MEXICAN BIRDS

First Impressions

MEXICAN BIRDS

First Impressions

BASED UPON AN ORNITHOLOGICAL EXPEDITION
TO TAMAULIPAS, NUEVO LEÓN, AND COAHUILA

WITH AN *Appendix* BRIEFLY
DESCRIBING ALL MEXICAN BIRDS

BY

GEORGE MIKSCH SUTTON

Illustrated
with water-color and pen-and-ink drawings
by the author

UNIVERSITY OF OKLAHOMA PRESS
NORMAN

By GEORGE MIKSCH SUTTON
Mexican Birds: First Impressions (1951)
Birds in the Wilderness (New York, 1936)
Eskimo Year (New York, 1934)
The Exploration of Southampton Island, Hudson Bay (Pittsburgh, 1932)
An Introduction to the Birds of Pennsylvania (Harrisburg, 1928)

Illustrated by GEORGE MIKSCH SUTTON
World Book Encyclopedia (section on birds) (Chicago, 1941)
Birds of Western Pennsylvania (by W. E. C. Todd) (Pittsburgh, 1940)
The Golden Plover and Other Birds (by A. A. Allen) (Ithaca, 1939)
American Bird Biographies (by A. A. Allen) (Ithaca, 1934)
The Birds of Minnesota (in part) (by T. S. Roberts) (Minneapolis, 1932)
The Burgess Seashore Book (in part) (by Thornton Burgess) (Boston, 1929)
The Birds of Florida (by H. H. Bailey) (Baltimore, 1925)
A Guide to Bird Finding (by Olin Sewall Pettingill, Jr.)
(New York, 1951)

COPYRIGHT 1951 BY THE UNIVERSITY OF OKLAHOMA PRESS
PUBLISHING DIVISION OF THE UNIVERSITY
COMPOSED AND PRINTED AT NORMAN, OKLAHOMA, U.S.A.
BY THE UNIVERSITY OF OKLAHOMA PRESS
FIRST EDITION

IN MEMORY OF *David Clark Hilton* WHOSE DEEP
INTEREST IN MEXICAN BIRDS
BRIGHTENED THE LAST YEARS OF HIS
FULL AND USEFUL LIFE

FOREWORD

W. H. Hudson, writing of Penzance in his scholarly and delightful book on Cornwall, has this to say of the peculiar value of first impressions: "Places are like faces—a first sight is almost invariably the one that tells you most. When the first sharp, clear impression has grown blurred, or is half forgotten or overlaid with subsequent impressions, we have as a rule lost more than we have gained: it is hardly too much to say in a majority of instances that the more familiar a place becomes to us the less well we know it. At all events we have ceased to know it in the same way; we no longer vividly, consciously see it in its distinctive character."

What Hudson is talking about is a psychological phenomenon, of course—a state of mental alertness or expectancy or awareness, stemming possibly from the instinct of self-preservation, and demanding that we pay special heed to anything recognized as being new to our experience. On meeting a new person we instantly put our antennae of perception to work on what he says, how he says it, what he laughs at, how he laughs, and so on, in our eagerness to discover where completely safe, common ground lies. In a new place we put our senses and wits to work at once, seeking to memorize certain details of the landscape so quickly and so thoroughly as to be able to regard them, a few moments hence, as part of our past experience, part of ourselves.

As ornithologists we observe a new bird half fearful that we may not see it again, and fully aware that we may never in our lives have a better look at it than this. Every move it makes, every cry it utters, is important to us. Observing it intently, we ascertain as quickly as possible what it is; not what its name is—that can come later—but how it compares with species we already know, what attitudes of body and expressions of face it repeats most frequently, what facts about it are so indubitable that we can safely add them at once to our personal store of knowledge. A wholly new bird is sometimes so bewildering that we cannot even place it in its proper genus or family. What ornithologist from Australia, unfamiliar with the latest general work on taxonomy, let us say, and not very well acquainted with our common birds, would instantly know that our American Redstart (*Setophaga ruticilla*) was a wood warbler and not a flycatcher? The question is not rhetorical. I think it quite possible that our Australian friend would be momentarily bewildered by the bird. I believe, furthermore, that a forthright statement from him concerning his *first impressions* of the living American Redstart might conceivably be illuminating enough, and revolutionary enough, to lead to a reinvestigation of the bird's anatomy, behavior, etc., and thus, eventually, to a much clearer understanding of its phylogenetic position.

So, firmly believing that a record of first impressions is important, I have written this book. I have presented the material autobiographically because bird students who visit Mexico for the first time will be apt to go through much that I went through in adjusting myself to the fact that many birds there are the same as, or very closely related to, those of the United States; that at such a place as Monterrey, Nuevo León, one only occasionally encounters distinctively Mexican genera and species in winter; that in tropical parts of Mexico one is apt to encounter a well known United States bird and fail to recognize it either because its winter behavior is unfamiliar or because its environment is so dramatically new. What I have written cannot hope to serve as a complete field guide or reference book. Such works as these will come later, when more is known.

The entire first draft of the manuscript I wrote on the Atlantic Ocean in my stateroom on the *S. S. City of Baltimore*. I was on my way to France, to attend an international ornithological congress at Paris and Rouen. Having returned from my first visit to Mexico, I found it hard to believe that I was bound for the Old World. Mexico was very much on my mind. All my Mexican field notes and sketches were with me. Realizing that once I set foot on European soil I should be meeting for the first time another lot of new birds, I wrote these chapters while clear-cut memories of motmots, tinamous, becards, and trogons still were fresh in my mind.

The plates in this book were reproduced from water-color drawings which I made in the field in Mexico, directly from living or freshly killed birds. Several of the species shown thus, notably the Blackish Crane-Hawk, Rufescent Tinamou, Bronzed Woodpecker, and Cabanis' Tiger-Bittern, probably have never been illustrated in this way before.

The engravings from which twelve of the plates were printed were lent by The Wilson Ornithological Club, a national organization of bird students, many of whom have become deeply interested in Mexican birds.

The pen and ink drawings I made very recently, using skins, photographs and field sketches as reference material. My drawing of the Laughing Falcon was based on a field sketch made in Veracruz by Robert W. Storer. The Masked Tityra, Groove-billed Ani, Social Flycatcher, Bronzed Woodpecker, and Derby Flycatcher drawings were based to some extent on photographs made in Tamaulipas by Olin Sewall Pettingill, Jr. The drawing of the Boat-billed Heron was based in part on a photograph made in Tamaulipas by Ernest P. Edwards and Robert B. Lea. The Caracara drawing was based in part upon a photograph appearing in Arthur Cleveland Bent's *Life Histories of North American Birds of Prey*. Certain drawings, notably that of the Long-billed Gnatwren, admittedly are somewhat imaginative, for I have never seen the birds alive. Particularly useful to me in my pen and ink drawing work was a boxful of fresh plant specimens sent from the border by Elizabeth Beard. My thanks to these friends for this help.

I wish to express my gratitude also to the following: the officials of the Dirección General Forestal y de Caza, for permits to collect specimens in Mexico; the officials of the Museum of Zoology at the University of Michigan for giving me a room in which to work and access to their remarkably fine collections of Chiapas, Yucatán, Tabasco, and Guerrero birds; Herbert Stoddard, Sr., Mr. and Mrs. Haven Spencer, Mr. and Mrs. Robert M. Mengel, and others who have been instrumental in bringing into being the Foundation for Neotropical Research; Rogers McVaugh, Robert T. Clausen, and Paul Standley for identification of certain plant specimens and drawings; William H. Burt and Kenneth Doutt for information concerning Mexican mammals; Eugene Eisenmann for his careful consideration of the problem of common names for certain birds; Mrs. G. Reeves Butchart for a critical reading of the manuscript; Luis de la Torre for assistance with the spelling and accenting of Spanish words; and Emmet R. Blake for so promptly sending me needed specimens from the Chicago Museum of Natural History.

A very special word of thanks to Dr. and Mrs. Powell Cottrille, of Jackson, Michigan, for their timely help with the Appendix; and to Elsa Hertz, Natalie Belkin, Maud Beebe, Marion Patton, Elvi Fitzgerald, and Mary Kier for their careful typing of notes and manuscript.

And, finally, a word about my friend, Dr. David Hilton, to whose memory I have dedicated this book. Dr. Hilton was our family physician during my early childhood years. His wise comments on the beauty and value of birds impressed me deeply. In 1944, the year before he died, he wrote me from Mexico, enclosing lists of the new and puzzling birds he had been seeing. I very much hope that the living members of his family circle will enjoy this book.

GEORGE MIKSCH SUTTON

June 18, 1951

CONTENTS

ILLUSTRATIONS

COLOR PLATES

PEN-AND-INK DRAWINGS

MEXICAN BIRDS

First Impressions

I

I had my first glimpse of Mexico one spring when John B. Semple and I were studying the birds of the Big Bend country of Texas.

One of our bases that season was Hot Springs, on the Río Grande. From the thick-walled, dark little *apartado* in which I prepared specimens, made water-color sketches, wrote notes, and slept, I could look southward across the dry mouth of Tornillo Creek and the bed of the Big River into the Mexican states of Coahuila and Chihuahua. My eye found rest and diversion there, roving the rocky, sun-baked wilderness, following the rims of distant canyons, memorizing the details of the rugged horizon. The mountains off to the southeast were known as the Del Carmens. They were strange and unpredictable: one never knew what to expect of them. At times they drew close, towering bold and black above the river. Again they receded, becoming diaphanous and ghostlike. In the fierce glare of the sun they looked flat, worn down, done in; but let the shadow of a little cloud fall on them and a certain vitality instantly returned. They were all but colorless at midday, but mornings and evenings they were blue or purple or lead-gray, and at sunset they sometimes became so bright that it would have been easy to believe them solid cinnabar or hematite or even gold.

The most striking feature of the Del Carmen skyline was a pinnacle known as the Shot Tower. This bold, symmetrical shaft of rock leaned slightly, calling to mind the Tower of Pisa. I looked at it often, wondering how far away and how high it was, and whether it had ever been climbed. Sometimes, as I gazed at it, a thick, low cloud moved in from the east, advancing slowly down over its top like a mass of yellowish-brown wool. The effect was startling and sinister. Never did the cloud hide more than the upper third of the range. Never did it rise to cover the sky. It curled down over the nearer edge, hanging thus sometimes for hours. Then slowly it withdrew, the Shot Tower emerged, and the familiar horizon became visible once more.

Every evening, there at Hot Springs, hundreds of nighthawks gathered at the river. They came from all directions, swiftly, silently, flying but a few feet above the hot ground. We rarely saw the incoming birds unless, standing at the water's edge, we watched for their silhouettes above the banks. One by one, never in flocks, they appeared, each with long wings set for the final glide down to water level. In the gathering dusk they circled gracefully, catching insects, skimming a drink with their tiny bills, perhaps cooling their feet with a swift dip. Not a cry did they utter, though their wings sometimes rustled.

A little before dark they went away, each to its own special part of the desert. Always a good many of them flew southward, straight into Mexico. These I watched a bit wistfully, wondering how far they would go. Did some of them nest in the foothills of the Del Carmens, perhaps at the foot of the Shot Tower? Theirs was a land I very much wished to see.

Five years later I went. Not into the Del Carmens, for that proved to be impracticable, but into the less mountainous region to the east and south of them. My companions were two of America's ablest field ornithologists, Thomas Dearborn Burleigh and the late John Bonner Semple. From latter January to early March we three journeyed about the states of Nuevo León, Coahuila, and Tamaulipas, becoming acquainted with wonderful new birds. This is the story of our expedition.

II

At Laredo, Texas, we took out special insurance for our two automobiles, gave the postal authorities our forwarding addresses, and had our hair cut short. The time was midwinter. We were on our way.

Some last minute purchases were to be made—cheap cotton for packing specimens, carbon tetrachloride for removing dirt and grease from bird plumage, a big sackful of excelsior, several flashlight batteries, some sulphur for chiggers and ticks, and a small Spanish dictionary. While Semple and I were rounding up supplies, Burleigh was to interview officials in Nuevo Laredo, on the Mexican side of the Bridge. He had with him letters from our government informing whom it might concern that our scientific collecting permits were awaiting us there.

Semple and I finished our shopping about noon. When we looked for Burleigh at the Bridge, however, no Burleigh was to be found. This roused us considerably, for, knowing our friend to be an incurable individualist, we instantly thought up several lurid reasons for his not being there.

We decided that I should walk to Mexico in search of Burleigh, while Semple would keep an eye out for him in Laredo. I paid a nickel at the tollgate, got halfway across the Bridge, then suddenly realized that I had not a red Mexican cent for the return trip. This made me vaguely uneasy. I was harmless enough in appearance, surely, and I had plenty of American money. But what about these Mexicans? Might they not be quick to suspect the worst? And, suspecting the worst, might they not seize and handcuff me and throw me into some vile jail? I did not stop walking. The expression of my face changed only slightly, if at all. I wasn't really afraid—of course not! It was only that I had a better than average imagination, and that I had crossed *that line*.

I glanced upstream and down, then off to the south. This country was all the same—brown with patches and smears of green, dust-covered, withered. The Río Grande was a queer little river, hardly more than a creek. Watching some birds as they flew rapidly past, I wondered what Mexican species they might be.

Odd, wasn't it? There I was: a biologist who had just stepped across a political boundary, an imaginary line. Being a biologist, I should have borne in mind that any bird I might see there belonged biologically just as much to Texas as to Mexico. Ecologically, the two banks of the river were much the same. Strong-flying organisms could cross and recross that bit of water without the slightest difficulty. Yet now that I was in Mexico, all things about me had become suddenly and overwhelmingly Mexican. I, and I alone, of all this vast, semiarid, half-visible world was foreign, out of place, not of Mexico.

Though I searched high and low for Burleigh, he was nowhere to be found. Inquiring at the customs office if anyone had seen him, I was instantly surrounded by sharp-witted, loquacious young men, not one of whom had the dilatory, somnolent bearing I had expected Mexicans to have. Accompanying me in a throng, they expressed their belief that Señor Burleigh had come this way; that, after looking at some strange fruit and cactus candy in the window of a little store, he had wandered on a block or so and crossed the street. Dismissing my cortege with a statement that I could surely find Señor Burleigh without further help, I walked southward toward the principal hotel. Here my sleuthing came to an end, for reason born of long experience told me that if my friend had got this far and had heard some strange bird farther on, there was no way of knowing where he would be by this time, nor hope of expecting him back were the creature still unidentified. Burleigh was that sort of ornithologist.

At the Bridge I paid another United States nickel and sauntered back toward my native land, this time noticing not so much the smallness of the river beneath me as the great width of its bed. What a powerful, savage monster the Río Grande must be when its banks were full!

To my surprise I found Semple and Burleigh together, waiting for me. Semple was in a veritable lather of impatience and restlessness. Having hunted all over Laredo before finding Burleigh, he could not view with equanimity my pensive returning. His heated comments concerning customs inspections in general and daydreaming scientists in particular need not be quoted, especially since at that moment I was paying little attention to them. A remarkable thing had just happened: above the racket of the busy street I had heard the cry of a new bird. There I stood, rummaging through the drawers and pigeonholes of memory, trying to place the sound. I listened to it carefully. It was a sharp, rather musical *kler,* which seemed to come straight from the building across the street. It was wholly unfamiliar. I had never heard anything like it before.

As I threaded my way through the traffic I wondered whether I was being misled by the squeaking of a hinge or by some other mechanical sound. But I kept on, following carefully the direction I had first taken, and found myself, presently, beside the United States customs building. There, sure enough, the bird was, up under the porch roof, perched on a rafter above the customs office door. Its underparts were light gray. It was somewhat smaller than a robin and its bill was short, but not heavy. As it fluttered down to snatch a fly from the wall I saw that its back was brown and that its outer tail feathers were tipped with white. I was enthralled—completely, hopelessly enthralled. Not for the life of me could I identify the bird.

Observing that it made no attempt to fly off, I decided that it must have been brought to Laredo from far to the south in a cage. It had a way of turning its head and looking at me with its large, dark eye as if it had singled me out of the crowd. The ringing timbre of its callnote suggested highly developed syringeal muscles and a beautiful song. But what sort of bird was it? Its species had never been recorded in the United States, of that I was certain. To what genus and family did it belong? I simply did not know.

6

Tourists who saw me standing there looking roofward probably thought me touched by the heat or mildly insane. Most of them were polite enough or preoccupied enough to pay no attention. As for Semple and Burleigh, they probably were wasting sympathy on me for being unable to capture this desirable specimen. What no one seemed to realize was that I had fallen in love with that little gray bird. I couldn't help myself. I just had to stand there admiring it, wondering what its name was, wishing I could give it a drink. Utterly forgetful of a bird's un-imaginativeness, and failing miserably to maintain an objective attitude, I was putting myself in its place. Somehow I couldn't forget how I had felt a half hour before, on the Mexican side of the river; how the whole world there—the horses and mules and burros, the signs along the street, the dust in the air, even my fellow human beings—had seemed hostile to me. No one had befriended me. No one had made much of an effort to understand me. Now the tables were turned. This time it was a poor little Mexican bird who felt lonely, friendless, and unwanted in a foreign land.

All this slamming of doors and rattling of girders, this clamor of horns and loud voices—what a terrifying pandemonium it was! The hot, dusty street! Men and women moving nervously about, all of them more or less miserable, none of them at peace! The tuneless, arrogant, self-sufficient chatter of English sparrows! Not a chirp of recognition, or of friendliness, or of understanding in the whole place!

As our two automobiles crossed the international boundary I was thinking hard about that little gray-breasted bird. Its big dark eyes haunted me. Its sibilant, forlorn cry lingered in my ears. I did not know its name but I would never, as long as I lived, forget it. And perhaps I would see it again.

III

By four o'clock that afternoon we had been queried, scrutinized, and passed by the customs officers. The numbers of our guns, motors, and tires had been written down and our ammunition had been carefully checked. How good it was to have this routine business behind us, to be on our way!

South of the city, in the open country once more, we could not dispel a vague feeling of disappointment. That curiously worshipful attitude toward boundary lines was at work again. Now that we knew ourselves to be outside the United States we expected the world to be different, but what we saw at either side of the road, and what stretched off ahead of us as far as we could see, was the same flat, monotonous, brush-covered country we had seen north of Laredo, the same "chaparral" through which we had been travelling, so it seemed, for days. What we failed to sense, in our eagerness to experience Mexico and things Mexican, was that the broad valley across which we were now moving was a vast unit, biologically speaking, throughout which soil, temperature, drainage, and plant and animal life were much the same. Had we been in an airplane this significant fact might have been more apparent. The true boundary between the United States and the Mexico we had dreamed of was neither the line nor the river which we had crossed, but the whole wide, semiarid valley which we were now traversing. Were we correct in calling this valley "Mexican"? Were we truly in Mexico? We could not quite make up our minds. Without quite realizing it, we were *experiencing* a lesson in zoogeography.

The day was hot and bright. Ahead of us the horizon wobbled with heat waves and the highway glistened as if wet with rain. Birds were scarce. The two species which we saw most frequently were the Mockingbird (*Mimus polyglottos*), which was easily identifiable from its plain gray upper parts and white under parts as it perched on the thicket-top, or from the white outer tail feathers, and white patches in the wings as it flew off; and the Pyrrhuloxia (*Pyrrhuloxia sinuata*), which was obviously closely related to the Cardinal (*Richmondena cardinalis*) in that it had a heavy, seed-cracking bill and high crest. In color this bird appeared to be gray, largely, but its wings and tail flashed dark red as it flew; and when we had a good look at a male we saw that there was red also on the crest and that the exquisite rose color of the face extended downward throughout the throat, breast, and middle of the belly. The female, though prominently crested and heavy billed, was much less colorful.

A common roadside bird was the Black-throated Sparrow (*Amphispiza bilineata*). This little finch was dark gray above, white below, with white tail-corners which showed in flight, very distinct black throat-patch, and (when we saw one closely enough) a distinct white line above the eye and another white line between the dark gray cheek-patch and the black throat-patch. Since their nesting season had not yet arrived these sparrows were feeding in loose flocks along the highway's shoulder.

Mockingbird (*Mimus polyglottos*)
10 inches

Middle-sized, white-breasted birds which had somewhat the appearance of Mockingbirds, but which were bigger-headed, and which had a distinct black mask extending backward through the eye, were Loggerhead Shrikes (*Lanius ludovicianus*). Their manner was somewhat hawklike. Perching in a prominent place on a dead twig, wire, or fence post, they watched for grasshoppers or lizards, paying little attention to us even when we passed close by.

And of course there were the Turkey Vultures (*Cathartes aura*). Through the motionless air these dusky scavengers flew—some far, far over us, floating from cloud to cloud; others a hundred yards above the highway, teetering from side to side; others so low that their breasts must occasionally have brushed the tiny new leaves of the mesquite and huizache—all drifting through a drowsy world on wings which neither flapped nor fluttered.

9

What an illusion of purposelessness in the Turkey Vulture's flight! Every one of these birds was hungry, every one of them on the alert, every one of them hunting as only a vulture can hunt, its round, bright, wart-encircled eyes searching the gray-brown wilderness beneath it for the dead. Yet, contemplating them, we might easily have believed them all half asleep.

Carcass hunting! Not only were those soaring vultures watching the ground. They were watching every hawk, every raven, every coyote, perhaps even the very flies and scarlet-spotted scavenger beetles, on the chance that one of these might lead them to a meal. In particular did they keep their eyes on all other vultures, lest one of these swing suddenly earthward, flap into the thicket, and alight undetected. A sharp coasting downward, a wingbeat abruptly changing the course of flight: no more than this was needed and the secret was out, the hunt for the moment over, the invitation to the feast extended. Almost never did one of those vultures dine alone.

There were two species of vulture in the country through which we passed—the Turkey Vulture and the Black Vulture (*Coragyps atratus*), the latter a shorter-winged, heavier-bodied bird, with stiff, laborious flight, and gray rather than red head. We saw our first Black Vultures at the outskirts of a village some forty kilometers south of Nuevo Laredo. Here, about the remains of a half-grown pig, the greedy company stood, heads high, beaks slightly parted, wings half lifted. We had but a glimpse of them in passing, but at that instant one bird hobbled to the dead pig's mouth, braced itself, and tugged savagely at the lip.

The village itself was a mere handful of houses, some of adobe, some of stone, most of them falling to pieces. At the top of a hill to one side stood a tiny white building surmounted with a cross. Leading down from this shrine, with directness remarkable for so steep a slope, was a well-worn path.

A hundred kilometers south of the border, we noticed that the sky to the west was pale lavender rather than blue. Not consciously curious, yet puzzled by this unfamiliar atmospheric effect, we let our eyes travel from the horizon upward to the clearer blue of the zenith, then downward again to the zone where the blue stopped and the lavender began. That lavender was not sky. It was mountains! Vast, jagged, rock-ribbed mountains, so high, so pale, so very nearly the color of the sky that they seemed utterly intangible and unreal. They were the Sierra Madre—the Mother Range. Their ruggedness and sheer bigness awed us.

Looking closely, we made certain that there were no snow-capped peaks in sight.

We were climbing now. The highway was leading us into yucca-studded foothills. Ascending by a series of well-planned curves, we reached a pass. Here we stopped to scramble about, looking for birds. In the dusty brush which half hid the ledges below us, a small bird was singing. The phrases of the song were varied and not very musical. At our approach they resolved themselves into a mere callnote, a harsh *chick-eer!* The sandy-colored bird was hard to see on the ground, but as it flew up we noticed that its rump was brown and that its widely fanned tail had a broad black subterminal band and buffy-brown tip. It was a Rock Wren (*Salpinctes obsoletus*).

Through the cooling air we glided downgrade. How gigantic and black were the mountains which loomed ahead of us! What mystery there was about them! We slipped through the village of Ciénaga de las Flores, across a bridge, into flat country again. Broad farmlands stretched out at either side of us. The lush fields of young grain were rich green in the waning light. Flocks of large, slow-flying blackbirds passed over us. A tiny dove shot off down a hedge. At a sluggish stream marked "Arroyo de Pesquerías" a cormorant and two white herons were fishing. We did not stop to watch them.

We passed some Mexicans with *serapes* wound over their mouths and noses. These soggy looking scarves would keep the poisonous night air out of their lungs, we had heard. Burro-pulled carts moved at a snail's pace along the highway's sun-baked shoulder. Children stared at us solemnly. It was growing dark.

The gaudy red, blue, and green of a neon sign sprang at us from the right. "Wait a minute!" shouted Semple. "Isn't that where we were going to stop? Isn't that the place the man told us about?"

We had reached Monterrey, the big, elusive, skyscraperless capital city of Nuevo León.

IV

The evening air was surprisingly cool. Not knowing the countryside at all, hence having no idea which way to turn for a birding ground in which we could work without disturbing the populace, we went to bed.

The shame of it all! Here we were in the land of which we had talked for weeks, yet sleep was the order of the hour. Back in those tangled woods a few miles to the north there would surely be night birds—goatsuckers of some sort, owls, herons possibly—fascinating and beautiful creatures some of which would almost certainly be new to us. Even the comparatively open country, with its knee-high brush, its ragged clumps of cactus, and its dry, winding stream beds, would be alive with little mammals at this very hour, and among the creatures feeding upon these mammals would be nocturnal birds of prey. Such things had to be, for that was the way a fauna was composed. There could be no wealth of small creatures without a wealth of larger creatures to feed upon them, to effect a control. The thought of having to sleep at a time when the night was so full of activity was hard to bear.

Early the following morning, wakened first by reveille which sounded from a military base off somewhere to the north, then by a burro which brayed as if having a convulsion just outside the window, we rose. The air was incredibly chilly. We began to wonder whether we had brought enough warm clothing with us.

At the first chirp of a bird, Burleigh was out. Returning, he informed us of an English Sparrow (*Passer domesticus*) he had seen in a palm tree, a "large-sized bird" which he thought might belong to an undescribed geographical race of this hardy, amazingly adaptable species. Whether this was "boundary-line worship" again at work or no, we agreed that these tourist court English Sparrows did look rather large, and during breakfast we reminded each other of old Professor Baird's injunction to his field collectors that they make a point of obtaining, first of all, the species which were obviously commonest in any region they might happen to visit.

Unable to put from our minds the woodland we had noted to our east as we had approached the city, we drove north a few miles along the main highway, then eastward on a dirt road into a section known as Anáhuac Park. Stopping the car in a grove of fine live oaks, we listened a moment, then got out.

So thrilling was this new world that there was an illusion of being on tiptoe in simply standing there. The day was mild, though not sunny. The veil of green over the wilderness of thorn and vine; spots of yellow here and there in the grass; a faint aroma in all but motionless air; and especially the clamor of the numerous birds—all these proclaimed that spring was at hand. The bird chorus was bewildering, completely so at first, less so once we realized that some species were capable of making many sorts of cries. During those first five minutes in the grove the world was disembodied, immaterialized, transformed into a realm of sound. Loud pipings, repeated with a machine gun's staccato rapidity, plaintive cheeps, harsh chatter—these were the actualities of this world, these the closest to the tangible. Now and then the dominant entity was a sweetly trilled whistle, not loud, but so firm and clear that it hung in the air with the self-assurance of a strand of spider's web.

A flash of color brought us to our senses, reminding us that we had eyes as well as ears. A yellow-breasted bird, big-headed, square-shouldered, and larger than a robin but with shorter tail, had flown to a bush only a rod or so away. Perching upright, it turned its head deliberately, giving us a good view of its heavy black bill, the broad white line above its eye, the sharp black and yellow of its crown, and the white of its throat. With a shrill, loud *geep!* it darted upward, snatched a moth from the air, and returned to its perch. A flycatcher, of course: a fine, big Derby Flycatcher or Kiskadee (*Pitangus sulphuratus*), a widely distributed South and Central American species known to range northward as far as the mouth of the Río Grande.

We listened for further callnotes or for a repetition of the loud *geep!* which still sounded in our ears, but the Kiskadee was in no mood for courting and had no nest-territory to advertise or defend, so it made no further outcry. We inspected it minutely, noting that the bright yellow of its breast extended throughout the belly and under tail coverts, that its wings and tail were of a bold shade of reddish-brown.

How the big, dignified Kiskadee got away without our seeing so much as a flash of its wings I shall never be able to explain. We were using our binoculars, to be sure, and birds may come and go while binoculars are being adjusted. Too, since we were in an unusually receptive state of mind and senses, slight sounds and movements probably were dividing our attention. In any event, the flycatcher was there one instant, so large, so conspicuous, that we took for granted its being easy to see and follow about; and the next instant it was gone, utterly gone, and in its place on the very same branch, not a stone's throw away from us, perched a wholly different bird. The newcomer was slender and gray, about average in proportions, and a bit larger than an English Sparrow.

The new bird was a male Rose-throated Becard (*Platypsaris aglaiae*), a species which at that time had been recorded but once in the United States. We didn't recognize it while its back was towards us, but when it about-faced, lifted its fluffy black crest, and let us see the pink of its throat, we knew what it was. We recalled that the female was very different in color: tan above, plain buff below, with dark gray crest.

13

We had handled Rose-throated Becard skins in museum collections many times. We were familiar with several members of the Cotingidae, the New World family to which the pretty creature belonged. But here was the becard itself, this time not a cotton-stuffed specimen with label and neatly crossed feet, but a being of warm flesh and blood, its soft plumage rising and sinking with every breath, the highlights in its dark eyes constantly shifting. With deep satisfaction we watched it,

Rose-throated Becard (*Platypsaris agaliae*)
7 inches

14

realizing that never before this moment had we known what the shape of a becard's head was—or the expression of a becard's face!

Like the Kiskadee, the becard was hungry. Not being interested in flying insects, apparently, it moved in and out among the twigs, inspecting bark, bud scars, leaves, and petioles. What it found we did not know—aphids, perhaps, or scale insects. At ease it stood erect, rather high on its feet.

Finding these two distinctly Mexican species almost the instant of our arrival, we were now prepared for anything. But since no other bird appeared we gave our attention to the jumble of sounds which had confused us so badly. We could distinguish without difficulty the boldly whipped-out song of a Cardinal and, in the distance, the clear whistle of a Bob-white Quail (*Colinus virginianus*). But the most noticeable sound of all was a loud, shrill piping which we did not recognize— an odd, mechanical sound which had made us think of a machine gun the instant we had first heard it. We decided that no single bird could produce so considerable a din. At that instant the piping ceased, harsh *chacks* sounded, and a flock of Great-tailed Grackles (*Cassidix mexicanus*) passed overhead. The males were almost as heavy-bodied as Common Crows (*Corvus brachyrhynchos*), and shiny black; the females about half that size, and dull brown. All flew somewhat laboriously, as if their long tails were more burden than help. They settled in a dead tree and the piping started again.

The males did all the singing—if singing it was. They pointed their beaks straight upward as they piped, then puffed out their body plumage, flapped their wings, spread their tails wide, lowered their heads, and shook all over as they disgorged a series of wheezy *k-thicks*. The whole flock kept going at a fearful rate, as if each bird were determined to outdo the others in sheer noise.

The grackles flew off to feed in a plowed field. Their going left the woodland oddly still. Presently, however, a new sound, a rough *cra, cra, cra, cra, cra,* issued from the depths of the grove. Obviously this was no song nor display performance; it was the raucous chatter of birds used to foraging together. We instantly guessed them to be jays. But which jays lived here?

They were Green Jays (*Xanthoura yncas*), medium-sized, uncrested birds, rich green above, greenish-yellow beneath, with light yellow outer tail feathers. Like the Kiskadee Flycatcher, they were known to range northward as far as extreme southern Texas. Walking toward them, we found them to be busy hunting acorns. What all their scolding was

15

about we could not determine. They chased each other constantly, staying high in the trees most of the time, giving us no glimpse of the black on the throat and face, nor of the beautiful blue crown and moustache-patch, unless one chanced to fly to the ground.

Northern Green Jay (*Xanthoura yncas luxuosa*)
11 inches

Here again, pictures and museum specimens had given us a wholly inadequate concept of a common Mexican bird. It took the living, flying Green Jay, seen against the dark green of the live oaks, to reveal its outstanding field-mark—the yellow of its outer tail feathers. And it took careful checking with the binocular to ascertain that the eye was dark brown rather than yellow. For years we had entertained the notion that the Green Jay was a yellow-eyed bird, for in Louis Fuertes' portrait (published in *Bird-Lore,* in 1919) the eye indubitably had been represented

PLATE I
Mexican Cormorant, immature
(*Phalacrocorax olivaceus*)

as yellow. The explanation was this: in Veracruz, a Mexican state Fuertes had visited in 1910, the Green Jay *is* yellow-eyed. Fuertes had had no way of knowing, when he had painted his yellow-eyed bird, that the Green Jays of Tamaulipas, Nuevo León, and extreme southern Texas had dark brown eyes.

One of the jays was so preoccupied with pounding open an acorn that it let us approach closely. It held the acorn in its feet, lifted its head high, and drove its sturdy bill downward with enough force to produce a considerable noise. It had given the acorn eight or ten whacks when another jay sailed into the tree, slipped quietly from branch to branch, then made a rush forward, screaming *cra! cra! cra! cra!* at the top of its voice. This plainly startled jay No. 1, which grasped the acorn with its foot, screamed out a *cra! cra!* of its own, and flew to the next tree. Jay No. 2 started in pursuit, cackling obstreperously. Here the chase ended. A new note, a shriek of genuine alarm, sounded from one of the flock. The acorn dropped. We heard it distinctly as it hit a leaf, then a twig, then the ground. The babble had ceased. A Red-tailed Hawk (*Buteo jamaicensis*) was circling low over the trees.

The jays were dead silent as long as the hawk was in sight. But the Golden-fronted Woodpeckers (*Centurus aurifrons*), once they had ascertained that danger was not imminent, resumed their search along the shadowed boughs, tapping at the bark, pausing now and then to call *chuff! chuff!* in a voice which reminded us of a gray squirrel's. They were beautiful birds, each with back and wings sharply barred with black and white, under parts light gray, forehead deep, rich yellow, and crown (in the male) glossy red. There were Ladder-backed Woodpeckers (*Dendrocopos scalaris*) in the woodland, too, birds about the size of the Downy Woodpecker (*D. pubescens*) of the United States and Canada, with barred black and white upper parts, light gray under parts, the crown red in the male, black in the female. Their callnote was an incisive *peek*. Their tapping, though businesslike enough, was much lighter than that of their big, golden-fronted allies. This Ladder-backed Woodpecker ranged northward well across the border. The subspecies found in the United States were known variously as the Texas Woodpecker, Cactus Woodpecker, "Little Ladder-back," and so on.

A low callnote which rose from the shrubbery beyond the live oak grove continued to assail our ears. The companionable cry called to mind pussy willow buds, light flashing from cool water, thin-winged flies moving through gentle air. Its very familiarity made us distrust it. We listened carefully. *Fit-i-bee!* it sounded, clear enough. *Zhee-bee!* with a downward inflection. A phoebe, of course; a plain and common phoebe from back home in the States! To identify the bird beyond all doubt, we followed the sound. There on a bare twig, not far from the ground, tail wagging properly, perched the Eastern Phoebe (*Sayornis phoebe*). Its song had a meditative, far away quality, as if it might be pondering the migratory flight it would soon be taking northward.

Ladder-backed Woodpecker (*Dendrocopos scalaris*)
7 inches

V

Now that we had our bearings, ornithologically speaking, we settled down to the task of identifying the nondescript small birds which flitted ahead of us wherever we went. Obviously a good many of these were United States and Canadian species which were spending the winter here. Recognizing them was not always easy because very few of them were singing and many were molting.

A common species which fed in bushes close to the ground, as well as in the trees, was the Orange-crowned Warbler (*Vermivora celata*), a plain little bird, olive above, dull yellow, vaguely streaked with gray, below. Occasionally we saw a full-plumaged male in which the orange crown-patch was visible, but many of the birds were females or molting, immature males without any crown-patch whatsoever. Equally common, and also molting, was the Myrtle Warbler (*Dendroica coronata*), which went about in small companies and which was identifiable by its four yellow spots—one on the crown, one on the rump, and one at each side of the chest. The Black-cap or Wilson's Warbler (*Wilsonia pusilla*) was the most confiding of the three warbler species which we continued to see. It was olive above and bright yellow below, and had a habit of jerking its tail loosely. The black cap was very distinct in the males, less so in the females.

A bird which we thought at first was a warbler proved to be a White-eyed Vireo (*Vireo griseus*). It kept itself so well-hidden in a smilax tangle that we had to watch it for some time before seeing its gray-green back, yellowish-white under parts, yellow eye-ring, and pure white eyes. Its song was an explosive *pit, pit-a-wheer, chip!* Unlike the warblers, which moved all about through the grove, it stayed in one thicket. It probably had selected a nest-territory, and may even have had a mate.

The sparrows which inhabited the underbrush were puzzling because they were so difficult to see clearly. The dark-looking ones which flew up ahead of us were, we found, likely to be Lincoln's Sparrows (*Melospiza lincolni*), but final identification depended on our seeing the buffy chest band and streaking of the chest and sides, or the fine crown and facial markings. Less dark, slightly larger ones were apt to be White-crowned Sparrows (*Zonotrichia leucophrys*). Full-plumaged adults of this species were easy enough to recognize from the clear black and white of their crowns, but young birds, which were molting into

Pyrrhuloxia (*Pyrrhuloxia sinuata*)
8 inches

their first breeding plumage, had only a sprinkling of black and white feathers on the tops of their heads. Green-tailed Towhees (*Chlorura chlorura*) were fairly common. They were a bit larger than the White-crowned Sparrows and were olive above, gray beneath, with white throat and chestnut crown-patch. Their cry was a mew, not unlike that of a small lost kitten. There were Spotted Towhees (*Pipilo maculatus*) too,—robust, terrestrial birds, the males with glossy black head and upper parts, red-brown sides, white belly, white tail-corners which showed plainly in flight, and more or less concealed white streaking or spotting on the back; the females browner (less black, that is) throughout the head and upper parts. Cardinals and Pyrrhuloxias were common. Unlike the other above-mentioned finches, these two species nested in the region, hence were to be heard singing frequently. Both were heavy billed and strikingly crested. The male Cardinal we identified easily at any distance from its bright red color and longish tail. The male Pyrrhuloxia was much less bright, being gray with dark red wings

20

and tail, and rose-red patch down the middle of the throat, breast and belly. Female Cardinals and Pyrrhuloxias were dull in comparison with the males, the female Cardinal being fawn-colored, the female Pyrrhuloxia gray.

But what were these mousey, olive-backed finches which moved like shadows from bush to bush; which so reminded us of undersized Green-tailed Towhees; and which had that species' amusing habit of kicking up the dead leaves while searching for food? If we walked toward them, even though slowly and noiselessly, they kept well ahead of us. But if we sat down and remained quite still, they resumed their feeding, chased each other playfully, and gave their faint chirps of alarm and beady squeals of contentment almost under our noses. Their eyes were light brown. Frequently as many as three or four of them fed close by, scratching diligently a moment or two, then racing across an open stretch to the shelter of the next thicket. They were birds we had never seen before—Olive Sparrows (*Arremonops rufivirgatus*), a species found in the United States only along the coast of southern Texas, hence frequently referred to as the Texas Sparrow. The neat brown and gray striping of the head, gray of the breast, and touch of yellow at the bend of the wing made the Olive Sparrow a very attractive bird, we thought, and its manners were winsome. We judged it to be a common nesting species in the vicinity of Monterrey though we heard no songs and witnessed neither courtship nor pairing.

Olive Sparrow (*Arremonops rufivirgatus*)
6½ inches

Beyond the borders of the live oak grove, in thinly thicketed country, we put up flock after flock of Clay-colored, Brewer's, Chipping, and Field Sparrows—all winter residents. The first of these, *Spizella pallida,* was the most noticeably streaked on the face, crown, and back of them all. The second, *Spizella breweri,* was similarly but less coarsely streaked. The Chipping Sparrows (*Spizella passerina*) were still largely in winter plumage, so only a few incoming feathers of their crowns were reddish-brown. The Field Sparrows (*Spizella pusilla*) were the least common of the four. The pink bill was a good diagnostic mark by which the species could be recognized.

The most distinctively Mexican finch of the brushlands near Monterrey was the Black-throated Sparrow—a pretty little songster which liked especially the drier stretches of country throughout which the prickly pear cactus throve. This bird we had seen repeatedly along the highway south of Laredo.

The common thrasher of the live oak grove was the Long-billed Thrasher (*Toxostoma longirostre*), a vigorous, long-tailed bird, brown above and buffy-white, heavily streaked with black, below. It was very much like the familiar Brown Thrasher (*T. rufum*) of the eastern United States, but had darker, less rufous upper parts. Another thrasher, the Curve-billed (*T. curvirostre*), inhabited the more open country close by. This was a light gray, indefinitely marked bird which sometimes raced from cactus clump to cactus clump like a tiny deer. Both these thrashers were in full song. Both were mimics, too; not so versatile as the Mockingbird, perhaps, but clever mimics nevertheless. For a while we could not be sure which species we were hearing.

As for the wrens, we noted two species that day, the House Wren (*Troglodytes aëdon*) and the Bewick's (*Thryomanes bewicki*). The former, a plain grayish-brown bird without any noticeable field-mark, was not singing, hence probably was wintering in the region; the latter—gray-brown above, ashy-gray below, with white line over the eye, and longish, rather "loose-jointed" tail—sang occasionally and probably was on its breeding ground, but subspecific identification of specimens collected would have to come later. Both these wrens lived in brush piles and thickets and kept close to the ground, although the Bewick's often hopped or flew to the top of a bush to sing.

The biggest bird of the grove was a Horned Owl (*Bubo virginianus*), a solitary individual which I discovered, remarkably enough, without any help from the Green Jays. Our party had separated for the time being, and I was making my way under low-spreading trees when out from the thick boughs overhead flew the owl. No sooner had it swept into the open than a general alarm was sounded and a troop of jays came on the double-quick. The owl flew to a distant tree. Here the jays continued their loud abuses, the whole bird community gathered, and I added species after species to our list: Ruby-crowned Kinglets (*Regulus calendula*), which bustled from twig to twig, crying *chud-ah,* and flicking their wings; Blue-gray Gnatcatchers (*Polioptila caerulea*), which whined noisily and wagged their tails as they flitted closer; Black-crested Titmice (*Parus atricristatus*), which scolded just as vehemently as the jays but less loudly because they were smaller; two small flycatchers of the genus *Empidonax*—species I could not be certain of; and a fire-bright male Vermilion Flycatcher (*Pyrocephalus rubinus*), breathtaking to behold.

The owl sat on a high branch, its eyes almost closed, turning its head slowly downward as I walked beneath it. Now the jays kept a discreet distance and made little outcry, as if wondering how wise it would be to express themselves freely under circumstances such as these. The owl, deciding that I had come close enough, lifted its head, opened its eyes wide, popped its heavy beak, and flew off. The jays, screaming bloody murder, followed.

Learning the language of birds is sometimes useful. When, an hour later, I heard the jays' sudden screaming of their phrases for "Off with him!" "Down with tyranny!" and "Nip him in the rear!" I instantly knew that the big owl had flown again, that it was flying to some distant haven of refuge, that the organism most likely to be frightening it into so extended a flight was another human being like myself—Tom Burleigh perhaps. Tom Burleigh it was!

On our way back to the car, we found the nest of a small member of the titmouse tribe, the Verdin (*Auriparus flaviceps*). The nest was globular, built of slender, thorny twigs, and so compact as to look like a solid ball. The entrance, which was at one side and surprisingly well-hidden, was less than an inch in diameter. Poking our fingers somewhat reluctantly within, we felt first the thorns which guarded the opening, then the warm, silk-smooth feather lining. That the nest was not in use we surmised because the twigs at the entrance were covered with the white droppings of the departed young, but it was as trim and strong as a nest finished that very day, so far as we could see. Pulling it apart, we realized anew how well it had been built. In the lining were neatly spotted belly feathers of the Red-shafted Flicker (*Colaptes cafer*), round feathers from the neck of a "Cotton-top," or Scaled Quail (*Calli-*

23

pepla squamata), and coarse, frayed feathers from the back of a Roadrunner (*Geococcyx californianus*). Fancy listing the birds of Nuevo León by examining the linings of Verdins' nests!

The Verdins themselves—gray midgets with dull yellow heads and red-brown shoulder patches—were not common. We saw one or two of them and occasionally heard one scolding. Their song, which reminded us a little of the clear whistling of a Solitary Sandpiper (*Tringa solitaria*), we heard infrequently. Spring had not yet really come to the live oak grove.

VI

The Monterrey countryside was something of a disappointment to us. We had expected to find deep forest and tropical birds and had found brush and Myrtle Warblers instead. To be sure we had seen some half-dead banana plants and the Rose-throated Becard, but where were the orioles, hummingbirds, trogons, and parrots for which Mexico was so famous? Had we not come expressly to see such birds as these?

We decided to push farther south or west. Having no definite plan, we studied the map trying to decide which road to take. Obviously there were excellent highways south to Mexico City and west to Saltillo, San Pedro, and Torreón. Perhaps we would find trogons in higher country. At Saltillo we might learn of a negotiable road leading northward into the Del Carmens. Or—at that instant my eye fell on a big spot of blue off in southwestern Coahuila: the Laguna de Mayrán. That was the place for us: a big lake with cattails and water hyacinths and jacanas—those queer, long-toed, spur-winged waterbirds which I had all my life wanted to see!

There were objections to my plan, but I defended it stoutly. At Saltillo we would have to jog northward, but from that point on the route would be direct. The whole distance was only two hundred miles and the road was good. We probably would be able to get gasoline at La Rosa or Parras. Not far beyond these villages, we would come to the lake. A road of some sort would lead to the lake, of course, and there would be willows or cottonwoods under which we could make camp. It would be a wonderful place for bird study.

Early next morning, we started. Beyond the outskirts of Monterrey the highway climbed gently, winding through bold, scantily forested

24

mountains. From the slopes to the south of us thin extrusions of rock towered into the clouds. Birds were not numerous. Here and there a Sparrow Hawk (*Falco sparverius*) balanced on a telephone wire, a Loggerhead Shrike surveyed its thorny domain, or a Road-runner slipped off into the cover. Vegetation was sparse.

Westward from Saltillo the prospect became steadily more arid. Dust covered the vegetation along the highway and even the greenest of the great maguey plants looked as if they had died long ago and been carefully preserved in an attitude of life. The day was hot, almost disagreeably so; the sky, hot blue and white. In the open country the Turkey Vulture was common, but we saw no Black Vultures at all. Occasionally, where trees lined an arroyo, we noted a Harris's Hawk (*Parabuteo unicinctus harrisi*),[1] a dark brown hawk with white rump, under tail coverts, and tail-tip, a noticeable red-brown patch on each wing, and red-brown flags; or small flocks of White-winged Doves (*Zenaida asiatica*), a species which was easily recognizable from the big white spot in each wing. In cultivated districts near the little towns, mixed flocks of blackbirds fed about the barns.

The ravens of the region interested us, for there were two species— the so-called American Raven (*Corvus corax sinuatus*), which nested, presumably, on cliffs back in the mountains, and the White-necked Raven (*C. cryptoleucus*), a smaller species, which nested in trees in the lowlands. To all outward appearances the White-necked Raven was solid black. But the basal part of its plumage, particularly that of its neck, was snow-white. Occasionally this whiteness became visible when the plumage was rumpled by the wind, and the birds' deliberate lowering or turning of the head so as to allow the wind to lift or part the feathers was apparently a form of courtship display.

Commonest of the small birds were the Mockingbird, Curve-billed Thrasher, and Black-throated Sparrow. Close to the highway we saw small flocks of Horned Larks (*Eremophila alpestris*) and Clay-colored Sparrows. On rough hillsides we occasionally glimpsed a Rock Wren or Brown Towhee (*Pipilo fuscus*),[2] the latter a plain brownish-gray, ground-inhabiting finch. In the thickets there were scattered pairs of Pyrrhuloxias. But nowhere did birds appear to be common. Surely we

---

[1] Harris's Hawk is really the name of only the more eastern of the two North American races of the species *Parabuteo unicinctus*, a hawk which breeds from southern Texas, southern Arizona, and southeastern California southward through Mexico and Central America to Argentina and Chile. I have not yet hit upon a completely satisfying species-name for this bird.

[2] See page 255 for a complete description of this bird.

could not hope to see trogons or parrots in this sort of habitat. We began to feel that we had left the really "good" bird country behind.

To relieve the monotony we took turns driving. About four o'clock that afternoon, while Semple and I were together in the first car and Semple was at the wheel, a shimmering line of white, well below the horizon and off to the northwest, attracted our attention. Neither of us spoke of it at first, but as it broadened and became distinct we began to believe our senses. How could it be anything but the much-talked-of laguna, the lake we had come to see?

Keeping our eyes on the nearer shore as we sped forward, we descried tussocks of grass, a bush or two, a stand of sedge or cattail. The water sparkled as if rippled by a light wind. But we could not tell how far away it was and, to our annoyance and bewilderment, it seemed to recede as we approached. Watching carefully, we saw tufts of grass waver, sink, vanish, and reappear farther away. The faster we drove, the faster the lake receded. We could not overtake it.

The mirage gave us a topic for lively conversation. My companion, who had not been very enthusiastic about the laguna from the outset, agreed that this thing looked very much like water and wondered if the real lake, lying somewhere off to the northwest, were not being projected toward us by tricks of light. As for myself, I was beginning to distrust everything I saw. If the mirage hadn't been exactly where the laguna was supposed to be, just to the right of the highway and obviously in the lowest part of the plain, I shouldn't have argued so vigorously. I was dejected. The Laguna de Mayrán was, in a sense, *my* lake. But for my insistence that we see it, we should never have taken this long, hot journey.

Suddenly, as the highway swung northward from the base of a long ridge we had been skirting, the mirage disappeared. At that very instant we passed a small, battered sign with blood-red letters which read: MAYRÁN. There was an arrow too—not a particularly straight one— pointing toward the flat where the "lake" had just been showing. The road leading that way was very poor. We decided to go on to San Pedro.

The highway was alive with goats, cattle, chickens, pigs, burros laden with faggots, and men who appeared to be going home from work. About a stagnant pool flew a mixed flock of blackbirds.

San Pedro amazed us. Though a city of thirteen thousand inhabitants, it appeared to be only a big village. Nowhere did its buildings dominate the scene. No hum of wheels nor column of smoke gave token of industry. At a filling station we had trouble figuring up what we owed for gasoline and let it be known that we wanted to hire for a few days a camp-man who could speak English.

The loquacious throng which quickly gathered had us tongue-tied with embarrassment. We shut up like clams. It was obvious that no one was eager to act as interpreter for us, no matter what we might be able to pay. Semple suggested that we give up trying to find a guide and camp-man, and center on locating the laguna.

Our questions brought a veritable flood of answers, all of which emphasized the fact that the laguna was close about us in all directions, if not actually underfoot as well. Never had we been more puzzled. We had, up to that moment, supposed a *laguna* to be a lake, pure and simple; but all this gesticulating seemed to indicate that such a concept was wrong: a *laguna* was low-lying farm land or something along that line. Our queries about water got us nowhere. The villagers at first thought that we wanted to fish, but when we explained that we were not interested in sport, they decided that we wanted a drink.

Hot, testy, and bitterly disappointed, we drove back to the cracked, weather-worn signboard which read MAYRÁN. Looking at the network of roadways which led off to the north, our hearts sank. They were miserable roads, all of them. In the distance we thought we saw some cottonwood trees, but, remembering the mirage, we said nothing. We decided to find a nook in the hills off a way from the main road, to tuck the cars in for the night, and to resume our search on the morrow.

The nook we selected was half a mile south of the highway, at the base of a rocky hill. It was, at best, an unprepossessing spot. From the bits of paper, charred sticks, and wisps of fleece which littered the place, we guessed that goatherds had camped there before us. A considerable area had been cleared. Heaps of dead agave and creosote-bush would, we foresaw, supply us with fuel.

Burleigh and I, bearing in mind a thin patch of mesquite trees we had passed back toward San Pedro, decided to go after birds. Semple volunteered to watch the cars and find what he could close to camp. Within a quarter of an hour the dustiness and glare of San Pedro were forgotten; our failure to find the lake was forgotten; even the long, hot trip from Monterrey was a thing of the half-remembered past—for we were finding birds. Mourning Doves (*Zenaidura macroura*) were common. The musical whistling of their wings sounded wherever we went. Mockingbirds scolded and sang on all sides. Gnatcatchers whined and lisped snatches of song as they fed among the lacy leaves. Interested in determining what these were, we collected one, finding it to be a

27

Plumbeous Gnatcatcher (*Polioptila melanura*), recognizable from its glossy black cap and almost wholly black tail. This species we had not seen in the live oak grove near Monterrey.

The two warblers which we listed were winter resident species. One was the Orange-crown, which had been so common at Monterrey. The other we took at first to be the Myrtle, but careful inspection revealed the fact that its throat was yellow rather than white, so we knew it was the Audubon's Warbler (*Dendroica auduboni*), a species whose summer home was in the western United States, western Canada, and Alaska. We must have seen a hundred of these Audubon's Warblers, and every one of them, even the dullest females, had at least some yellow on its throat.

In the densest part of the grove some small, greenish-gray birds with upright posture attracted our attention. They were flycatchers of the puzzling genus *Empidonax*, no doubt—but which species? Looking at them carefully through our binoculars we decided that some of them were Wright's Flycatchers (*Empidonax wrighti*); but others appeared to be a trifle large and pale for that form. These wagged their tails phoebe-wise and gave a gentle, two-syllabled cry which reminded us somewhat of the *chebec* of the Least Flycatcher (*E. minimus*). We shot one, finding it to be a Gray Flycatcher (*E. griseus*), a species Burleigh had not seen before. I had become acquainted with it in the Big Bend country of Texas and now identified it in the hand by the narrowness of the bill and the light straw color of the lower mandible.

To our surprise we found a Great Horned Owl in this hot, thin woods. What a widespread, adaptable species *Bubo virginianus* was proving to be! Frightened from its hideout in a little gully, it flew to a mesquite a hundred yards off, alighted on a branch about three sizes too small for it, and looked about guiltily as if expecting some jay, crow, or hawk to pounce from somewhere. Its big eyes were wide open, the pupils contracted to mere pinpoints of black. Splashes of whitewashing on the ground here and there indicated that it probably had inhabited the grove for some time, yet apparently the smaller birds did not regard it as an enemy. Not even the high-strung Mockingbirds scolded as it sat there, looking clumsy, uncomfortable, and out of place in the tiny tree.

Handsomest of the feathered beings of this desert copse was a male Vermilion Flycatcher, a veritable flower of a bird, brilliant red on the crown and under parts, and dark gray on the face, back, wings, and tail. The sun shone through its fluffy crest, fashioning a flame-bright halo. Watching for insects, it perched daintily on dead weeds and leafless twigs; then, sensing the imminence of spring's return, it fluttered upward to perform a flight-song above the topmost plumes of the trees. While beating its fanned wings slowly, it sang its simple lay over and over, punctuating the phrases with loud snappings of its bill. The female was a plain little creature—grayish-brown above, white below, with gray streaking on the breast and sides, and a pink wash on the belly and under tail coverts.

Yet another member of the flycatcher family lived in this thinly shadowed bower—a sober, almost pensive bird, somewhat larger than the Vermilion Flycatcher, and gray above, soft tan below. This was Say's Phoebe (*Sayornis saya*), a common nesting species throughout much of the western United States and western Canada.

Burleigh and I returned to camp just as the sun was setting. Flocks

Vermilion Flycatcher (*Pyrocephalus rubinus*)
male, right; female, left
6 inches

29

of Long-billed Curlews (*Numenius americanus*) passed over us, their bodies dark against the bright sky. Their voices trembled through the still air as they set their wings for a long glide earthward.

Our friend Semple was elated over a beautifully marked chipmunk he had obtained on the hillside. He had seen several of them. Since the afternoon had been hot we skinned the little mammal immediately.

The wind from the hills was so strong that we had trouble with our campfire. Starting it at last, we found its odor unendurable. We built it up again, farther off, wondering as we worked how the coffee would taste. Gathering fuel was no pleasant task, for every bough and twig bore spines. Eventually we learned to drag the stuff in by the roots. After supper from cans and a cracker box, we made our beds. Out came the brightly striped mattresses, fresh from the Saltillo store. Out came all the sleeping bags, topcoats, hunting jackets, and sweaters that we had. In this country the night might turn out to be cold.

No sooner had our fire died down than a Horned Owl began booming on the hill just east of us. How solemn, how utterly without humor or friendliness, were those far-carrying syllables! How they served to recall the incidents of the day—the mirage, the battered sign along the highway, the futile harangue at San Pedro!

For more than an hour I lay with eyes wide open, watching the fading embers, listening to the sounds of dry plants shaken by the wind. Mackerel clouds drifted in from the east. So uniform in size and shape were these, and so symmetrically arranged, that the sky became a wondrous sort of Great White Way, whole sets of stars coming on and going off, coming on and going off, with the precise punctuality of electric signs. Wondering a little at hearing neither the yipping of coyotes nor the scuttling of pack rats through the brush, I fell asleep.

VII

Our waking thoughts on the morning of January 30 were of the laguna. Refreshed by ten hours of sleep, we crawled from our beds in the mildly cool air, listened in vain for a chorus of bird song, and briefly discussed plans for the day.

Burleigh and I decided to have a look from the hilltop just to the east of us. Following tortuous goat trails which led through clumps of sotol and across jagged outcroppings of rock, we made the summit in time to see the sun come up. A fresh wind struck us in the face, but heat seemed to emanate from the rocks at our feet, and waves of air warmed by yesterday's sun continued to rise from the lowlands.

The world about us was serene. Save for the faint rustling of dry pods and grass stems, and the distant trilling of a Rock Wren, there was no sound, nor was there movement save for the shaking of these same pods and grass stems, a barely perceptible drifting of clouds, and a gentle undulating of the horizon line. Now that the sun was up there was little color in the sky. The flat which stretched off to the north and east was a mass of indefinite gray to which no house, nor tree, nor winding bed of stream gave pattern. Looking toward San Pedro we thought we descried the red of roofs and yellow of adobe walls, but of this we could not be certain.

Closer by, especially among the rocks at our feet, bold spots of color enlivened the scene—the orange of tiny daisies, the pale yellow and magenta of cactus flowers, the waxy pink of a trim desert blossom whose name we did not know.

Off in the grayness to the northeast, so faint and dust-filmed as to be but half visible, two thin lines of white showed below the horizon. Even as we watched these glistening threads they disappeared, as if covered by a cloud. Then they showed again, this time reflecting the faint yellowness of the sky. We thought they might be the laguna. There was a fugitive quality about them, a come-and-go shimmer, which suggested the mirage—but we saw them, whatever they were, and they were enough to revive hope.

We started down the hill. The smoke from Semple's fire clung to the brush, adding an element of mystery to the scene below us. We had gone a hundred paces when Burleigh emitted a wild cry, asked for my pocket knife, and bade me go on. He had spied a mascot for our expedition—a tiny cactus about the size and shape of a ping pong ball, with a pink bud exactly on top. This he dug up, making certain that no part of the root was damaged and that a goodly lump of earth came with it, and displayed it with much satisfaction at breakfast. A trifle amused at this sudden appearance of a cactophile in our midst, we dehorned a tomato can, watched our friend pot the little plant, and helped him give it what was possibly the first real watering of its life.

Breakfast over, we climbed into the cars and resumed our search. On our way back to the main road we saw a jack rabbit and a "big" raven, and collected a specimen of Vesper Sparrow (*Poœcetes gramineus*), the first of this species which we had seen. It was readily identi-

31

fiable, as it flew up from the roadside, by its distinctly white outer tail feathers.

At the forlorn signboard we turned north from the highway, Burleigh and I in the first car, Semple following. There was no such thing as keeping to the road, for a scramble of cart tracks and cattle trails led off ahead of us. We steered our course by the big cottonwoods. Clouds of dust rose from the foliage we brushed in passing. We moved slowly, but moved ahead. This we knew because the cottonwoods gradually assumed more definite shape and color.

Burleigh and I frisked merrily along at fifteen miles an hour,

Loggerhead Shrike (*Lanius ludovicianus*)
8 inches

through narrow, brush-lined aisles, into and out of ruts, round sudden curves. The air back of us was so filled with dust that we hadn't the faintest notion where the other car was. All at once there was a furious roar, the sound of shifting gears, the blast of a horn, and a fresh cloud of dust to our right as a black automobile whirred past us at thirty miles an hour. We slowed up instantly, astonished, bewildered, half frightened.

It was Semple of course. Who else in this savage and unaccountable world would dare to do such a thing? Swinging into the road directly

PLATE II
Green Kingfisher
(*Chloroceryle americana*)

ahead of us, he slammed on the brakes, thrust out his hand with an imperious flourish, and came to a stop. We almost ran into him. There followed a lecture, delivered in a voice befitting the wildness of the scene, on careless driving. Burleigh and I were given to understand that if we kept on at the rate we had been going we could expect blowouts the rest of the trip from thorns picked up by our tires while running over mesquite brush.

Wondering how many spines Semple's tires had gathered during that wild spurt round us, but chastened nevertheless, we moved forward again. Within half an hour we reached Mayrán, which was not a lake, nor a pond, nor even a mudhole, but a village, a poor, sorry, hot, little *poblado* where nobody seemed to be making anything or going anywhere or even dreaming dreams. The streets were crawling with half-naked chickens, limp dogs, and scrawny pigs. The houses, trees, and cane fences were gray with dust. Half-heartedly we asked about the laguna, but our query seemed only to bewilder those to whom we spoke, so we took what appeared to be the main street and went on.

Beyond the village we entered a carefully cultivated and less dusty district where the roads were few but well defined, and green fields lay to either side of us. Here Loggerhead Shrikes were numerous along the hedgerows. Off to the north we heard a trumpeting of Sandhill Cranes (*Grus canadensis*). What a thrilling sound! Since we could not see the birds in the sky we felt sure they must be on the ground, feeding.

We gave up our search for the Laguna de Mayrán late that morning. Reaching the improved highway once more about noon, we sped eastward. We had with us several specimens we had collected the day before. As the heat of the day increased we realized that these would have to be skinned if we were to save them at all. So, watching the side of the road for a suitable place, we drew off and stopped, ate half a grapefruit apiece, and set to work.

Burleigh could change the front seat of his car into a sort of workroom in a twinkling. Out came the box of tools, corn meal, preservatives, and cotton; the whistle blew, so to speak, and he was at work. He was grand that way. As for me, I was obliged to establish myself under a low bridge. Taking specimens and tools hither, I sat down with my back against an abutment, picked pebbles from under me until I was comfortable, and began. My table was the cigar box in which I carried my taxidermic kit. I had trouble keeping the cotton from blowing off and the corn meal out of my eyes. A shower of dust and gravel fell whenever anyone passed over the bridge. But the place was cool and airy, and there was an element of excitement in hearing the footfalls of unknown persons so close above my head.

While working I continued to hear the spring song of a flicker. The wind was so strong that I had difficulty in ascertaining from which direction the sound came; but finally I saw the bird fly into a tree not far away. It climbed rapidly to a stub near the top, carefully selected a spot in which it was sheltered from the blast, and continued to sing. It was a Red-shafted Flicker.

Near the village of Parras we stopped for a close look at a fine, large Ferruginous Rough-legged Hawk (*Buteo regalis*) which was perched on a pole at the side of the road. Its breast and belly were gleaming white, its flags and tarsal feathering rusty-brown down to the very claws, its tail buffy-white at the base, gray toward the tip. It was a winter visitor to the region.

A few miles west of Saltillo we saw a puzzling hawk which we had to inspect with considerable care before deciding what it was. It was solid black, with yellow cere and feet, and three white bands on the under side of its tail. When it flew, we noted that the tail-bands were distinctly gray above,[1] and that lightish areas showed on the under side of the wings. The bird was a Zone-tailed Hawk (*Buteo albonotatus*), a species known to range northward into southwestern Texas, southern New Mexico and Arizona, and extreme southern California. It was much like a Red-tail in behavior and proportions, but was a little smaller than that species.

Between Saltillo and Monterrey we saw several Harris's Hawks, most of which appeared to be paired. The docile birds sat in the tops of trees not far from the highway, giving us a good look at the red-brown patch on each wing. As we drove past they roused themselves reluctantly, revealing the prominent white rump patch and narrow white tail-tip as they spread their wings and flew off.

We reached Monterrey that night. Not during the entire day—indeed not during the whole of the rather wearisome dash westward—had we seen a *distinctively* Mexican bird!

VIII

We spent most of the morning of January 31 among the fine old live oaks of Anáhuac Park, just north of Monterrey. How good it was to

[1] See page 196 for a drawing of the upper and under sides of the tail of the Zone-tailed Hawk.

be back! With appreciation born partly of the disappointment we had just experienced, we set to work with new vigor and determination. We were, by this time, fully aware of our failure to find certain well known and easily recognizable species—the Hooded Oriole (*Icterus cucullatus*), for instance—which we had assumed would be resident and common throughout the district. Where the birds of this category were, we could only surmise. At that time no one fully realized how migratory some of these species were, so our *not* finding them was, paradoxically enough, something in the nature of a contribution to knowledge.

Shortly after daybreak we saw our first Collared Seedeaters (*Sporophila torqueola*), little finches with blunt, not very conspicuous bills, round faces, and double callnote which resembled the syllables *tick-tick*.

Collared Seedeaters (*Sporophila torqueola*)
left, subadult male; middle, adult male; right, adult female
4 inches

They were quite confiding. Indeed, we found ourselves in their midst before we realized what they were.

Long-billed Thrasher (*Toxostoma longirostre*)
11 inches

The males were easily distinguishable from the females, for they were gray and glossy black above and buffy-white below, with an almost complete white collar, clear-cut white wing-markings, and, in some individuals, spots on the upper chest which vaguely suggested a black band. Fully adult males, in which this chest band was complete, were known to be rare in collections, and most of the males which we saw were presumably immature. The females were dull olive-brown above, buff below, and somewhat nondescript, though they had inconspicuous wing-bars. We saw no sign of the flock's breaking up into pairs, and heard no singing even from the most brightly colored males.

In the brushland off to the north we heard from time to time a loud, rhythmic song which was so amazingly similar to the *teakettle, teakettle, teakettle* or *which jailer? which jailer? which jailer?* of the Carolina Wren (*Thryothorus ludovicianus*) back home, that we felt certain that this bird, whatever its name, would prove to be of the same species. But we failed to catch so much as a glimpse of the elusive creature.

We became well acquainted with the Long-billed Thrasher. This bird occupied the same sort of ecological niche as that occupied by the Brown Thrasher in the farmlands and forest edges of the eastern United

States. It was, indeed, strikingly like that bird in some particulars—
notably in its harsh *tchuck* of alarm, which sometimes startled us as we
threaded our way through the shrubbery, its energetic scratching on the
ground, and its song. It had a habit of hopping upward through a bush
to a perch full in the open, then suddenly diving back toward the ground
with closed wings. Its eyes were rich golden orange, bright as live coals.
One of its characteristic callnotes was a mellow, somewhat bluebirdlike
too-ree. Its song was like the Brown Thrasher's in that each phrase was
once repeated; but we were uncertain about a good many of the songs
which we heard, for we were beginning to realize that the Mockingbirds
imitated the thrashers a good deal, and we suspected that the thrashers
did some imitating on their own. The confusion was considerable.

Curve-billed Thrasher (*Toxostoma curvirostre*)
11 inches

We ascertained that the Long-billed Thrasher was primarily a bird of the smilax tangles and thick shrubbery. The Curve-billed Thrasher, on the other hand, was especially fond of areas in which the prickly pear cactus flourished. In its song there were no obviously repeated phrases. Its most frequently given callnote was a sharp, loud *whit-it-it!* Occasionally it chattered or made grating, angry-sounding cries.

Our studies took us into an open, somewhat formal part of the grove—an area we had avoided because we had heard men at work there. No one raised objection to our presence, however, so we wandered about watching the Green Jays and Black-crested Titmice, and looking for new birds. Suddenly the whining cry of a middle-sized woodpecker attracted our attention. The bird flew across a clearing, alighting in a live oak not far from the workmen.

We went after the woodpecker at once, and had no trouble shooting it; but to our dismay the dead specimen caught in a crotch and would not come down. We tossed sticks at it until our arms ached. Finally we had to climb for it. Imagine our surprise at finding it to be a Yellow-bellied Sapsucker (*Sphyrapicus varius varius*)—a species we had seen hundreds of times in the United States and Canada. It was in mixed plumage, having only a fleck or two of red on the throat and crown. In our enthusiasm to discover something new and *Mexican* we had failed to recognize its callnote (a nasal *mew* or *kew* which we knew perfectly well); to note that it hitched *downward* on the tree trunk an instant after alighting—behavior we should instantly have recognized as characteristic; above all to pay attention to an obvious field-mark—the large white patch in each wing. Thus, bit by bit, did we discover that the process of learning Mexican birds involved becoming acquainted with our own "home" birds all over again!

As we crossed a bit of open grassland, we put up a loose flock of middle-sized, chunky birds which had short tails and distinctly white outer tail feathers. We recognized them at once as meadowlarks, but since they uttered neither song nor callnote we were obliged to collect one in order to be sure of the species. The specimen proved to be a Western Meadowlark (*Sturnella neglecta*), for the yellow of the throat ran well up onto the side of the head. What the local status of the species was we had no way of knowing. Our failure to hear its song suggested that it did not nest in the Monterrey district but only wintered there.

A low *chuh* which sounded from a thicket attracted our attention to another well-known United States bird—a Yellow-throat (*Geothlypis trichas*). We scrutinized this member of the warbler tribe with great care, making certain that it was not the unfamiliar bird which we all wanted to see—the so-called Río Grande or Thick-billed Yellow-throat (*Chamaethlypis poliocephala*). The bird before us was far too small-billed, obviously, for *Chamaethlypis*. Furthermore its over-all size was too small, it was too short-tailed, and its black facial mask was too extensive. The Thick-billed Yellow-throat was a wholly different bird, distinguishable at once by its proportionately (as well as actually) longer tail and heavier bill. In addition to this, the male was distinctly gray on the crown and had a partial, white eye-ring.

We were by this time beginning to realize what a mistake it was to make a snap identification of any bird we saw. As we were casually watching a company of Myrtle Warblers we noticed that one of the little birds was yellow-throated. That individual was not, in other words, a Myrtle Warbler at all, but an Audubon's—a western species which we had not expected to record at Monterrey. Again, when a flock of bluebirds flew over we observed them somewhat perfunctorily, hardly suspecting that they could be anything out of the ordinary. But those which we saw clearly through our glasses proved to be either brownish-gray or light blue on the breast. They were, in other words, Mountain Bluebirds (*Sialia currucoides*), a species known to nest in western North America from Chihuahua to Yukon. From that time on, needless to say, we identified all bluebirds with care. Those which had distinctly reddish-brown throat and breast we knew to be Eastern Bluebirds (*S. sialis*), but those with grayish-brown breast were female Mountain Bluebirds. The male Mountain Bluebird was recognizable at virtually any distance, even in its dullest winter plumage, because it was light turquoise blue all over.

Certain elusive, brown-backed, all but silent birds which occasionally flitted ahead of us through the brush were Hermit Thrushes (*Hylocichla guttata*). Their only callnote, so far as we could discover, was a low *chook* or *took*. Their tails were reddish-brown—a color which was fairly strong in certain lights, but not in others. The geographical race to which these birds belonged was a matter of conjecture. They probably were not the well-known bird of the eastern United States, *H. guttata faxoni,* for their coloration, particularly that of the tail, was not rich enough.

During our four or five hours afield that morning we saw several Marsh Hawks (*Circus cyaneus*) beating back and forth over the brushland in easy buoyant flight. Most of these were brown first-year birds or adult females, but one was a beautiful pale gray adult male, which was downright gull-like in appearance as it flapped past, giving us a good look at its clean white under parts and black wing-tips. All these Marsh Hawks were white-rumped, of course. The field-mark was a well known one. Experience had long since taught us, however, that even the Red-tailed Hawk appeared white-rumped at times, especially when seen from above or behind; we knew from what we had read, as well as from specimens we had handled in museums, that one of Mexico's famous and puzzling "black hawks" was white on the upper tail coverts; and we were daily becoming more familiar with the fact that even the Harris's Hawk was white-rumped. In short, we didn't identify those Marsh Hawks by their white rumps at all. We identified them by their manner of coursing back and forth a few feet above the ground, and we merely checked the identification by noticing the white rump now and then.

A small hawk which we collected as it darted through the trees proved to be a male Sharp-shin (*Accipiter striatus velox*). It was heavily barred with reddish-brown below. The several Red-tailed Hawks which we saw circling or perched in the tops of trees were so darkly colored on the under parts that we decided they probably were Western Red-tails (*Buteo jamaicensis calurus*). Occasionally we saw a Sparrow Hawk hovering or dropping to the ground for prey. Once a fair-sized, short-winged, gray-backed accipiter dashed ahead of us, angling between the bushes as if chasing a smaller bird. This was more than likely a Cooper's Hawk (*Accipiter cooperi*).

Two large buteonine hawks which we recorded that morning were of special interest to us. One of these was like a Red-tail in size, bearing, and proportions, but its under parts and tail were gleaming white, the latter being crossed by a broad subterminal band of black. This was the White-tailed Hawk (*Buteo albicaudatus*), a South and Central American species known to range northward to middle Texas. The other was a slightly smaller bird which resembled an immature Red-tail in that its tail was grayish-brown, narrowly barred with black; but its chest was crossed by a distinct brown band. This was a Swainson's Hawk (*B. swainsoni*), a species easy enough to identify in its ordinary "light" phase of plumage, but very puzzling, even to the ablest of field ornithologists, in its rarely seen melanistic or black plumage-phase.

We were delighted to find the region so well populated with these several beautiful birds of prey. Their presence indicated not only that a food supply abounded, but also that the Mexicans were not slaughtering them for sport. To our great disappointment, however, we did not see a White-tailed Kite (*Elanus leucurus*); and we looked in vain for the two large, sluggish, black hawks which we so much wanted to see—

the Black Hawk (*Buteogallus anthracinus*), which in its adult plumage was black with narrow white tail tip and a single broad white tail band; and the puzzlingly similar Urubitinga (*Hypomorphnus urubitinga*),[1] a long-legged, rather short-winged hawk which was, when adult, solid black save for the two (or three) white bars on the tail, the *boldly white upper tail coverts,* and obscure white flecking on the leg feathers.

The various black hawks of Mexico were a knotty problem for the field student, that we well knew. There were at least five of them in the more northeasterly parts of the Republic: the two just mentioned; the Zone-tailed Hawk, which we had seen once in southern Coahuila; the dark or black phase of the Western Red-tail; and the black phase of the Swainson's Hawk. The last of these was easy enough to identify in the hand from the notching of the *three* outermost primaries; but the free-flying bird was impossible to place with absolute certainty. Even the Harris's Hawk often looked solid black.

From our experience with museum specimens we suspected that the various subadult plumages of the Black Hawk and the Urubitinga would be very confusing. In neither of these species was the young bird truly black. It was, generally speaking, dark brown above; white or buff, much streaked with brown and black, on the head and under parts; and light gray or white, barred with black, on the tail. For a further discussion of the identification of the black hawks of Mexico, see the appendix.

IX

Since we did not obtain many specimens that busy morning, we finished our skinning by four o'clock in the afternoon. Eager to discover what sort of country lay beyond Anáhuac Park, we set out again, finding ourselves this time in a scrubby woodland possibly half a mile east of the main highway.

Coming upon a flock of Clay-colored Sparrows along a little-used

[1] The name "Urubitinga" admittedly is difficult, but confusion will result from any common name using the words "black hawk" in view of the fact that *Buteogallus anthracinus* has long been called that. The North American race of the Urubitinga, *Hypomorphnus urubitinga ridgwayi,* has been known as the Ridgway's Black Hawk. Henceforth this bird may well be called Ridgway's Urubitinga. Those who object to the difficulty of pronouncing *Urubitinga* should bear in mind that no one now hesitates to use such "difficult" words as *Phainopepla, Pyrrhuloxia,* and *Phalarope.*

road, we collected one. At the sound of the shot, several soldiers armed with huge machetes burst from the thicket, shouts rose on all sides, and a distant slamming of doors suggested that the infantry might be turning out for a skirmish. We displayed our permits and the specimen —which looked curiously small in the midst of so well-armed a company—and were good-naturedly dismissed; but common sense directed us to seek a birding-ground farther away from the city.

A mile or so to the north we found a woodland through which ran an old irrigation ditch. This watercourse was perfectly straight for half a mile, but it had been there so long that it had almost lost its man-made appearance. The stream itself was two or three feet wide, about a

Black-throated Sparrow (*Amphispiza bilineata*)
5½ inches

foot deep, and quite clear. It was too swift for a growth of cattails and elephant-ears, but its banks were thick with dead weeds, shrubbery, and fallen branches, and considerable stretches of it were obscured by green masses of cat's-claw smilax, which clambered over it supported by trees.

So glorious was the late afternoon that we were conscious of a desire to move deliberately and silently. The day had been gray, but now the low-hanging clouds parted and a gentle brilliance enveloped the world. Off to the south, Saddle Mountain stood clear and dark against the sky. As if brought to life by the sun's slanting rays, birds hopped upward through the thicket, chose perches on the topmost twigs and cactus pads, and began to sing. A veritable symphony rose from the brushland about us.

Most noticeable of the songsters were the mockingbirds and thrashers. Wherever we looked one of these birds was to be seen, head lifted, tail down, mouth open, throat quivering lustily. The thrashers were content with singing; but the mockingbirds were so ebullient that they turned flip-flops too, fluttering upward for a somersault, coming down with wings and tail widespread, singing all the while without missing a syllable.

Whole flocks of Black-throated Sparrows were singing. Each song was clear and sweet, but its pattern was lost in the chorus. From the low bushes came the monotonous *churr, churr, churr, churr* of Clay-colored Sparrows, a thousand miles from their nesting ground, but induced to song by the generous warmth of the sun; or the half whispered *cheery-weer, cheer, cheery-weer* of a White-crowned Sparrow. The Lincoln's Sparrows, though fairly common, were not singing; and from the abundant Chipping Sparrows and Olive Sparrows came only low chirps of alarm and the squeaks and squeals of petty bickering.

The peevish complaints of Blue-gray Gnatcatchers and chattered cries of Green Jays were so incessant that we paid little heed to them. The piping of Great-tailed Grackles became a sort of organ point so all-pervasive as to be unnoticeable. Even the songs of the thrashers, mockingbirds, cardinals, and Black-crested Titmice were such a jumble that only an occasional phrase stood much chance of being heard. But when, from a branch above the irrigation ditch, the bold *geep!* of a Kiskadee Flycatcher sounded, we were instantly on the lookout for the fine bird.

The Kiskadee's usual call-note at this season was the single *geep!* or *weep!* just mentioned. But sometimes this was followed by a clearly enunciated *career,* the whole cry thus becoming *geep career!* If two Kiskadees wrangled, the phrase became loud and incisive and harsh chatter mingled with ferocious snappings of the mandibles.

We watched two Kiskadees for some time. They were dignified and unhurried. Sitting upright, they turned their heads slowly, eyeing each insect which flew past as if taking careful note of its size and calculating its precise caloric value. Obviously they were in no great need of food. But when a fair-sized moth or beetle appeared, their whole bearing changed, their crests went down, and their red-brown wings spread for the chase.

They spent much of their time near water. At first we thought this

43

Derby Flycatcher or Kiskadee (*Pitangus sulphuratus*)
10 inches

was because the insect supply was good there; but we soon discovered that they caught small fish now and then. Frequently they perched on rocks or snags which barely protruded from the stream, and they fairly soused themselves when snatching a minnow from just below the surface.

As we walked along the irrigation ditch scores of small birds bustled about us—all of them busy feeding, none of them singing. They were so confiding that in identifying them we had but to stand perfectly still and wait for them to move upward into plain sight one by one. Most of them we had already listed; but the Macgillivray's Warbler (*Oporornis tolmiei*) we had not seen before, and we were interested to discover that it was fairly common here. It was a ground-inhabiting species, obviously; but now and then it hopped high enough in the shrubbery to give us a good look at its olive back, wings, and tail, and clear yellow under parts.

The male had a dark bluish-gray head, slaty-gray bib, and distinct, though interrupted, white eye-ring; while the female was olive above, yellow below, with brownish-gray head and indistinct, as well as incomplete, white eye-ring. The species' summer home was in far-removed northwestern parts of the continent. It was another of those distinctly western birds which wintered regularly in the vicinity of Monterrey.

Rufous-capped Warbler (*Basileuterus rufifrons*)
4¾ inches

Our next new bird was a real surprise, for it belonged to a genus none of us had ever before seen alive. Again it was a warbler—of that we were quite certain—but it was so different from anything we had seen in the United States that we were considerably puzzled. Fortunately for us, it was not very secretive, so we had a good look at it. It had bright yellow throat and breast, rufous crown- and ear-patch, clear white line above the eye, olive back, wings and tail, and white belly. Its tail was longish and noticeably *narrow*. It seemed to be terrestrial, but it hopped

45

up through the smilax wagging its tail in the manner of a gnatcatcher, and fed in the tops of bushes not far from the water's edge. Its alarm cry was a *chip* or *chup,* not unlike that of a yellow-throat. Occasionally it gave a series of these *chups.* But what we heard of its song seemed to be bright, tuneful, and somewhat suggestive of that of an Indigo Bunting (*Passerina cyanea*). It was a Rufous-capped Warbler (*Basileuterus rufifrons*), one of the most northward-ranging members of a large South and Central American branch of the warbler family. Not even knowing what it was at the time, we collected it with great care, wondering whether it had ever before been recorded in the Monterrey region.

The new warbler was exciting, but the thrill of thrills came with the Brown Jays (*Psilorhinus morio*), five of which inhabited this woodland. We were standing there eyeing little birds through our binoculars when the big, dark, loose-jointed jays flopped across an open space in front of us. Their spread wings were noticeably rounded. We observed that their primaries curved upward sharply on the down-strokes of the wings and that their tails pumped comically. The general effect they created in flight was of five small hawks clowning shamelessly. Their loud, resonant cries sounded like *peeah! peeah!* The woods rang with the noise.

The screaming stopped, the five birds flopped off, the woodland grew still. Waiting for complete silence, we "squeaked" loudly. The jays instantly returned, yelling at the tops of their voices, perching not far above our heads. Here they sprang noisily from twig to twig without lifting their wings, peering at us first with one eye then with the other, so intent upon their protestation that they did not even shut their beaks between screams. It was high time they were finding a roosting place, but banish the enemy they must while yet there was daylight. Listening carefully, we noticed a rattling quality in their cries. Each scream stopped with extraordinary abruptness in a sort of hiccough, as if a valve somewhere had snapped shut, cutting off the sound.

The jays were not brightly plumaged. Their charm lay in their boldness, their noisiness, their candid inquisitiveness. They were about as large as crows, but were somewhat longer-tailed. They were plain grayish-brown all over the head and upper parts, light gray or white on the belly and under tail coverts. Two of the flock were black-billed, but in the other three the bills were yellow, marked with black along the top of the upper mandible and at the tip. We had no idea what color a Brown Jay's bill should be, but concluded, naturally enough, that if the five birds were a family, the two black-billed ones must be the parents.

The Brown Jays' tirade attracted a band of Green Jays, which added their rowdy chatter to the hue and cry. Smaller birds, too, hopped up through the thicket—Olive Sparrows, which chirped faintly; Green-tailed Towhees, which *mewed* at us; and Audubon's and Orange-crowned Warblers, which were so nonplussed that they remained discreetly silent.

Wishing to make a sketch of a Brown Jay, I collected one of the yellow-billed birds. Examining it at once, I noted that the eyes were dark brown, oddly patched with silvery gray, the eyelids thick and wrinkled, the tarsi straw-yellow, the toes black. The feathers of the forehead stuck up and forward a little, forming a slight crest, but the nostrils were completely uncovered.

By this time night was gathering. The remaining four Brown Jays were silent. But the Green Jays' raucous chattering continued. For a time it waxed so fervent that we thought they must be badgering an owl.

On our way back to Monterrey we saw a night bird near the road. We would never have known it was there had not its eyes shone brightly pink in the light from our car. We had little more than a glimpse of it as it flew up, showing white patches in its wings and long tail, another glimpse as it fluttered into the blackness of the thicket. It was a Pauraque (*Nyctidromus albicollis*).

After supper we skinned the Brown Jay. It was a tough, bloody specimen. The most notable of its several queer anatomical features was a little pouch of flabby skin hidden among the chest plumage. This appendage was covered with short, downy, white feathers, and was directly connected with the respiratory system. Pressing the dead bird under the wings, we were able to inflate the pouch instantly, causing it to spring up from the plumage. It now was spherical, slightly translucent, and about three quarters of an inch in diameter. When we released the pressure, the pouch collapsed with a curious clicking sound—the hiccough we had heard from the living bird.

X

Anyone who expects Monterrey weather to be bright and warm all winter is sure to be disappointed. Early on the morning of February 1 we were so cold we were miserable. We rose eagerly enough and enjoyed a hearty breakfast; but afield we found ourselves in a wretched, half-congealed state of scrooched-up shoulders, stiff hands and watery eyes, and wondered why we hadn't brought with us our heavy underwear. Clouds hung low over the valley, hiding the mountains, and fine rain fell.

Making our way first to the live oak grove north of the city we drove about until we found a somewhat hidden spot in which to leave the car. Hardly had we stepped out when a familiar sound greeted us—the lisping of Cedar Waxwings (*Bombycilla cedrorum*) overhead. There must have been fifty birds in the flock, all of them milling about shaggy clumps of mistletoe, eagerly snatching off the berries as the green stems sagged. The scream of a Red-tailed Hawk silenced them momentarily. Taking sudden alarm, they shot off en masse.

Another new bird for our list was the Blue-headed Vireo (*Vireo solitarius*), a winter visitant species easy to identify first because it was deliberate and confiding, again because its color pattern was so clear-cut. Its upper parts were dark, its under parts light. The top of its head was bluish-gray, and its white eye-ring was very distinct. Its sides were pale yellow. It had two white wing-bars.

Black-crested Titmouse (*Parus atricristatus*)
5¼ inches

PLATE III
Bronzed Woodpecker
(*Piculus aeruginosus*)

We were especially interested in determining the name of the wren whose *teakettle* song we had heard the day before. To reach the thorny tangles in which we believed we would find this bird, we followed a cart road a way and pushed through the underbrush to a tiny vine-hung pool. The route was known to us, for we had visited the spot several times.

That certain individual birds spent most of their time about this pool was becoming clearer to us day by day. There was, for example, the big Kiskadee Flycatcher which we could count on finding directly above the water, sitting quietly on a dead branch. It could hardly have had a mate for no other Kiskadee lived anywhere close by. We had seen the one bird time after time, noting that it seemed to regard the pool as its own. Today the clear yellow of its breast and belly added a note of cheer to the somber woodland.

Then there were the Black-crested Titmice which sometimes scolded us as we walked about the pool. Six or seven of these little birds went about together in a loose flock—probably a family group. They were here as usual, pounding busily at galls which they carried about in their feet, whacking at tough cocoons, or investigating cavities in trees. Somewhat to our surprise they accepted us without protest. Like the wood gatherers and cattle drivers who so frequently passed, we were only human beings and therefore to be accepted as part of any well-organized titmouse habitat. One of the birds even broke into a clear, whistled *peeto, peeto, peeto* which belied the coolness of the air.

As for the four or five Olive Sparrows which we had repeatedly noted feeding among the leaves at the water's edge, we thought at first they were going to fail us. But here they were—two in plain enough sight under a fallen branch, kicking away like little towhees; another off in the shrubbery, invisible but scratching noisily; and two more in a vine, a short way above the ground, busily preening their wings.

One by one the birds which belonged here put in their appearance: a Long-billed Thrasher, which called *too-ree* from a smilax tangle, gave a low *chuck* of alarm, and flew across the pool; two Orange-crowned Warblers, which we recognized *as individuals* from the way in which the facial feathers were molting; a male Cardinal, then a female, which chirped sharply, and darted off between the oaks; a dirty little female Ladder-backed Woodpecker; even the big Horned Owl which had flown now from this hideout, now from that, but always from some thick tree near the pool.

We knew that these birds did not spend all their time in this circumscribed area, of course. The Horned Owl might wander miles afield

49

during the course of a single night's hunting. The two Cardinals we sometimes came upon a hundred yards away. Even the relatively sedentary Olive Sparrows wandered out into the dry weed patches, some distance from the water. But this woodland was their winter home, the pool a sort of focal point of their existence.

Northward from the pool led a stream or ditch along which other birds lived. Hither we walked, choosing our course carefully so as to make little noise. Smilax flourished here; but the broad leaves of the elephant-ear plants, which grew at the water's edge, were blotched with brown and partly dead, perhaps from the cold.

A spot of white in the top of a small tree attracted our attention: a tiny spot which looked like a blob of cotton lodged among the twigs. Fancy our surprise at finding this to be a dead Blue-gray Gnatcatcher, hanging by its foot from a narrow fork! It could hardly have been put there by a shrike. No shrike would have preferred a forked twig to a thorn; nor would a shrike have gone off without eating at least part of its prey. Furthermore, examination disclosed no trace of wound. The gnatcatcher had caught its foot, twisted and jerked and fluttered trying to get free, and died at last. The carcass had dried perfectly and was virtually odorless.

Squeaking in imitation of a crippled bird was part of our wren-hunting plan. This morning, however, perhaps because the weather was so cool, our squeaking produced unusual results. The small birds heeded us little. But the birds of prey came with a rush—on one occasion a Harris's Hawk, which flapped rapidly in, swept to the top of a tree not more than twenty feet away, and eyed us fiercely; again a Cooper's Hawk, which dashed in from behind, striking vines, leaves, and twigs in its headlong approach, and actually brushed my arm roughly with its wing as it turned.

Finally we heard one of the wrens scolding in the depths of a thicket. It did not sing and we could not squeak it out. Its cries roused a second wren, then a third. The harsh-voiced birds were all about us, hidden in the smilax. We finally got a specimen. Elated, we looked at it critically, noting its rich reddish-brown upper parts, the buffy-white line over the eye, the buffy-brown under parts, and barred flanks. We were not surprised at its appearance, for it was essentially the very bird we had seen repeatedly in West Virginia, southwestern Pennsylvania, Georgia, and Mississippi—the Carolina Wren. It was, of course, a geographical race of this species, the bird known as Berlandier's Wren (*Thryothorus ludovicianus berlandieri*); but we all felt, after observing it carefully and listening to its callnotes and songs, that the only really correct name for it was Berlandier's *Carolina* Wren.

Our wren was not very noticeable at this season. To see it we had literally to beat the dense clumps of vines, forcing it to fly out. Most of the time it was silent. Now and then, however, its impulse to sing gave its whereabouts away. A loud *teakeetle, teakeetle, teakeetle* would burst from a thicket close by, a scolding *djeer* would issue from the tangle beyond, and before we had recovered from the shock, a half dozen other *teakeetle* songs had sounded from as many thickets. That the song of one bird inspired the other wrens to sing was obvious. Sometimes even the roar of our shotguns would set one bird to singing, whereupon the others would take up the challenge and the woodland would ring with merry music.

At noon we returned to our rooms to skin specimens. As we approached Monterrey we noticed that the sky over one section of the

Berlandier's Wren (*Thryothorus ludovicianus berlandieri*)
5¼ inches

51

city was minutely flecked with black. Using the binoculars, we beheld an immense congregation of vultures, hundreds if not thousands of birds, circling in a funnel-shaped cloud.

XI

The flat country immediately about Monterrey has an elevation of 1,500 to 1,700 feet. This somewhat arid plain is almost completely surrounded by mountains, the most conspicuous and famous of which is Saddle Mountain to the southeast, a bold and picturesque peak which frequently is obscured by clouds in winter. South and west of the city rises the Sierra Madre itself—massive, forest-clad, topped with cliffs which look like vast battlements. The rough country to the north is really foothills of this sierra. From them a low spur leads northeastward across the plain.

Soon after reaching Monterrey we heard of the Mesa de Chipinque. The Mesa was, we learned, on the big mountain just to the south. The Mesa's elevation was about 5,000 feet, and an improved road led to it. From it one could look down upon the city and the whole length and breadth of the lowland to the north and east. No one seemed to know whether there were birds on it, but when the spot was pointed out to us we perceived, with our binoculars, that the whole mountainside at that level was covered with pine forest. The more we thought of that far-removed place, and of the birds which would surely be living there, the more eager we were to make the ascent.

On the second day of February we drove to the Mesa. Turning south at the western edge of the city, we made straight for the big mountain. After paying one peso apiece at an *Alto!* (Stop!) sign at the foot, we began climbing. So gentle was the grade that we moved forward in high gear. The vegetation about us was low and exceedingly thick. Now and then the delicate aroma of opening flowers reached our nostrils. The purple buds of a squat, leguminous shrub set our eyes to roving for hummingbirds. The slope to our left was gashed with innumerable gullies, some of them veritable canyons.

Even on the lower levels the hairpin curves made us hold our breath. As we climbed we were startled by the steepness of the slope above and below us, and by the narrowness of the road. The slow unfolding of the haze-filmed lowlands exhilarated us strangely. We said but little. Instead we listened—for the sound of a horn round the curve ahead, for the cry of an unfamiliar bird. We leaned forward eagerly, a little apprehensively, as we glanced down the sharp declivity at the left.

As for birds, they were few. The only ones we identified satisfactorily were a phoebe, a Mockingbird, and some Turkey Vultures. The vultures were now as frequently to be seen below us as above us.

At length we entered the pine belt. The trees were fine and large, with red-brown bark and deep green leafage. There were oaks, too, not live oaks nor scrub oaks, but well shaped spreading trees whose gnarled boughs were shaggy with lichens. We continued to climb. Below us we beheld loop after loop of the highway up which we had come, and, off in the rolling country to the north, the tiny ribbon of road which led to Monterrey.

Had we been obliged to walk, this world of pine and oak might have seemed more real. Walking would have given us time for adjustment. But riding, ascending so quickly, reaching so effortlessly this new life-zone, gave us the feeling of being in a huge museum, of passing from exhibit to exhibit, of looking through glass at trees made of papier-mâché and wax, with a vast and wonderful painting at the back.

The Mesa was a surprise. Not so much the cluster of small, well-constructed buildings, one of which we had seen from the foot of the mountain; not so much the magnificent view, for we had expected that; but the Mesa itself, which was in fact not a tableland at all, but a broad, gently sloping shelf, extending for several hundred yards along the mountain's bold front. Two thousand feet above this shelf towered the mountain's real top—a realm of gigantic, cloud-hung cliffs and deep ravines. At all levels there were trees, even at the tip of the highest pinnacle.

One glance at the woodland about us, one instant of tense listening, and we knew we had come to a wonderful place. Not even the Turkey Vultures could break the spell. Familiar though these widely ranging birds were, there was a newness about them as the golden brown of their sun-struck backs and wings stood out against the rich green of the pines far below us.

The most noticeable bird of the Mesa was the Mexican Jay (*Aphelocoma ultramarina*).[1] Hardly had we got out of the car when three of these noisy mischief-makers flew up, bespoke their curiosity with harsh squawks, and inspected us impudently. They were about the size

[1] The common name "Mexican Jay" has not had very wide use, but since the bird inhabits much of the Mexican plateau, is not found south of Mexico, and occurs in the United States only in mountains near the border, "Mexican Jay" seems entirely appropriate.

of the well known Blue Jay (*Cyanocitta cristata*), but were strikingly different from that species in that they had no crests. Their color-pattern was very simple—plain blue above, light gray below, but what they lacked in variety of hue they certainly made up for in brightness of eye and alertness of manner. Plain in appearance, they were sturdy, almost without fear, and intelligent. Since they obviously were common, we made no attempt to collect a specimen at the moment.

Laying our plans quickly, we decided to go separate ways, thus to obtain as quickly as possible a broad knowledge of the mountainside. My companions elected to take a trail which led westward at the Mesa's level. As for myself, I looked upward toward the gray cliffs which showed through the trees, and decided on a climb. Curiously enough, not one of us so much as considered retracing our way down the road by which we had come.

I soon found that birds were not common, and that the climbing was anything but easy. The slope was deeply covered with pine needles and these were so dry and slippery that I could scarcely keep my feet. For more than an hour I toiled upward, annoyed with the inadequacy of my shoes, and surprised and disappointed with the silence of the place. At last, reaching the base of one of the cliffs, and completely charmed by the wild beauty of the spot, I sat down. Delicate white flowers were blooming at my feet. Surely they must be spring beauties! That little mass of pink off in the gray forest—could that be anything but a blooming redbud tree? I put my hand on the cliff. It was rough, like slag. Close by I could find no moss. But I saw ferns in shadowy niches to one side, and just above me spread a giant maguey, firmly rooted in the rock.

Through the stillness spilled a cascade of bird-song: notes so liquid I felt they must surely splash somewhere—eight, perhaps nine, clear whistles in a descending scale, tossed from a ledge or crevice far above me. I had heard that bird before—in the Black Mesa country of the Oklahoma Panhandle and in the Big Bend country of Texas. It was a Canyon Wren (*Catherpes mexicanus*).

I did not see the bird. I looked for it hard enough, for a Canyon Wren from this locality would have been interesting indeed. But it eluded me. For a time it was so directly above me that a pebble dislodged by its feet struck the needles behind me. But it kept itself hidden even while its singing roused echoes from the distant crags.

Before descending to the Mesa, I encountered a roving bird flock. All the species were small and restless to the point of fidgetiness—bustling from twig to twig, preening themselves nervously, uttering sharp little notes whereby each informed the others as to its whereabouts, while at the same time warning them to keep their distance and find their own caterpillars, moth eggs, and aphids.

One member of this flock was easy enough to identify. Even if I had not seen its colors, I would have recognized it by what Gilbert White of Selborne would have called its "air," for it was our own Black and White Warbler (*Mniotilta varia*). It crept about the larger branches, investigating crevices in the bark, keeping somewhat to itself. The Mesa was, then, part of the Black and White Warbler's winter home.

Tiniest of all were the Ruby-crowned Kinglets, fluffy, round-bodied midgets which surveyed me with their beady eyes, flicked their wings, and expressed their disapproval with the harsh *chud-duh!* which I had heard hundreds of times in the Canadian spruce woods. There were Black-crested Titmice, too, the very same species we had been seeing in the lowlands.

But what was that chickadeelike cry, that fine *see, zee, zee, zee, did-did-did-did-did!* so rapidly and buzzily given? Surely no Black-crested Titmouse ever sang such a song; surely no Ruby-crowned King-let had any such cry. As I watched and wondered, a small gray bird flitted toward me, alighted on a branch close by, and gave me an excellent view of its jaunty crest and bizarre black facial markings. Without even lifting my binocular I knew it was a Bridled Titmouse (*Parus wollweberi*), the first I had ever seen. It was a species found in the United States only in the mountains of southwestern New Mexico and southern Arizona.

Eager to inspect it more closely, I squeaked. Down it came with all its companions, a dozen or more Bridled Tits, all of them calling *see, zee, zee, zee, zee, did-did-did-did-did-did!* in unison. The Black-crested Tit-mice came too, and the Ruby-crowned Kinglets, and a host of pretty wood warblers all of which appeared to belong to the same species—a species which was wholly new to me. In general these warblers re-sembled Parula Warblers (*Parula americana*) in that they were yellow below and had sharply pointed bills; but a round reddish-brown spot in the middle of the chest declared them to be quite different from any-thing I had ever seen, and further inspection revealed another well-defined field character—the bold white line over the eye. The upper part of the head, otherwise, was bluish-gray, as were the wings and tail. There were no wing-bars. The back was olive-green, the flanks brownish-olive, the belly white. The only callnote that I heard was a sharp *chip*.

55

Bridled Titmouse (*Parus wollweberi*)
5 inches

This new bird was Hartlaub's Warbler (*Vermivora superciliosa*),[2] a species known to inhabit the Middle American highlands from Mexico southward to Nicaragua. How disappointed I was not to hear its song!

Before descending to the Mesa I had a good, though brief, look at a Canyon Wren—a handsome, dark rusty-brown bird with long, slender bill and white throat. Also, somewhat to my surprise, I came upon several Rufous-capped Warblers, the very species we had seen in the low country just north of Monterrey. Again I noticed that their behavior was much like that of gnatcatchers in that they wagged their tails as they hopped upward through the shrubbery.

At the Mesa we had a surprisingly good look at a new and interesting bird which appeared to be common about the very dooryard of the hostelry—a sparrow in which the under parts were sulphur-yellow; the upper part of the head ashy-gray with clear-cut, reddish-brown crown-patch; and the back, wings, sides, and tail olive-brown. In behavior and size it was not unlike a White-crown. It was ground-loving, somewhat

2 "Hartlaub's Warbler" is, admittedly, a somewhat bookish name. If a more descriptive common name is desired, "White-browed Warbler," suggested by my friend Eugene Eisenmann, will suffice.

secretive, and fond of kicking up leaves while searching for food. Six or seven of the pretty creatures frequented a ravine not far from one of the guest houses. They were Rufous-capped Sparrows, or to employ a less easy, but more distinctive name, Rufous-capped Atlapetes (*Atlapetes pileatus*), a species whose range was restricted to the Mexican plateau.

The outstanding bird of the day was a beautiful male Sharp-shinned Hawk which Semple collected. He displayed the specimen somewhat diffidently, as if fearful that he had brought in too common a bird. I took one look at the little hawk's face and fairly shouted my surprise and delight, for the eye, which I knew to be bright red or orange in the adult male Sharp-shin of the United States and Canada, was dark rich brown. I am not sure that my friend comprehended my enthusiasm. He may have thought that I was merely trying to encourage him, for he had seen very few birds. But I had painted the United States Sharp-shin direct from life or from a freshly killed specimen many a time, and I knew we had a *Mexican* Sharp-shin this time. The specimen subsequently became the type of a subspecies new to science, a race characterized in adult plumage by the almost immaculate light reddish-brown under parts and dark brown eye.

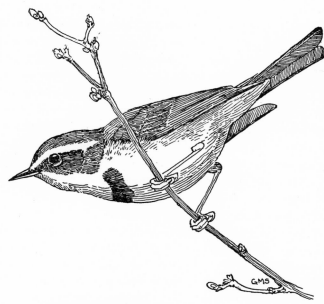

Hartlaub's Warbler (*Vermivora superciliosa*)
4¾ inches

So anyone studying Mexican birdlife in winter has to be on the alert for two sorts of Sharp-shinned Hawks—this ruddy-breasted, brown-eyed one which *nests* in Mexico; and the one with heavily barred under parts and red or orange eye, which winters there and migrates northward into the United States and Canada to breed.

XII

We returned to Monterrey in time for a sketch, before dark, of the eye, cere, bill, and other fleshy parts of our Mexican Sharp-shinned Hawk specimen. After supper we worked late preparing skins and writing notes. It was a busy session.

Next morning we drove straight to the brush country north of Anáhuac Park. We saw some more Collared Seedeaters, put up a Cooper's Hawk which had been bathing at the edge of a woodland pool, and saw three species which were new for our list—the Barn Owl (*Tyto alba*), whose melancholy face, "hornless" head, and golden-brown and white coloration were unmistakable; the Arkansas or Dark-backed Goldfinch (*Spinus psaltria*); and the Water Pipit (*Anthus spinoletta*). The Dark-backed Goldfinches were a motley company, not one of the males being in full breeding plumage; but all of them, males and females alike, were yellow below, and all had fairly conspicuous white wing-markings. The pipit, which sprang from the ground at our feet, called *chi-chi* as it flew up. Its outer tail feathers were marked with white. On alighting, it pumped its tail as it walked off daintily through the grass.

In the afternoon we drove northward five miles to a little stream we had noted on our way south, the Arroyo de Pesquerías. We saw so many cormorants, herons, and other interesting fowl along this sluggish watercourse that we all decided we should spend a day there at our first opportunity. The most notable specimen we obtained was a Mexican Cormorant (*Phalacrocorax olivaceus*), an exceedingly plain looking creature with dull green eyes.

The morning of February 4 was mild. Clouds shut from sight all the mountains to the south and hung low over the city. Fine rain fell. Although this was far from what we desired in the way of weather, we knew we might have to wait a long while for a bright day, so off we went, straight for the Arroyo de Pesquerías. As we passed the bridge spanning the arroyo we put up a flock of small white herons. These Semple identified as Snowy Egrets (*Leucophoyx thula*), insisting that he had clearly seen their black legs and yellow toes. As for myself, I was equally certain that they were Little Blue Herons (*Florida caerulea*) in white plumage-phase, for I had thought that the legs and toes looked dull green. We had rather a hot argument as we drove the car off the highway, hid it in a mesquite thicket, and walked back to the stream. Again the white herons flew up, and we collected one. It proved to be a Snowy Egret, so there was nothing for me to do but hang my head in chagrin and go to the foot of the class. The specimen was in perfect breeding feather, the filmy, flowing crest and recurved back plumes being exquisite beyond belief.

During our first hour along the arroyo almost every bird we saw was new for our list. A small flock of sparrows which were feeding in the short, thin grass were Savannah Sparrows (*Passerculus sandwichensis*). They were molting, so the yellow of the fore part of the superciliary line was not very distinct; but the black streaking of the breast and sides was clearly visible, and a little white showed at the sides of the tail in flight. A Spotted Sandpiper (*Actitis macularia*) teetered as it ran ahead of us, then circled low over the water on widespread, quivering wings. A male Pintail Duck (*Anas acuta*) sprang from a pool at one side, towering swiftly. A flock of Killdeer Plovers (*Charadrius vociferus*) flew up noisily from a gravel bar. A Black Phoebe (*Sayornis nigricans*) perched on a tiny clay islet, calling plaintively. It was black all over save for the white belly and narrow, white wing-bars. Upstream a way, a Great Blue Heron (*Ardea herodias*) flapped up, announcing its departure with a hideous squawk.

We walked westward, taking the left bank. The bushes were so low that we could see a long way ahead. Using the binoculars we had little difficulty in determining that two distant points of red were male Vermilion Flycatchers, that two spots of clear yellow were Kiskadee Flycatchers, that a square of white was a Belted Kingfisher (*Megaceryle alcyon*). How odd that for the naked eye that kingfisher's white collar should stand out so much more clearly than the bird itself—so clean-cut, so noticeable, so like a little square of paper pasted casually on a picture of a stream!

A Golden-fronted Woodpecker flew in from the right, swung to the top of a dead Spanish bayonet, called *chuff! chuff!* and settled down for a doze. Small flocks of Great-tailed Grackles continued to pass slowly overhead. A covey of Bob-white Quail sprang from a thicket, rocketed off in all directions, and alighted in the brush. *Per-lee! per-lee* they called, each letting the others know where it was, as the flock reassembled.

The bushes were alive with small birds. Most conspicuous of these were the male Cardinals, Pyrrhuloxias, and Vermilion Flycatchers, whose bright colors flashed. Black-throated Sparrows were numerous. Their striking white head-markings were visible at considerable distance. The Field Sparrows and White-crowned Sparrows made their presence known chiefly through sputtered conversation and low, sweet fragments of song. As for the numerous Green-tailed Towhees, Spotted Towhees, and Olive Sparrows, the average passerby would never have

Golden-fronted Woodpecker (*Centurus aurifrons*)
10 inches

become aware of them at all, for they kept themselves hidden most of the time.

In midmorning a flock of Long-billed Curlews flew over. The forty or fifty birds kept almost abreast, forming a wavering bow across the sky. They were no surprise, for we had been hearing their far-carrying callnotes from time to time. Now they set their wings for descent and a high, shivering *coo-leeeeeeee* sounded as they alighted in a cultivated area half a mile to the south.

One very small bird of the thicket was quite new to us. It was greenish-gray above and grayish-white below, had inconspicuous wing-bars, and reminded us vaguely of a female Ruby-crowned Kinglet as it hopped briskly about snatching at insects. Presently it paused, stood upright, threw back its head, opened its mouth wide, and emitted a spasmodic, wholly unmusical *eeee-yuck!* This performance over, it resumed its hopping from twig to twig, again reminding us of a vireo, kinglet, or warbler. Surely this was the drabbest, least striking of all the new birds we had seen; moreover, it was annoying in that it did not behave quite like any bird with which we were familiar. It was a Beardless Flycatcher (*Camptostoma imberbe*), a curiously tiny-billed bird for a flycatcher. It was known to range northward across the border a short way into the United States.

While walking along the edge of an old field, we heard a whistle which was so much like that of a carefree boy that our first impulse was to change our course lest we frighten the lad out of his wits by appearing before him too suddenly. We heard the whistle again, then several whistles at once, each of them with a disarming tunelessness which called to mind bare feet in the dust, crude fishing poles, and rolled up overalls. How extraordinary, we thought, to encounter a whole company of absent-minded lads in a place like this!

As we moved forward cautiously, we saw them—not boys of course, but a little flock of orioles, feeding in a low bush. They were somewhat larger than Baltimore Orioles (*Icterus galbula*), and were black on the head, wings, and tail, yellowish-green on the back, and clear lemon-yellow on the breast, belly, and under tail coverts. Their sharply pointed bills were grayish-blue at the base. Their wings were trimmed with white. Seeing us, they scolded harshly and flew off. Following their whistling, we relocated them without much trouble in a clump of giant yuccas where, climbing about like so many parakeets, they hunted insects in the coarse, fibrous bark at the bases of the big leaves. They were Black-headed Orioles (*I. graduacauda*), a bird known to range

61

as far north as the lower Río Grande valley. The race of the species which nested in southern Texas was known as the Audubon's Black-headed Oriole (*I. g. auduboni*).

Along a narrow stretch of the stream we had our first glimpse of the Green Kingfisher (*Chloroceryle americana*), a beautiful, comparatively uncrested little bird, about half the size of the familiar Belted Kingfisher, with glossy, bronzy-green upper parts, white throat and belly, rich rufous chest, and white spotting on the wings and tail. Like the Black-headed Oriole, it also ranged northward into southern Texas, where it was known as the Texas Green Kingfisher (*C. a. septentrionalis*). The female, we recalled, had no rufous on the chest.

In a weed patch along a little used path we put up a flock of Lark Buntings (*Calamospiza melanocorys*) which flew directly to some fence wires close by and began singing boisterously. Since they were largely in winter plumage, these good sized finches were predominantly gray; but the black breeding plumage of the males was beginning to show, and every male had a bold white patch in each wing. These patches gave the flock a curiously flickering appearance as they flew about.

A waterbird which flew over us appeared to be very dark gray without markings of any sort. Its tail was paddle-shaped, and no feet were visible sticking out behind. The beak was hooked at the very tip. This was a Mexican Cormorant, a species obviously not strictly coastal in distribution.

As we headed the car for the highway, we saw a pointed-winged hawk flying swiftly across the flat ahead of us. It was about the size of a Peregrine (*Falco peregrinus*), and, like that species, was heavy-bodied and muscular. It spurned a fence post as a perch, sped past a low tree, made straight for a mound of earth not far from the main highway, and, swooping upward on widespread wings, revealing an intricate and delicate pattern of spotting and barring, came to rest. Here it bobbed its head vigorously, watching us with its bright dark eyes. It was a Prairie Falcon (*Falco mexicanus*), a species identifiable even at considerable distance by the distinctly sandy-brown tone of the upper parts and the narrow black streaking of the under parts. We followed it with the car, hoping to get close to it; but it was nobody's fool and made off the instant the car stopped, beating its way low over the ground to a distant boulder.

That evening, after several hours of work at our rooms, we returned to the arroyo. The sun had just set and the whole western sky was yellow. The quiet stream, with its grassy south bank and the clay bluff opposite; the brush-lined tributaries, all dry as a bone; the giant yuccas, towering above the mesquites, some straight as pines, others grotesquely bent—all these were steeped in mellow, amber-golden light. A small flock of Mexican Cormorants flew overhead, their bodies sharply black against the bright sky. Six Snowy Egrets followed, flapping slowly, their plumage so perfectly reflecting the colors of clouds, vegetation, earth, and water that no part of them appeared to be truly white. Flocks of Mourning Doves shot in from all sides for their evening drink.

At dusk, just as we were beginning to have difficulty in seeing anything below the horizon, a small hawk flew past. We followed it across the stream by jumping from stone to stone, but lost sight of it as it swooped suddenly earthward. Presently it reappeared, flying toward us laboriously, as if burdened. Believing it might be a Merlin (*Falco columbarius*), a falcon we had not thus far recorded, we shot it. As we lifted the specimen from the gravel of the stream bed we noticed a thin, squeaking sound. Looking closely, we found a living free-tailed bat (*Tadarida*) in the tightly clenched talons. The hawk was not a Merlin, but a Sparrow Hawk. We marvelled that it should be capturing food so late in the evening.

XIII

A woodchopper we happened to meet near Monterrey told us of Santa Rosa. Displaying genuine interest in our specimens, he described this village, which was several miles northeast of Monterrey and well off the main highway, as a sort of paradise for birds. Opening his eyes wide, spreading his arms, and employing his most graphic superlatives, he made his meaning clear: there were birds of all conceivable sorts, birds everywhere, at Santa Rosa. Tolerant of his exaggeration because he was so enthusiastic and friendly, we smiled knowingly, thanked him, and went our way.

Something took us, nevertheless, to Santa Rosa. Some subtle power in the beautiful words themselves, perhaps; some challenge flung at us by the little sign along the highway; some deep belief in the expression on the woodchopper's face. Who were we to explain the forces which were taking us there? We simply went. The date was February 5.

Santa Rosa hopped, fluttered, and squawked with birds. Never, during a lifetime of bird study, had we seen anything like it. The narrow

63

streets were alive with middle-sized blackbirds and doves. The fences back of the houses were lined with Black and Turkey Vultures, Great-tailed Grackles, more middle-sized blackbirds. The trees literally sagged with grackles. On houses in the very middle of town perched sedate birds of prey, most of them Red-tailed Hawks. Here and there through the birds could be seen the white of a hen or goat, the brown of adobe, the red of oleanders. Odd whirlwinds of birds rose where children romped or dogs ran.

The river which we had been obliged to ford as we entered the village was attractive to birds, no doubt; so also were the fields of young grain and innumerable irrigation ditches; but the place the birds quite obviously loved was the village itself, the hard-packed dooryards, the low adobe houses with their pink and blue painted fronts, the puddles and weed patches and vine-covered walls.

The middle-sized blackbirds were of four species. The commonest was the Brewer's Blackbird (*Euphagus cyanocephalus*), the males of which were quite handsome with their glossy, purplish-blue heads and white eyes. The females were dark-eyed. The Red-winged Blackbird (*Agelaius phoeniceus*) was of about the same size, and dark-eyed. Adult male Red-wings were easy enough to recognize by their scarlet wing-patches, but immature males were less clearly marked, and females were brown rather than black, much streaked below, and rather sparrowlike in appearance. The Red-eyed Cowbird (*Tangavius aeneus*) was actually red-eyed, but this eye-color was sometimes hard to see, especially in the females. The males were noticeably larger than the females and their neck plumage was so long that it sometimes bulged out like a hood or cape. They were bronzy-black on the head, back and under parts, blue-black on the wings and tail. The Dwarf Cowbird (*Molothrus ater obscurus*), a relative of the Common Cowbird of the eastern United States, was the smallest of the four. The males were glossy black with coffee-brown heads, the females dull grayish-brown all over.

Of doves there were three species—the Mourning Dove, which was the largest and least common, but most likely to be seen flying overhead; the trim, long-tailed, diminutive Inca Dove (*Scardafella inca*), with its prettily scaled plumage; and the even smaller Ground Dove (*Columbigallina passerina*), with its short, rounded tail. So numerous were the latter two species that they sparred for choice positions on the manure heaps, hooting out fierce threats which stood no chance of being heard more than a few feet away, lifting their sturdy wings, and thumping each other soundly. Watching them was like watching the foam of a

PLATE IV
Mexican Sharp-shinned Hawk
(*Accipiter striatus suttoni*)

rapid. There was no following a single bird, no escaping the round and round motion. Not even looking up, nor looking to one side, nor shutting the eyes, gave relief. Wherever one looked, the whirling and eddying continued.

The abundance of birds embarrassed us. Here were more specimens than we could collect and prepare in a month of Sundays, more birds than we knew what to do with, all so confiding, so completely sure of our innocence, that we were ashamed of our hunting garb and guns. We drove through town slowly, wondering if we should ever find our way out of this labyrinth of narrow streets; carefully, too, lest we knock down the flimsy fences. Birds rose in front of us in clouds so dense that whole trees and houses were for the moment obliterated. At last we reached the farther side of the village, where a deep ditch precluded our going on.

Leaving the car, we walked across the fields to the river. The instant we reached the water's edge we saw a Green Kingfisher. The bird flew past not more than fifteen feet away, giving us a fine view of its glossy back and white-spotted wings and tail. It flew directly, alighting on a small rock at the head of a riffle. Here it lifted all that it had of crest, bobbed its head, gave a sharp cry which sounded like two small pebbles being struck together, and flashed off.

The river was not lovely. Scum on the stagnant pools, gray-green ooze all over the stony bottom, and a strong odor of dead fish or sewage warned us not to drink. But the birds found it adequate for their needs. A Vermilion Flycatcher, wet from bathing, flew up a few paces ahead. A screaming sounded from Kiskadee Flycatchers playing in the water downstream. Green Kingfishers shuttled back and forth like change carriers in a department store.

For several minutes we enjoyed ourselves watching one of these little kingfishers. During this time it changed its perch thrice. Failing to discover even a crayfish near the rock at the head of the riffle, failing again at a deep pool below, it darted between the willows swiftly downstream to a low bank from which protruded a stiff root. Here, after a surprisingly brief wait, it plunged with a whisper of splash, reappeared in an instant, fluttered back to the root, and gulped a silvery minnow about three inches long.

All was not peace and quiet in the little angler's world, however. Hardly had the minnow gone down when another Green Kingfisher appeared, darted at the bird we had been watching, and drove it so fiercely our way that pursued and pursuer passed within a few feet with-

65

out veering in the least. Now a third kingfisher flew upstream, made straight for this most popular of roots, and took up the vigil. When bird No. 2 returned to find its favorite perch again usurped, it went into a rage, rattled fiercely, made a swift lunge, and knocked the offender into the water. Not content with half a victory, it continued its pursuit, diving instantly. When the two birds reappeared their beaks were interlocked and their wings outspread. They floated downstream a short way thus; then arriving at some manner of understanding, they separated, one flying downstream, the other returning to the root. Here, after a vigorous shake, it rattled defiantly.

Great-tailed Grackles were never out of sight or hearing. We were thoroughly accustomed by this time to their shrill pipings. But their mingled *chacks, chucks,* and *k-thicks* produced an effect which sometimes took us wholly by surprise. So like a rough trampling of corn stalks was this sound that more than once we turned to see what beast might be bearing down upon us.

We saw several ducks along the river—two Shovellers (*Spatula clypeata*), four Green-winged Teal (*Anas crecca*), a flock of Cinnamon Teal (*A. cyanoptera*), and a female Lesser Scaup (*Aythya affinis*). Wilson's Snipes (*Capella gallinago*) were fairly common. At a quiet pool we saw a Solitary Sandpiper. Wherever we went one or more Spotted Sandpipers were nearly always in sight. None of these various waterbirds was exclusively Mexican, of course; we had seen them all in the United States.

We walked a considerable way downstream, following the north bank. A mile or so from the village we came upon a sort of colony—three pairs, to be exact—of Harris's Hawks, perched in low trees a short way from the water's edge. As we approached we expected to see them fly, but they did not budge. Although we continued to walk straight toward them, they held their ground, eyeing us calmly. By the time we were directly under them they were looking straight at us, so it stood to reason that the position of their heads must have changed, but certainly we had perceived no movement. Never were full-grown birds of prey more docile and imperturbable.

Wondering what could possibly be wrong with them, we clapped our hands sharply. This unheard-of insolence roused them to the point of lifting their heads, standing on two feet instead of one, and tucking in the rough plumage of their under parts, but fly they would not. Never before had they flown from anybody in this blissful valley, and they did not intend to do so now. At our last look they were standing again on one

66

foot, their heads low against their shoulders, the picture of complete indifference and complete repose.

The birds along the river kept us busy. There were yellow-throats which we inspected one by one in the hope of finding the much-talked-of Thick-billed Yellow-throat; a Long-billed Marsh Wren (*Telmatodytes palustris*), which kept itself hidden most of the time in a dense clump of cattail; and Rough-winged Swallows (*Stelgidopteryx ruficollis*) which circled us repeatedly. Pipits seemed to be fairly common. White-necked Ravens, which looked for all the world like Common Crows, but cawed more hoarsely, flew over now and then. An interesting new bird for our list was the House Finch (*Carpodacus mexicanus*), the male of which was rosy on the head, breast, and rump; the female very plain, streaked, and ordinary looking.

The bird of the day was a beautiful Least Grebe (*Colymbus dominicus*), a diver about the size of a Bob-white Quail, which flew slowly downstream only a foot or so above the water, just as we were about to leave the river. Its wings were narrow and the white of the secondaries showed plainly. Seeing us, it flopped from the air straight into the water and dived instantly. We crouched, hid as well as we could, and crept quickly forward. In a twinkling the sleek gray head emerged, a strand of waterweed clinging to the slender bill, and we had one unforgettable glimpse of the wild and gleaming eye—the pupil of which was black, exceedingly small, and ringed with white. The rest of the iris was pale yellow. The gray body did not reappear. The head slowly sank as if being pulled under, the bright eye staying wide open as it went down. Though we searched for half an hour up and down the river we did not see the grebe again.

At the car three uniformed men were waiting for us. We showed our permits, displayed the birds we had collected, and were forthwith presented with a handsome *aguililla,* or "little eagle," which they had shot. This bird was actually a Western Red-tailed Hawk. Thanking our new-found friends for the specimen, we made our way once more through Santa Rosa's bird-filled streets, and drove back to "headquarters" in Monterrey.

All our smaller specimens we prepared immediately upon our return. The larger ones could wait, however, since the night promised to be cold and the morrow was to be a day of rest. After supper we went to town to see the sights. The most memorable of these was a "Horrible Monster," advertised as half man and half ape, who was chained to a chair in a dimly lighted tent. Bestowing upon us far more than our money's worth of leering, this creature jabbed with a pencil at a beetle which wandered about on the table in front of him.

XIV

Sundays in the field are a delight. On Sunday one is not obliged to rise with quite the rush of the ordinary day, and breakfast may be regarded as a social rather than a purely physiological function. One may take a walk if one wishes, wandering through the woods or open lowlands more reposefully, more thoughtfully than usual, letting colors and shapes and sounds penetrate to one's inner consciousness.

When far from home one prefers to follow a familiar route on Sunday, to jog along easily, even aimlessly—not as a collector of specimens, nor as a representative of some institution whose research work must be carried on, but rather as an humble sort of lower animal, a being among fellow beings, seeking in no very effortful or aggressive way to comprehend its place in the Great Scheme.

February 6 was Sunday. From half past nine o'clock that morning until noon Burleigh and I were afield near Monterrey. We went out together but soon separated, each recognizing the other's right to enjoy the leisure hours in his own way. As usual it was raining—a slow drizzle. So low and dense were the clouds that there was no horizon, but all the paths were familiar and we needed no landmark.

Nowhere was the prospect especially attractive. The leafless bushes were heavy with moisture, the plumage of the birds damp and dull. But the fact that the twigs did not crackle underfoot made it possible for us to move about noiselessly, the grayness of the day was easy on the eyes, and the air was so fresh that being abroad was, in itself, invigorating.

Off in the thicket to the north a Berlandier's Wren sang briefly. Farther away a Mockingbird attempted a phrase or two, then lapsed into silence. It was no morning for bird song, that was obvious. But the birds were there, literally thousands of them if one remembered to include in one's count the great flocks of sparrows which were wintering all through the brushlands.

Bending low and moving slowly forward beneath the bushes along an old cattle trail, I approached an opening in which I knew there would be birds. I had visited this spot before and had never been disappointed.

68

This morning I heard in front of me the fluttering of little wings and the low *chips, chups,* and *tseeps* which small birds make while they are about their small affairs. The birds neither heard nor saw me. I did not enter the opening, but crouched motionless in the trail, resting on one knee.

A Green-tailed Towhee hopped to within ten feet, looked straight at me, looked again. Because my eyes were so nearly shut that the bird could see no highlights in them, it went on scratching in the leaves as if I had been a mere stone. Now that it had accepted me, my principal difficulties were over. I had only to keep motionless, with eyes not too widely opened, to watch at close range the White-crowned Sparrow which chased the towhee off; the three Lincoln's Sparrows which hopped farther and farther into the open, but moved toward shelter the instant the slightest chirp of alarm was sounded; the company of Chipping Sparrows which argued with, threatened, and bit each other over seeds the size of pinheads. It was Sunday for me, a day of peace and quiet. But it was any old day for the Chippies. For them the task at hand was the time-honored task of keeping the gizzard neatly packed and—well, in a world full of Chippies, where each was trying desperately to get ahead of the next, the only thing to do was find the seed first, cry *tsip* and bite if necessary, and let the devil take the hindmost!

A White-eyed Vireo discovered me. While I was watching a Long-billed Thrasher, the vireo slipped in from behind, flew so close that its wings fanned my ears, and alighted about a yard from my face. Instantly it perceived that I was no stump, so, suspecting the worst, it hopped closer. I did not budge. But when those little ghost-like eyes looked squarely into mine, I knew that I had been recognized, that the jig was up, that I was done for.

At the first note of scolding from the vireo the Lincoln's Sparrows vanished. But the Long-billed Thrasher came in great haste, sounded a loud *chuck* of alarm, and, ascertaining that I was indeed just what the vireo had said I was, it set up a clamor far louder than I deserved. Two or three White-eyed Vireos gathered promptly, for small brush-inhabiting birds love a mob scene. Two Verdins came too, cheeping shrilly. Some Blue-gray Gnatcatchers flew in, drawling their protestations. Six or eight Cardinals and several Pyrrhuloxias arrived. A Sparrow Hawk hovered directly overhead. I began to wonder if the Monterrey police force might not be on its way.

Sunday, in other words, is not quite what I said it was. Sunday is a state of mind.

XV

The Pauraque or Cuiéjo was a Mexican "night bird" which I had long wanted to observe. Its odd, supposedly onomatopoeic names had intrigued me for years. I wanted to hear its cry so as to be able to spell out the syllables for myself. When first I had heard of the bird—twenty-five years or so ago—it had been known principally as the Parauque, and the word had been pronounced *par-auk,* with the accent on the second syllable. But latterly someone had pointed out that the correct spelling was Pauraque, and the correct pronunciation *pow-rah' kay;* and even more recently certain field ornithologists had reported that the bird's characteristic cry did not in the least resemble the syllables *pow-rah' kay* and that the native name Robert Ridgway had employed in his great work on the birds of North and Middle America was more suitable. This Ridgway name was Cuiéjo (pronounced *koo-yay' hoe*).

I knew that the Pauraque was a goatsucker, related to the Whippoorwill (*Caprimulgus vociferus*) and Chuck-will's-widow (*C. carolinensis*). I knew that it was a South and Central American species which ranged as far northward as the lower Río Grande valley. I knew from examination of museum specimens that it was larger, or at any rate longer, than the Whippoorwill, that both the male and female had a noticeable patch of white on each wing, and that the outer tail feathers of the male were boldly marked with white. But how did the bird behave? To what special use did it put its longish tail? Did it rest during the day on the ground or on a branch? Did it capture insects high in the air, nighthawkwise, or did it, like the Whippoorwill, prefer to hunt close to the ground. Above all, what was its characteristic cry? Our party had, it will be remembered, encountered a Pauraque briefly the last of January, but we had not seen the bird at all by daylight.

I met the Pauraque face to face on February 7, along the Río Salinas, not far from the village of Ciénaga de las Flores, twenty miles north of Monterrey. The meeting was, as meetings so often are for a collector of specimens, completely unexpected and a trifle disappointing. The day was dull. Rain had been falling gently all morning. As I had made my way along the river's south bank I had continued to beat the edge of a thin patch of cane, hoping to put up some unusual warbler or sparrow, or perhaps a rail. Having crossed a barbed-wire fence, I was clomping along the margin of a muddy, recently plowed field. Suddenly, from the scant shelter of some dead weeds only a step or so ahead, and as noiselessly as a shadow, a shapeless, dull brown thing flopped up, fluttered as if to shake the moisture from its wings, and zigzagged across the field, flying only two or three feet from the ground.

The instant I realized that the creature was a bird, I raised the gun and fired. The Pauraque dropped, dead as the weed stalks from which it had flown. I ran forward, lifting the flimsy wet carcass from the earth. So sudden and so complete was this conquest of a bird I had long wanted to know, that for a moment I failed to realize how little about Pauraques I could ever hope to learn from this one. I forced myself to think back: the bird had flown from the ground, not from a tree or fence post; it had spread its long tail only slightly; its behavior had been that of a Whipporwill in that it had kept close to the ground, but there had been something of a nighthawk, too, in its manner of flight. I opened its huge, pale mouth, spread the beautiful wings, examined briefly the dark lambent eyes, the tubular nostrils, the tiny combs on the claws of the middle toes; then, perceiving how wet the plumage was, I wrapped the specimen carefully in a handkerchief before placing it in the collecting creel. To thrust such a delicate bird into a paper cone might, I knew, mash some of the damp feathers hopelessly out of shape.

Back and forth I walked along the river bank, hoping to put up another Pauraque. But I did not find one. In fact, not during the course of our expedition did we record the interesting species again. I had to wait until the following year to learn that its usual cry was a full-throated, slightly rasping *gu-weer* or *go-wheer,* the first syllable frequently so faint as to be scarcely audible.

There were birds aplenty along the Río Salinas that drizzly day. Small flocks of Pintails, Cinnamon Teal, Green-winged Teal, and Blue-winged Teal (*Anas discors*) rose ahead of me. A loud squawk attracted my attention to a Black-crowned Night Heron (*Nycticorax nycticorax*) which was flapping over. Flocks of Great-tailed Grackles continued to fly from field to field. My list of species included the Spotted Sandpiper, House Finch, Golden-fronted Woodpecker, Clay-colored Sparrow, Black-throated Sparrow, Kiskadee Flycatcher, Vermilion Flycatcher, Bewick's Wren, Rock Wren, White-crowned Sparrow, Bob-white, Red-tailed Hawk, Green Kingfisher, Pyrrhuloxia, Black-crested Titmouse, and Black-headed Oriole. This was not a wild country. Wherever I went there were roads, paths, and cattle trails. I wandered into a grove of orange trees, all fully leaved but not in bloom. The ground beneath them was covered with brightly colored but bitterly sour fruit.

On my way back to Ciénaga de las Flores, I followed the north bank of the river. At the outskirts of the village I had to jump over a deep, foul ditch, probably a sewer, make my way completely round a high-walled cemetery, and finally retrace my course altogether because of a twenty-foot-high, precipitous, clay bank. Going through town was a somewhat embarrassing experience, for I was escorted by no fewer than twenty boys and dogs of assorted sizes, whose mingled yipping, woofing, whistling, and laughter brought everybody to the front door for a look.

On our way back to Monterrey we stopped at the Arroyo de Pesquerías to watch a company of swallows circling above the stream. They were shining green above and plain white below. We collected one of them, finding it to be the well known Tree Swallow (*Iridoprocne bicolor*) of the United States and Canada. The species could not have been a very common winter resident in the region, for we did not record it otherwise.

Skinning the Pauraque was an experience worth recording. When I took the bird from the handkerchief in which I had wrapped it, I found to my delight that it was perfectly dry. The delicate color-patterns had been completely restored—the fine traceries and criss-cross barring of the under parts, the velvety black sagittate markings of the scapular feathers, the exquisite silvers and lilac grays and buffy yellows of the head and throat.

I began my work with fear and trembling, for I knew that all goat-suckers were delicate. The plumage stayed with the skin, however; there was but little fat to scrape off; and I soon had the satisfaction of showing my companions a perfect specimen. It was a female. The outer tail feathers were marked with buff rather than white. The stomach I examined with care. So firmly packed with food was this organ that for some minutes the process of skinning had been one of getting round and over this great knob, this sort of golf ball, which protruded from the abdominal region. When I cut the stomach open I found a hawk moth, the body of which was as big as a hummingbird's, some large beetles with iridescent wings, and a mass of smaller beetles, flies and orthopterans, the identification of which would have entertained an entomologist for many a day. Most of these insects were partly digested, of course—a leg or wing here, an antenna or claw or bit of thoracic muscle there. I counted the remains of almost a hundred insects, most of them ground inhabiting beetles. They had been swallowed whole, for the Pauraque had neither claws for grasping them, nor beak for tearing them apart.

The following morning we were pleased to note that the cloud had lifted a little, that a warm brightness had returned to the thicket-lands, that the foot of Saddle Mountain was visible once more. The sky did not open, however, nor the sun emerge.

Among the live oaks of Anáhuac Park we collected a puzzling small flycatcher which proved on careful identification later to be a Hammond's Flycatcher (*Empidonax hammondi*), a species which nested in the western United States and western Canada. We had seen these puzzling little flycatchers before (notably on January 28) but did not trust our field identification of them for they resembled the Least Flycatcher very closely.

We had by this time worked the low country of the Monterrey district for over a week. With most of the nonmigratory and winter visitant bird species we had, therefore, become fairly familiar. Our failure to find hummingbirds, trogons and Hooded Orioles continued to puzzle us. We suspected that some dull-colored, secretive species, such as the Cassin's Sparrow (*Aimophila cassini*), had eluded us simply because we had not worked hard enough in ferreting them out. We had begun to wonder whether such tropical or subtropical forms as the Rose-throated Becard would indeed become commoner as the days lengthened, and with this thought had grown the conviction that we were not in a tropical region at all, despite our being well south of the border. We were, in other words, still slightly under the spell of the belief that in Mexico all things were wholly Mexican. Our not finding the Road-runner, Scaled Quail, Black Hawk and White-tailed Kite we attributed—to some extent correctly—to the fact that the district was heavily populated.

Spring was at hand, there could be no doubting that, for flowers were blooming and birds singing everywhere. But the Clay-colored, Lincoln's, and White-crowned Sparrows were not yet departing for their breeding grounds, the individual Eastern Phoebes which we knew so well were still with us, and we had noted no nest-building even among the White-necked Ravens. Furthermore, we had not listed one species which we believed was passing through the region on its way northward. The spring migration had not yet started.

That afternoon we packed specimens, sketches, and equipment for a move to the Mesa de Chipinque. Though we had not for days been able to see the higher parts of the mountains because of cloud, we had not forgotten the big pines, lichen-covered oaks, and towering cliffs of that upper realm. Spring would be returning now to those enchanted slopes, and thought of what we might be missing made us restless. We had not given up our dreams of trogons.

73

Hardly had we begun our climb to the Mesa when we found ourselves shut in by dense, heavy cloud. So oppressive was the all-encircling
grayness that we felt a wild desire to lunge through it, to back out, to
take a deep breath in hope of being able to rise to light and freedom.
Seen through the cloud, the trees were like motionless shadows—without substance, without color. So vague was everything beyond the roadside that the silence did not surprise us. What right had we to expect
clarity of sound when every visible thing was dim, amorphous, robbed
of its third dimension?

Slowly, carefully, for half an hour we climbed. The road, while not
steep, was narrow, and we remembered vividly, though unable to per-
ceive it now, the abruptness of the declivity to our left. The suspense was
nerve-wracking. The fact that we heard nothing save the sound of our
own voices and the hum of the two motors added to our feeling of
uneasiness.

Suddenly, like arctic seals popping from the dark water through
their breathing holes out onto the ice, we emerged. So bright was the
new-found day that for an instant we could hardly see. All things above
us—the trees, the cliffs, the Turkey Vultures circling against the far blue
—were bathed in warm, steady light which poured from the sun. Below
us, like a vast brownish gray ocean stretching off to the northward as
far as the eye could see, lay the cloud. The higher mountains rose from
it like islands. Its surface was rough, as if lashed into irregular waves
by squalls. For all we could see of Monterrey, that city had been en-
gulfed and forgotten long ago.

As we rounded a sharp curve, with our eyes on the road and our
minds anywhere but on birds, a small, black, long-winged creature shot
past us down the mountainside. Another flashed by, then another. They
were not bats. Nor were the swallows. They were swifts!

But which species were they? If Chimney Swifts (*Chaetura pelagica*), then perhaps we had made a significant discovery. At that moment of time, it will be remembered, no one knew just where the Chimney Swift spent the winter. Or, supposing they were not Chimney Swifts,
might they not belong to a species wholly unknown to science? We were
sorely tempted to stop; but mad determination to keep above that awesome cloud, to reach the Mesa before night, to have done with that en-
ervating ascent, drove us forward. We did not even pause. The swifts
would have to be identified later.

We established ourselves in a little house built along the Mesa's
rim, a truly elegant brick structure with tile roof and floors, a fireplace,

and bathrooms which would have delighted the soul of old Chipinque, the chieftain for whom the Mesa had been named. Hardly had we got our luggage in when, in a ravine near the front steps, we saw a little company of Rufous-capped Atlapetes. The partly hidden and shadowed yellow of their under parts was not at all noticeable. Neither was the reddish-brown of their crowns. They were busy scratching among the leaves.

After supper we had an hour afield before dark. Followed by those disturbers of the peace, the Mexican Jays, we walked back down the road, wondering if the swifts might still be flying low. It was a beautiful, windless evening. Far above us ravens wheeled about the crags, croaking solemnly. These were not the White-necked Ravens we had been seeing in the low country; they were "big" American Ravens, close relatives of the raven of the wind-scourged Aleutian Islands, of Scandinavia, and of northernmost Greenland. In the distance a Canyon Wren sang. But we saw no swifts.

Returning to the Mesa, we passed through a grove of fine oaks. Here a flock of fair-sized birds were moving restlessly through the topmost branches, making their way to some roosting place, apparently. Approaching them cautiously, we were surprised to find that they were plain, everyday Robins (*Turdus migratorius*), just about the last species we had expected to see on the mountain. Whether they belonged to a Mexican race of this widely ranging form, or were migrants from the western United States, we did not know.

From shrubbery to one side came the *chup* of a Rufous-capped Warbler and the *chook* of a Hermit Thrush. In trees farther away we heard the chatter of Bridled Titmice, the clear-voiced *peeto-peeto-peeto* of a Black-crested Titmouse, and the *mew* of a Yellow-bellied Sapsucker. What an odd mixture of the familiar and unfamiliar! Little-known birds were all about us, keeping us on tiptoe with their strange cries. But Robins and Hermit Thrushes and Yellow-bellied Sapsuckers were here too.

A new bird for our list was a dull-colored, ground-inhabiting sparrow which seemed to prefer loose rock piles and steep, brush-covered slopes of little canyons. It was a difficult bird to see, for it kept hidden in the grass or brush, or under rocks, most of the time. It was gray, generally speaking, with reddish-brown cap, back-streaks, wings, and tail, and a *narrow but fairly distinct black streak at either side of the throat*. Neither the reddish-brown crown-patch nor the gray superciliary line was distinct. Its song was bright and pleasing, and when it sang it perched conspicuously on a rock, usually somewhere above us. This bird was Boucard's Rufous-crowned Sparrow (*Aimophila ruficeps boucardi*). It was a Mexican race of a species which ranged well northward into the western United States. It was, of course, a wholly different bird from the Rufous-capped Atlapetes, a distinctively Mexican finch with sulphur-yellow under parts.

XVI

We wakened early on the morning of February 9 to find the rocky summit two thousand feet above us bright as gold. The effect was breathtaking, for at our level gray mist floated through the trees and the sun itself was nowhere to be seen. The talus below the summit cliffs, as well as the whole broad front of the mountain, was dark and indistinct, but the jagged pinnacles at the very top gleamed like a burnished crown against the sky.

Standing in the mist, we watched the splendid brightness as it crept slowly downward. Where the distant cliffs were sheer this evidence of the sun's rising was easily observable; but the instant the strong light struck the talus, pine tops all over the high slopes turned rich yellow-green, narrow ravines took on sharp definition, and a rosy flood swept over the fold to our right too swiftly for the eye to follow. As the light moved toward us steadily down the mountain, little plumes of clouds lit up, and shadows changed shape as they shrank and disappeared. Suddenly a branch overhead became bright, we were conscious of a gentle warmth on our faces, and lo—there was the sun itself hurling broad-swords of light through the trees. The vapors whirled and spun as they rose and drifted away. Everywhere the day became stronger, the details of the woodland clearer. Looking once more toward the pinnacles, we perceived that their aureous brilliance had faded.

Astonished by the silence of the birds at this promising hour, I headed up the mountain for a narrow shelf from which I knew I should be able to survey the ravine beyond. Despite the dampness of the atmosphere, the carpet of pine needles was so slippery that I had frequently to resort to clambering upward on all fours. Redbud trees were blooming everywhere. These and the myriad buttercups and violets reminded me of the spring woodlands of Pennsylvania and West Virginia. I would, in fact, have felt quite at home had it not been for the peculiar cactus, sprawling maguey, and other unfamiliar xerophytes I continued to encounter.

After half an hour of steady climbing I reached the shelf. Making my way along cautiously, I peered round the mountain's shoulder. The ravine appeared to be utterly uninhabited. Somewhere I heard a drop of water striking a leaf, then the faint rustling of a mouse or lizard, then, far overhead, a raven's croaking. I sat down, happy at being in such a beautiful spot. A thousand feet below me the cloud stretched off to the north. Back at the Mesa a dog was barking. How good it was to smell the pines, to feel the clean, dry earth beneath me!

Yielding to this ecstacy, I lay back and looked upward through the trees. Forgetful of the problems of ornithology and zoogeography, I stretched out, wriggled down into the bed of aromatic needles, and closed my eyes. I should have been asleep presently but for some devil's plaguing me into believing that I had heard a faraway bit of bright sound. Roused at length, yet hardly trusting my senses, I sat up, made certain that neither belt buckle nor shoe had misled me with its squeaking, held my hand carefully to my ear, and placed the sound several hundred yards away at about my level on the mountainside. It was so faint that I feared I must be missing a good deal of it. But what I heard was surely no rattling of harness nor susurration of hidden spring; it was the song of a bird!

Checking the direction carefully, I started straight across the ravine. The nearer slope was almost devoid of undergrowth so I was obliged to let myself down as best I could, sliding part of the way. Reaching the bottom, I stopped to listen. Not a sound did I hear. The silence filled me with dismay.

Distressed by the suspicion that I had chosen a wholly wrong direction, I toiled up the farther side. The ascent was anything but easy, for there was a veritable rubble of loose, angular rocks, all of them covered, though not held in place, by thorny vegetation. A short way from the top I paused for rest, leaning against a stout young oak. Suddenly I caught my breath. There was the song again—this time so distinct that I knew it could not be far off. It was so brilliant, so amazingly complex, that I could scarcely believe my ears.

Waiting motionless, I heard the song through from start to finish. The opening notes were only chirps. But the body of the song, the song proper, was a slowly descending, sadly sweet whistle accompanied by such a profusion of grace notes that I found myself instantly comparing it with what, as a child, I had called an "electric sparkler." It was so

77

beautiful, so wondrously like musical fireworks, that I opened my mouth and gasped. Never in all my journeyings had bird-music wrung from me such ineffable applause, or filled me with such wild, half-furious exultation. "I've never heard! I've never heard!" I whispered to myself, as if confessing that up to that high moment my ears had never fully functioned.

Wretched with apprehension that my next move might frighten the bird away, that I might not even get a glimpse of this wonderful singer, I crept over the rocks toward the big pine whence the song seemed to come. Failing to find any shrubbery behind which to approach, I crouched and looked the tree over with my binocular. The search was vain, but at least I saw no bird fly out. Keeping my eyes on the tree as best I could, I stumbled forward. Hardly had I found firm footing beneath the spreading branches when the song began again, directly overhead.

This time the opening syllable—a sharp, ringing note—stirred my memory. This time I wondered if I might not have heard the song before. *Kler!* it started. Then another *kler,* and another, then that sparkling shower, that "bright effluence of bright essence increate," which poured over and all around me. It was incredible. The song was so loud and clear that I could almost feel it falling. Yet nowhere could I see the singer. Was this the voice of some celestial spirit I could never hope to see? Had I, in crass eagerness, blundered into the ruins of some ancient cathedral, defiling a sacred and forbidden place?

At last I saw the bird—directly above me, at the end of a dead branch just thick enough to hide its body. It was plain gray and a bit smaller than a robin. It was not in the least frightened, apparently, and was watching me with its large, dark eye. Its bill was rather short and I could see white on its outer tail feathers. A turn of its gray head, a note from its swelling throat, and I recognized it as the bird I had seen at the bridge in Laredo, the bird I had actually called *Kler* for want of a better name. So this was Kler, this wild and lovely spot Kler's home! But to what species did the bird belong? My ignorance humiliated me.

I did not know it at the time, but Kler was a Brown-backed Solitaire (*Myadestes obscurus*), a truly celebrated songster, beloved of the Mexicans as a cage bird and called by them the *jilguero*. All these solitaires were really thrushes, members of the family Turdidae. One species of the genus *Myadestes* was the Townsend's Solitaire (*M. townsendi*) of the United States check-list.

An hour after my meeting with this delightful bird, the cloud caught me. Thick, gray, vaguely sinister, it rose through the trees, shutting out the pinnacles above me, then the blue of the sky, finally the sun itself. With the cloud came a complete cessation of bird voices. The Mexican Jays, which had been screeching in the ravine, stole off silently as if going to roost. A Macgillivray's Warbler, which had been singing off in the brush, stopped as if it had been choked. A stillness far deeper than that of a clear night descended upon the mountain.

I made my way quietly up the slope, now picking a quadrupedal course across the vast rockslide, now crawling through the vine-covered branches of a fallen pine, finally reaching a narrow canyon at the base of a perpendicular cliff. The denseness of the cloud oppressed me. I could not quite dispel the feeling of being lost. Reason told me that I

Brown-backed Solitaire or *Jilguero* (*Myadestes obscurus*)
about 8 inches

79

had but to go far enough down the mountain to find the road; but caution born of experience reminded me that this was a place I did not know. It would have reassured me to hear a rooster crowing back at the Mesa.

The canyon was an eery place. Its rocky walls, which were studded with cactus, huge century plants, and jagged-leafed sotol, were anything but inviting. Making my way round a gigantic, fern-crowned boulder, I almost stepped into a gaping cavern fifteen feet across. The trees about me were tall and slender. Their lowest leaves, twenty or thirty feet above me, were dimly visible through the shifting mist.

It occurred to me that I might call up an owl or other bird of prey, so I squeaked loudly. All that I got in answer was an echo from up the canyon, then silence deeper than before. Alert for any sign of life, I watched a leaf sag as a big drop of water gathered at its tip.

A sudden rustle made my spine tingle. This was followed by a louder rustle, then a harsh *querr! querr!*—half-sneezed, half-coughed— off in the brush. It was a squirrel. No jaguar, no ocelot, no puma, no ferocious member of the weasel tribe—only a gray squirrel, for all the world like those back home, looking at me with bright black eyes, probably not seeing me very clearly, probably not smelling me much, agitated as squirrels often are, and more than all else, curious.

I squeaked again, moving only enough to lift my hand to my mouth. This time the squirrel came on the run—across a rock, through the dead leaves with a flourish of its tail, up a tree not more than fifteen feet away. Here it must have been following a familiar route, for it went straight to a certain branch, stood on its haunches, tucked its front feet in as if scratching its ribs—and began scolding in earnest. Its outcry attracted other gray squirrels, some Mexican Jays, and a company of Bridled Titmice. All these pretty creatures berated me roundly. I didn't mind. In fact, the hubbub dispelled the eeriness of the canyon and made me feel more at ease in the fog.

Back at the Mesa we gave a complete account of ourselves, as was our custom. Semple, who had hunted on a fold to the east, had flushed a covey of quail, more than likely those bizarre, little-known Harlequin Quail (*Cyrtonyx montezumae*), a more northward-ranging though close relative of which he and I had encountered in the Chisos Mountains of Texas. They had burst from a thicket at his feet and shot off through the cloud-hung brush, straight up the mountainside. Burleigh, good bird-man that he was, had collected a fine specimen of Blackheaded Grosbeak (*Pheucticus melanocephalus*).

PLATE V
Gray Hawk
(*Buteo nitidus*)

At four o'clock that afternoon the cloud retreated. The lower part of the mountain remained shut from view, but for us the sun shone and the day became its own bright self once more. After sunset a brilliant moon rose. From high on the mountain, indeed from the very canyon I had visited, came the savage whooping of a large owl—possibly a Spotted Owl (*Strix occidentalis*).

XVII

The following morning Burleigh brought in a strange, middle-sized woodpecker which none of us had seen before—a male Bronzed Woodpecker (*Piculus aeruginosus*). It was richly colored, with moss-green back, wings, and tail, and heavily barred green and light gray under parts. Its head was somewhat like a flicker's in proportions and color-pattern, ashy-gray on the forehead and cheeks, deep red on the crown and nape, with clearly defined deep red moustaches. Semple and I examined the specimen eagerly, with a trace of cupidity I must admit, wishing that such a wonderful woodpecker might have flown our way.

This bird puzzled us. To be sure we did not know its name at the time—that was bad enough; but what was worse, its appearance led us to wonder whether it might not have been responsible for the "flicker" callnotes we had been hearing, hence for various statements concerning flickers which we had been entering in our notebooks. We had heard what we had thought to be the spring song of a flicker several times about the Mesa, but not once had we actually seen the bird.

Asked where he had been finding all these wondrous new birds, Burleigh showed us a trail which led northwestward to another shelf, another so-called Mesa, perhaps two miles farther along the mountain-side. It was an excellent trail, narrow but distinct, and easy to follow for it kept at about the same level the whole way. What a boon! Following it one would be able to move comfortably, swiftly and noiselessly forward. Nor would one ever need feel lost, no matter how thick the cloud.

Out this trail I started, hopeful that I might hear the Brown-backed Solitaire again, eager to find a Bronzed Woodpecker of my own, and especially eager to discover, if possible, a Red-shafted Flicker. A thread-thin squeal from the shrubbery beside the path I recognized as one of the characteristic callnotes of that common and confiding finch, the Rufous-capped Atlapetes. A little band of them fed regularly about a trash pile back of the house, and frequented the vine-covered fence round the chicken yard. Far up the slope sounded the gay song of a Berlandier's Wren. Birds of several species were tuning up or scolding below the trail not far ahead.

All at once the cloud closed in. Quite without warning, for the sun had been shining strongly, the air filled with mist, the bright blue of the sky went out, and a sort of twilight descended. I was deeply disappointed. The prospect had been very encouraging.

For more than an hour I walked along that beautiful trail without seeing or hearing a single bird. Hoping to startle a wren or warbler into flight, I thrashed through the shrubbery, but no bird flew out. I tried climbing the slope to the left, but was led on by neither chirp nor twitter. As if some powerful anesthetic had killed them or put them all to sleep, the birds were nowhere to be found.

I had actually turned back, wholly disappointed, when I heard a low, measured tapping off down the mountain. It was not a loud sound. In fact, it was scarcely more audible than the beating of my heart, but it was definite enough to stop me in my tracks. It was the tough, strong bill of a woodpecker at work! Investigating, I found not the Bronzed Woodpecker I had been hoping for, but a pair of Hairy Woodpeckers (*Dendrocopos villosus*), the first we had seen in Mexico. A few hundred miles to the north, in eastern Texas, a wholly different race of this species was known to inhabit wooded low country; here the bird was obviously montane. Nor were the woodpeckers the only birds I came upon. In the mossy oak with them was a male Black-throated Green Warbler (*Dendroica virens*) with light yellow cheeks. In the brush at one side were two Rufous-capped Warblers, and a Spotted Towhee which I recognized by its drawled alarm cry and white-tipped outer tail feathers. In some weeds not far off were three Black-headed Orioles. Not one of these nine birds was calling. All were moving quietly about, feeding, occasionally preening, keeping a lookout for enemies, but making no vocal sound. The cloud had hushed them.

Finding this mixed bird flock seemed natural enough when I recalled that the nesting season had not yet started. Especially natural did it seem when I noted the familiar-looking oaks, nettles, buttercups, and other spring flowers which grew all about me. How often, in the winter woods of West Virginia, had I encountered Hairy and Downy Woodpeckers, Carolina Chickadees (*Parus carolinensis*), Tufted Titmice (*P. bicolor*), Brown Creepers (*Certhia familiaris*), and Cardinals moving about together in this very way, feeding almost side by side, apparently enjoying each other's company, staying together from morning to night as if they all had been members of one big happy family. Here in Nuevo León the birds were an odd assortment, to be sure. Why odd? Only because some of the species were unfamiliar to me.

The Hairy Woodpeckers were different from any I had theretofore handled. Their wings were sparsely spotted with white, their under parts light brownish-gray. On the whole they were noticeably darker than the Hairy Woodpecker of the northeastern United States, the geographic race of *Dendrocopos villosus* with which I was most familiar. Recalling that in many bird species the breeding form found along the humid coast of Oregon and Washington was dark, I could not resist believing that the darkness of these Hairy Woodpeckers of the Sierra Madre was in some way correlated with humidity. This line of thought was easy enough to follow as I contemplated the dripping foliage, the wetness of my clothing, and the darkness of the cloud which hung over and through the woodland.

Climbing back to the trail I retraced my steps a way, feeling that my luck had changed at last. As I made a sharp turn round a great rock I came face to face with a trim pigeon, standing high on its legs in the very middle of the path. For an instant the handsome creature seemed wholly out of place. What business had a big blue pigeon in a wild, out-of-the-way spot such as this? Bobbing its head as all pigeons do when they walk, it took three mincing steps, paused to regard me with startled eye, and leaped into the air. As it vanished into the mist, the flapping of its strong wings echoed from the cliffs. Of course it was no ordinary barnyard fowl. It was a Band-tailed Pigeon (*Columba fasciata*)—a species I had studied in the wildest parts of the Chisos Mountains in Texas, and on Vancouver Island. That afternoon and late that evening we heard the Band-tails hooting among the pinnacles far above us.

I found my own Bronzed Woodpecker first thing the following morning. It was sitting in the top of an oak near our house, not climbing nor propped against the trunk or some thick bough, but perched, flicker-wise, on a horizontal twig, its tail hanging straight down. It called as I watched. An answer sounded from far up the slope. Assuredly this *was* the "flicker" I had been hearing, the "flicker" I had been writing about in my notes.

Observing that the sky was clear and the valley-cloud low, I decided to climb to the very top of the mountain. This I had for some time wanted to do, not so much to enjoy the view as to ascertain what birds

83

might be inhabiting the higher elevations at this season. The trail zig-zagged through the woods and up a slope of rough rocks to a point not far below the summit. A short way above the Mesa I encountered a flock of small, insectivorous birds—Bridled and Black-crested Titmice, Ruby-crowned Kinglets, a Black and White Warbler, several Orange-crowned Warblers, and a few Hutton's Vireos (*Vireo huttoni*). These trooped actively through the trees, giving their thin alarm notes, keeping close to each other as if bound together by a common cause. The Hutton's Vireo bore a strong superficial resemblance to the Ruby-crowned King-let. Though heavier, bigger-headed, and stouter-billed, it had the king-let's not quite complete eye-ring, inconspicuous wing-bars, and yellow-washed sides.

Three-quarters of the way to the top I came upon a wren which was new to me. It was obviously too small for a Berlandier's Wren or Canyon Wren, and it appeared to be closely related to the House Wren. It was a silent, furtive bird with gray-brown upper parts, *light brown throat and breast,* and rather distinct buffy-white line above the eye. I had no easy time collecting it, for it ran among the rocks and underbrush, refusing to take wing. It proved to be a Brown-throated Wren (*Troglodytes brunneicollis*).

The vista which spread out to the north was notable chiefly for the vast, flat, valley-hiding cloud which stretched from a point just below the Mesa to the base of the mountains north and northwest of Monterrey. What a cloud! Contemplating it, I was reminded not so much of a fog-hung lake as of a field of rotten ice in Hudson Strait—the chunks irregular, jammed tight, and all dirty white. The illusion was the more perfect because the breeze from the north was sharply cool.

The character of the vegetation did not change at all radically as I ascended the trail. Near the top of the mountain the thickets of smilax were denser than any I had seen at lower elevations, and here, somewhat to my surprise, I found all the wrens we had thus far recorded about the Mesa—the dark brown Canyon Wren, with its long bill, white throat, and clear song of nine or ten descending notes; the shorter-billed, rufous-backed Berlandier's Wren, apparently the very species we had encountered in the lowlands north of Monterrey at an elevation of only 1,500 feet; and two sorts of House Wrens: the gray-breasted species, *Troglodytes aëdon,* which was so well known throughout the United States; and *Troglodytes brunneicollis,* the Brown-throated Wren of Mexican extraction. How I longed to hear this last-named species sing, to examine its nest, to see its eggs!

The only bird I found on the very top of the mountain was a Hutton's Vireo. No eagle, no hawk, no high-flying swift, but a dull, greenish-gray little bird with indistinct eye-ring and wing-bars, singing his conversational song from a thicket which he evidently felt would make a good nesting place. No female bird that I could see was with him, so I fancied he had simply taken up residence there, and was announcing to all female Hutton's Vireos who happened by that here was a fine place for a nest, here a spot where food was abundant, here a male bird who considered himself to be the best of mates and fathers.

Disappointed at not finding some striking species as a reward for my four-hour climb, I descended to the Mesa in time to prepare my wren specimens, compare notes with my comrades, and go out Burleigh's trail before nightfall. It was a lovely evening. The air was so still that no leaf stirred. In its high canyon a Brown-backed Solitaire was singing. In a tree above me a perfect gem of a bird, a Painted Redstart (*Setophaga picta*), snatched flies as it tumbled from bough to bough. It was glossy black above, bright red below, with flashing white wing and tail markings. Close by the trail a dozen Acorn Woodpeckers (*Balanosphyra formicivora*) sparred with each other noisily. We had not seen these conspicuous birds anywhere about the Mesa proper. I wondered if they were a migrating flock enroute from southern Mexico to a more northerly nesting ground.

I soon decided that all these woodpeckers belonged here, for with the aid of my glass I discovered stubs in which literally hundreds of acorns had been driven neatly into little holes dug in the wood or bark by the energetic birds. The woodpeckers were paying no attention to the acorns now; instead, they were eating insects which they snatched, flycatcherwise, in mid-air. How handsome they were as they sailed out above the treetops, the red of their crown-patches and white markings of their wings flashing in the rich light! Again using the binocular, I observed that the birds were all white-eyed, and that the crown was wholly red in the males, black in front and red behind in the females.

The whole company of woodpeckers was garrulous and quarrelsome. They chased each other up and down the mountainside, two of them sometimes coming to grips and tumbling, a mass of black and white shot with red, to the very ground. I could not help thinking how silent all but one of them would suddenly become should a Sharp-shinned Hawk dash into their midst intent upon a kill.

At nightfall I watched one of the woodpeckers climb deliberately to a hole in a dead stub, look about a bit, force itself in, then, miraculously enough, appear at the entrance as if it had been looking out the whole time! At this very instant the hue and cry of the company ceased utterly. I looked about for woodpeckers but saw not another one. As if hurried off by some curfew which I had not heard, they had all retired. I focussed my glass on the bird I had actually seen turning in. Its brightly colored head was still visible. Its white eyes were wide open. There was on its face almost the expression of a small boy who has gone to bed with his clothes on intending to steal forth as soon as the house is quiet. A bat flapped past the tree. The woodpecker eyed this fellow citizen, whose presence so unequivocally proclaimed the imminence of night, blinked a sleepy eye (the binocular is a wonderful aid to bird study!), and crayfished back into its roosting place. The Brown-backed Solitaire, whose largeness of eye bespoke a liking for the dusk, continued to sing from the base of the mountain cathedral's now darkened spires. A Spotted Towhee scolded from the bushes. Somewhere off in the woods sounded a note which I thought was a small owl's.

Listening intently, I waited fully five minutes before starting back for the Mesa. My eyes were open wide, though I could see but little. Wings roared sharply as a heavy bird plunged valleyward at terrific speed. It was no Spotted Owl. An owl's flight would have been noiseless. It was no crepuscular hawk stooping. It was a Band-tailed Pigeon, descending from the pinnacle or from a favorite pine, perhaps for its evening drink.

XVIII

On February 12, a half mile or so down the winding road from the Mesa, we happened upon the largest mixed flock of birds we had yet seen in Mexico. The oak and pine forest at that elevation (3,500–4,000 feet) was surprisingly thick. Everywhere about us, up and down the wooded slopes, flitted titmice, warblers, vireos, wrens, kinglets, orioles, thrushes, jays, and various members of the Fringillidae, the finch family. The titmice were especially conspicuous because, impelled as they were by a curiosity all out of proportion to their size, they gathered in little groups about us scolding loudly. The Bridled Titmice and Black-crested Titmice were, so far as we could see, about equally common. In the low country north of Monterrey we had seen the latter species frequently, but the Bridled Titmouse was obviously a mountain bird. We looked for an *uncrested* titmouse with black cap and throat-patch—the Mexican Chickadee (*Parus sclateri*)—but, failing to see any such bird, we assumed that it must inhabit the spruce woods at considerably higher elevations.

A wholly new bird for our list was the Hepatic Tanager (*Piranga flava*), the first member of the tanager family we had seen in Mexico. The males were beautifully colored—rich orange-red below and on the forehead, dull reddish-gray on the back, wings, and tail. The females were wholly different in color, being plain yellow below and grayish-olive above. In both sexes the bluish-gray bill was so heavy as to impart a somewhat finchlike appearance.

All the orioles of the woodland were Black-headed Orioles. Nowhere did we see a Hooded Oriole, or any transient, northward-bound species such as the Baltimore, Bullock's (*Icterus bullocki*), or Orchard Oriole (*I. spurius*), all of which we knew would be making their way through some part of Mexico during the period of migration.

Of the wood warblers, the Hartlaub's Warbler, which we had already seen above the Mesa, was decidedly the commonest, although it was restless and not very easy to observe. Being struck anew with the great similarity between this bird and the Parula Warbler of the United States and Canada, we listened patiently for its song, confident that we would note a resemblance there, but no song did we hear. Neither the Myrtle nor the Audubon's Warbler was common, and the only other winter visitant members of the family which we noted were the Black-throated Green Warbler and the Black and White Warbler. The Rufous-capped Warblers, which we continued to see and hear from time to time, went about in pairs. The males, which were singing bright, buntinglike songs from smilax tangles and dense patches of undergrowth, probably had staked out their nest territories.

There were two species of vireos—the somewhat chunky, plain-colored Hutton's Vireo and the larger, more deliberate, and easily identifiable Blue-headed Vireo. The latter we had seen with the White-eyed Vireo in the low country; but Hutton's Vireo, like Hartlaub's Warbler, was a montane bird exclusively.

Commonest by far of the wrens was the Berlandier's, whose bright songs and loud scolding cries sounded on all sides. Far above us we occasionally heard a Canyon Wren—its song a series of startlingly clear, pure notes tripping effortlessly down the scale and ending with a faint trill. The whole slope was too well-wooded, apparently, and the elevation perhaps too great, for the Rock Wren. We saw the Long-billed Thrasher once or twice, but not the Mockingbird.

The only thrushes we saw were Hermit Thrushes, which flitted like ghost birds through the vegetation ahead of us, now and then giving a low *chuck* of alarm, or raising their tails in excitement as they eyed us from afar. We found that by hiding ourselves and squeaking loudly we could bring them up very close; but once they discovered they were being fooled they paid no further heed. The titmice, on the other hand, never learned what we were up to, and flew in belligerently each time we squeaked. They seemed to be driven by curiosity and a sort of headlong eagerness to help the stricken comrade which had cried out in distress.

The finches of the woodland were many. Commonest were the Spotted Towhees and Rufous-capped Atlapetes, which scratched noisily in the leaves all about us. We did not, however, see any Green-tailed Towhees or Olive Sparrows. Overhead we occasionally heard the *eek* or *zheek* of a Black-headed Grosbeak, a sharp cry which was quite unlike that of any other bird of the flock. The male Black-headed Grosbeak was easily recognizable by the warm, clear brown of the under parts, rump, and collar, the black of the head, and the black and white of the wings and tail. The females were much less colorful, but the white markings of the wings showed rather clearly when they flew, and their bills, like those of the males, were strikingly heavy.

A new fringillid for our list was the Common Goldfinch (*Spinus tristis*)—a plain little thing, surely, in this, its winter plumage. We saw a flock of four of them close together in the top of a bare tree. All of them appeared to be females, for very little yellow showed anywhere in the grayish-brown head- and body-plumage, and the black of the wings and tails was not very intense. The specimen we obtained, by way of confirming our identification, proved indeed to be a female.

To our surprise we noted a few Cardinals. We had not expected to find this low-country species so far up the mountainside, but here it was, and it seemed to be perfectly at home.

On rocky slopes, especially where there was grass or thick, low shrubbery, we occasionally put up a Boucard's Rufous-crowned Sparrow —a species we were learning to recognize by its dullness of coloration and secretive manner. It had a way of fluttering out from under foot, flying a short way up the slope, and dropping suddenly into the grass.

Of non-passerine birds we listed only a few, but they were exciting. One was a Red-tailed Hawk which soared far below us, giving us a wonderful look at its dark back and rich red-brown tail. Then there were the Bronzed Woodpeckers, several of which we saw hitching along the lichen-covered boughs, tapping quietly at the bark. So far as we could ascertain, they were unpaired. We watched in vain for "dancing" or other evidence of courtship amongst them. We were struck by the fact that the green of their plumage was not especially noticeable in any light. As they flew off, giving us a clear view of their upper parts, their spread wings had a decidedly bronzy or brownish tone.

The great find of the morning remains to be discussed. While Burleigh and I were concentrating on problems of identification, our friend Semple wandered off by himself—as was his wont—devoting himself

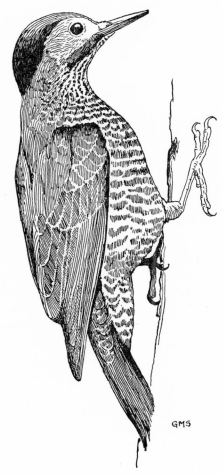

Bronzed Woodpecker (*Piculus aeruginosus*)
9½ inches

89

to a single objective. Paying no attention to the "small fry" which bustled about him, he examined carefully every tangle of vines and every shadowy place he could find, rapped with a stick all trees which had natural cavities or old woodpecker holes, and, as a direct result of this methodical search, obtained a bird we had not even expected to list—a Screech Owl! The specimen was not a Flammulated Scops Owl (*Otus scops flammeolus*), the very small, dark-eyed, mountain-inhabiting species which we had frequently discussed and fervently hoped to find, but a larger, grayer bird with pale yellow eyes. It belonged, obviously, to the wide-ranging species *Otus asio,* the very Screech Owl with which we were familiar back home. Finding it here gave us a special sort of thrill. But could this bird of the Sierra Madre actually be of the same geographical race as that which was said to inhabit the low country to the north? Was it dichromatic—that is, found in two color-phases, a red-brown and a gray—as were the races inhabiting the eastern United States? These questions we simply could not answer at the moment. Full subspecific identification would have to come later, when a series of skins would be available for comparison. The specimen in hand was a gray one, there could be no doubting that. Wholly because of Semple's prowess as an owl hunter we had establshed the fact that *Otus asio* was a Mesa bird. If the fates were kind, we might obtain another specimen, possibly even a red-phased one. The discovery of this unexpected owl gave us new enthusiasm, doubling our determination to make every moment of our sojourn count.

The day was the finest we had had on the mountain. When, by mid-afternoon, no cloud had threatened to close in on us, Burleigh and I decided to drive down the road after swifts. Not by any means had we forgotten these fleet-winged creatures whose identity was unknown to us. We had looked for them day after day, mentioning them repeatedly. We had even climbed to the summit hoping to find them there. Nowhere on or above the Mesa had we so much as glimpsed one of the birds.

We drove straight to the hairpin curve at which we had seen the swifts four days previously. To our delight the cloud did not envelop us. There it hung, not far off, to be sure. Parts of it drifted toward and over us. But the vast, thick body of it kept well below us. We waited five minutes or more before seeing a swift.

With a twist, a flutter, and a rapid slipping downward on long, set wings, a black *and white* bird shot past. So quickly did it pass out of sight that we had no time even to lift our glasses for a look. Everything about it had been swiftlike rather than swallowlike, that much was certain. It had had white on it too, so much white that we knew it could have been neither a Chimney Swift nor a Black Swift (*Cypseloides niger*). In a sort of daze we stood there, berating ourselves inwardly for not having shot when we had had the chance.

Hearing a squeal and sharp twitter overhead we looked up to see three more swifts rounding the shoulder of the mountain far, far above us. Suddenly a swift which we had not seen coming shot by so close that its image was only a blur. The whine of its passing was still in our ears when another appeared, then another, then still another . . . . Yelling at each other in our excitement, we watched the fleet creatures cross and recross in front of us. Up and down, up and down went our guns, but we fired no shot. There seemed to be no way of planning anything. As in a high old game of cross tag the birds cut in on each other, distracting our attention, fuddling us, making us half dizzy. Finally, with grim resolve, we began shooting. The roar of our guns echoed savagely all over the mountain. But the swifts played on, unscathed.

So far we had been shooting only at the incoming birds, for we had been determined not to lose the specimens on the steep, brush-covered slope below us. Now, half-desperate in our eagerness to ascertain what they were, we began shooting in all directions, heedless of the spot at which they might fall. Finally, luck with us, we got one. It whirled downward, wings still outspread, striking the hard ground beside us. It was a sleek, well-plumaged, fully adult White-throated Swift (*Aëronautes saxatilis*). We might have expected it to be of that species, but for some reason neither of us had seen the white *on the throats* of the birds which had flown by.

We took time out to examine the curious creature, whose short, strong feet were well feathered and whose whole body looked and felt so tough and firm. Now we perceived that the white of the throat extended in an irregular line down the breast and belly; that a spot at each side of the rump was white; that there was white at the tips of the secondary wing feathers, in a thin line above the eye, and on the middle tail feathers. The tail was distinctly forked. The lining of the wide mouth was brownish-yellow. In the moist gullet we found several unswallowed insects.

So our much-talked-of swift did not belong to an undescribed species. We were some thirty rounds of ammunition the poorer and slightly sore in the shoulders, but the feeling of satisfaction more than compensated. The problem had been solved. We could leave the Mesa knowing that the White-throated Swift lived there in mid-February. Looking up, we saw that the flock, which had so recently been disporting itself over-head, had departed.

That evening after supper we went forth in search of owls. Follow-ing the trail which led westward along the mountainside, we reached a broad rockslide just at dusk. After a short, laborious climb, we found a nook among gigantic boulders, took positions from which we could watch a leafless tree against the darkening sky, and waited. A huge beetle crawled noisily up through the leaves onto a rock, lifted its horny elytra, and flew off with a melodious roar. A bat fluttered by. Band-tailed Pigeons began hooting among the cliffs far above us.

Suddenly the soft, two-syllabled cry of some creature of the night began. Listening carefully, we agreed that the sounds came from a black spot of woodland possibly a hundred yards away, but they were so low and gentle that at times they seemed much farther off. Watching the trees for anything which might fly in, we squeaked in imitation of a mouse. The callnote we had heard now sounded from two directions—from the spot of woodland and from far down the slope, below the trail. We tried an imitation of the sound, but still no owl appeared. Thus, until the stars were shining brightly, did we wait, listening and watch-ing. But the creature of mystery did not reveal itself.

XIX

The Mexican Jay was by far the most noticeable bird of the Mesa. Not only was it fairly large, attractively colored, and noisy, but it was so unsuspicious and so inordinately curious that it spent much of its time about the buildings, frequently alighting in the paths or on the window-sills or porches. The workmen had no opprobrious nickname for it, however, calling it simply the *pájaro azul,* or "bluebird."

These particular Mexican Jays probably did not know what it was to fear human beings. Having spent their entire lives far from the populous low country, they had gained their knowledge of mankind wholly from the summertime guests at the Mesa, or from the few families who lived thereabouts the year round. Most of these people had fed and encouraged the pretty birds, shooing them off only when they became too noisy.

The jays had been interested in us the moment we had arrived.

Mexican Jay (*Aphelocoma ultramarina*)
13 inches

They had flown in to inspect us, screeching a lusty welcome. Our guns had held no terrors for them. Now that our comings and goings had become familiar to them, they gathered the instant one of us appeared at the door. This was no blind love for us, to be sure; it was a combination of hunger and common sense. The jays liked to eat the skinned bodies of small birds which we frequently tossed to them.

That the jays knew us as individuals I very much doubt. Had they come upon us in the woods at any considerable distance from the Mesa, they probably would have scolded us roundly. Indeed, a good many of the scoldings we got from jays may easily have been given by the very

93

birds we had been feeding. A human being is, in other words, a relative matter to a Mexican Jay. In the woods, whether armed or not, he is on about a par with a wildcat, something to be watched and followed about, screamed at, mobbed on occasion. At or near a house he is entirely harmless, need not be avoided nor scolded, and is to be regarded principally as a dispenser of food.

The jays went about in small companies by themselves, usually not associating with other species of birds. Sometimes, especially when the cloud shut down, they were secretive and silent, sneaking through the trees as if bent on some unsavory business; again, indulging in what appeared to be wholly unwarranted obstreperousness, they squawked and chattered at the tops of their voices. One of their favorite cries was a loud *oik! oik! oik! oik!* Another was a less raucous *wick, wick, wick!* Why they did not help us with our Screech Owl hunting was beyond us. The Green Jays down at Monterrey certainly would have done so. Jays and crows of all sorts usually consider owls their special problem, the finding and badgering of owls among their important duties or prerogatives; but the Mexican Jays on the Mesa de Chipinque never once led us to an owl, much as we hoped they would.

February 13 was Sunday, a quiet, cloud-smothered day. While my companions were skinning specimens, I took myself to the porch to paint an Acorn Woodpecker in water color. So damp was the atmosphere that I had a bad time with the paper, and the brush strokes would not dry. The all-pervasive cloud flowed in round the pillars, trailing past at arm's length between me and the door.

Semple brought his Screech Owl's stomach out to the porch for examination. Among the contents were parts of several beetles and the remains of one big centipede. We were disappointed at not finding more. It would have thrilled us to pick from a mass of fur the clean white cranium of a tiny shrew. Such a skull would have been identifiable. Nor would it have been beyond reason to look for parts of an unknown, undescribed, unnamed small mammal in the stomach of any owl whose hunting ground was the Mesa.

Looking up from our analysis of insect remains, what should we see in a tree close by but one of our Mexican Jays, full of meat scraps probably, tucking itself in for a nap. It was on a twig under a clump of live oak leaves, about fifteen feet from the ground. Its eyes were half closed. It turned its head, lifted its loose scapular feathers, and stuck its beak into their soft, grayish-blue depths. Along with all other orthodox Mexicans, it was taking a siesta.

So it was Sunday. We would have one more day on the Mesa if we were to follow our latest plan. Talking things over, we decided that, the cloud permitting, we would go to the foot of the mountain on the morrow, hunt for hummingbirds among the blossoming shrubs, obtain another White-throated Swift if possible, and continue our search for Screech Owls. We had now been in Mexico about three weeks. During this period not a day had passed but that we had recorded one or more species new to our list.

Monday morning did not dawn. The cloud which clung to the mountain was the darkest, wettest, and most forbidding we had yet experienced. Even in the midst of the buildings we seemed to be lost, ensnared in a vast cobweb, or moving about in an interminable dream. But a Spotted Towhee was singing brightly in the brush above the house and another was *mewing* close by. A trifle annoyed, if not depressed, we set out, following the road down the mountain.

Once we found birds to watch, we forgot all about the cloud. Just now there were two small, dull-colored birds in the tree overhead—a Hutton's Vireo and a Ruby-crowned Kinglet. Fancy finding these two, of all species, thus side by side, with not another bird of any sort close by! Two distinct species, representatives of wholly different families, yet so astonishingly alike that one general description would certainly have served for them both. The vireo was deliberate, even pensive, in manner, as vireos usually are. The kinglet was sprightly and restless. Occasionally, brimming with energy, it flicked a wing. Yet when the two birds paused to look at us, we might conceivably have thought one a male, the other a female, of the same species. We had never before had a reason, or, for that matter, a chance, to compare the two birds directly in life. The vireo paid little attention to the kinglet. The kinglet, on the other hand, followed the slightly larger bird closely, keeping at its side, even fluttering over and about it as if hopeful of attracting its attention. Who were we to attempt an explanation of this amusing behavior? To us the kinglet appeared to be puzzled, if not actually annoyed, by the vireo's sluggishness and indifference, and furthermore to be convinced that if it kept on nagging hard enough it could force its companion into a sprightlier, more kingletlike manner.

Farther down the mountain, among the big pines, we came upon a band of Black-headed Orioles. Since they were feeding close to the ground we had an excellent opportunity to observe them. They were not gorgeous birds, but we enjoyed the rich yellow-green of their backs, and the sunflower yellow of their breasts. Not often did they alight upon the ground, but they flew from weed stalk to weed stalk, jabbing at the leaves and leaf stems with their sharp beaks, or extricating insects from spiders' webs. Their casual, carefree whistling continued to charm us. Where had we ever heard bird music with quite this naïve, sweet-natured tunelessness?

Toward noon the cloud lifted, not alone from the mountain but from the whole valley to the north. For the second time that week we saw Monterrey, the highway leading north from the city, the little spot of green off to the right which had been our favorite birding-ground. Interesting it was to contemplate that distant bit of verdure, bearing in mind that the Pyrrhuloxias, Golden-fronted Woodpeckers, Kiskadee Flycatchers, and Rose-throated Becards which we had encountered there belonged to species which were nowhere to be seen on the Mesa about us. Listening, we could hear the *oik! oik!* of a Mexican Jay, here at this 5,000 foot elevation. At the same instant, with our glasses on the oaks in the valley, we could see the habitat of two other, and distinctly different, jays—the Green Jay and the Brown. Two worlds, a high one and a low: two worlds, ecologically speaking, as distinct, as separate, almost as cut off from each other, as two planets.

An interesting new bird for our list was the Red-naped Sapsucker (*Sphyrapicus varius nuchalis*), a handsome male specimen of which we obtained on our return to the Mesa proper. This woodpecker and the Yellow-bellied Sapsucker, which we had obtained just north of Monterey on January 31, were geographical races of the same species, both being winter visitors to Mexico. In the male Yellow-bellied Sapsucker the red of the top of the head was restricted to the crown-patch itself, while in the male Red-naped Sapsucker the red continued beyond the crown-patch and its encircling band of black *onto the nape*. This red nuchal area was distinct enough to be discernible even in the field.

Another new bird was the Pine Siskin (*Spinus pinus*), one of which we saw with a flock of about twenty goldfinches. It was much like the goldfinches in size, proportions, and behavior, but was heavily streaked all over, especially on the under parts, and its callnotes were rougher.

In the afternoon Burleigh and I drove down the mountain to the hairpin curve of the White-throated Swifts, waited in vain a full half hour, then descended the steep slope to the dry gorge directly below. The thicket was virtually impenetrable. Had it not been for animal trails and the stream bed itself we should never have been able to move forward without machete or ax. White-eyed Vireos sang their explosive songs in the densest tangles. Now and then an Inca Dove flew up, its

PLATE VI
Flint-billed Woodpecker
(*Phloeoceastes guatemalensis*)

wings producing a rough *flut! flut!* rather than a musical whistling. These two species we had not encountered on the Mesa proper. We saw no hummingbirds.

After ten minutes in the thicket Burleigh and I were completely out of touch with each other. Since I did not hear him shooting I assumed that he was not finding much, so I let him go his way while I ascended a rough, irregular tributary canyon which led up the valley toward a loop of the road. An hour passed before I saw him again.

On hearing the distant roar of a shotgun, as well as echoes which reverberated for several seconds, I decided that he had shot a twelve gauge shell rather than the small cartridge he would have used in collecting a hummingbird. There sounded another *baloom*—solemn, low, not at all close at hand—and more echoes. On the alert this time, I sensed that the report had come from somewhere above me, from across the valley, from the brow of the tablelike hill directly to the north. With my binocular I saw my friend (I recognized his hat and brown shirt) standing at the very edge of the high rock rim. I watched him raise the gun, saw the gun sharply recoil, then a full second later, heard the blast and its echoes. Why so much shooting? There could be but one answer to the question: he was after a White-throated Swift.

Joining Burleigh meant a rough scramble out of the arroyo and up the sharply precipitous, twenty-foot wall at the hill's top. Too much in a hurry, I broke a finger nail just as I made the last stretch. But the swifts! How they whirled and veered and volplaned about us, so close that we might have caught them with a butterfly net, now coming from this side, now from that, often two or three of them at a time! Occasionally one of them twittered, or chased another. Beyond this we observed nothing which suggested courtship or pairing.

We did not shoot very well that afternoon: so much must be said in strict honesty. But we did collect a specimen, and a beautiful bird it was with its long, trim wings and firm, black and white plumage. Holding it in our hands we could not help thinking how the Wright brothers would have thrilled at watching and studying those streamlined masters of the air as they shot so swiftly and so surely over the rocks.

We had no way of determining the speed of the birds' flight. Literally dizzy from following them with our guns while standing upright on the uneven ground, and fairly gasping at their pickup power as they whizzed by, we thought that 200 miles an hour would be about right. Not that we quite believed they were going that fast, nor expected any thoughtful person to agree that they were; but the day was fine, we

97

were off on a cliff-top by ourselves, nobody was there to argue with us, so 200 mph was a fair enough guess!

XX

The Mesa de Chipinque! With seven full days of searching we had discovered a few of the big mountain's treasures. We had seen its uppermost pinnacles turned to gold by the rising sun. We had felt the magic in the song of its Brown-backed Solitaire. We had captured its Screech Owl. But what of that creature of mystery whose low cries we had heard at nightfall? What of the unidentified quail which had whirred up the rocky steeps? What of the trogons and hummingbirds which would surely be nesting there a little later in the season?

With a pang of regret we departed—down through the cloud, which had returned full strength during the night; down through the great pines, in whose branches the Mexican Jays were squawking loudly; down past the White-throated Swifts' rock-girt citadel; down once more to the Sparrow Hawks, Great-tailed Grackles, Mockingbirds and Pyrrhuloxias of the low country. How odd it was, gliding along so quietly, so effortlessly, to come again upon these familiar birds, seeing them thus dimly through the cloud! So full had our life on the mountain been that the fact of their living elsewhere, of their existence at a definitely lower elevation, had never quite fully entered our consciousness. We had contemplated the "two worlds," to be sure, the high world of the Mexican Jay, and the low world of the Green and Brown, but seeing these low country species put them in their place, ecologically speaking, as they had never quite been before. The birds themselves had in no way changed, of course. It was we who had changed. Having lived for one glorious week on a mountain, we were descending with a new concept of the plain at its foot.

We continued to drive through mist until we were well past Monterrey. Having no set destination, we knew only that we were headed south. We might go as far as Victoria, the capital city of Tamaulipas, or we might stop at Linares. We might, if we found a good road, drive westward into the mountains. It was the fifteenth of February. As we moved forward along the excellent highway we noted certain new features of the landscape: clear, shallow streams with tall cypresses growing along their banks; festoons of Spanish moss hanging from the larger trees; extensive orange groves. The brush country was somewhat monotonous, as it had been between Laredo and Monterrey; but the thickets seemed to be more verdant here, the shrubby trees higher.

As for the birds, there were first of all the vultures. These scavengers, which the Mexicans called *zopilotes,* we had always with us. They circled over us or perched on fenceposts along the highway, spreading their sombre wings to the sun. Often they stood in the road itself, devouring the remains of rabbits, cats, dogs, and even larger animals which had been killed by the motorcars.

Listing birds from a moving automobile is never very satisfying, of course. Whenever we passed a Mockingbird we could not help wondering what unfamiliar species were lurking in the thicket beneath it. Never did we see a Mourning Dove without remembering other members of the pigeon tribe with which we wanted to become acquainted. We were disappointed at seeing so few hawks along the highway.

Several times, while passing from Montemorelos to Linares, we stopped to investigate a likely looking spot, but found very few birds. About the villages and vast orange groves there were mixed flocks of blackbirds; Mourning, Ground, and Inca Doves; and a few Cardinals and Pyrrhuloxias. Occasionally we were lucky enough to squeak up a White-eyed Vireo or wren of some sort. But the obvious fact was that, close to the highway at least, this was not a very good bird country. It was too thickly populated, too intensively farmed.

At the edge of the city of Linares, in the vicinity of the Canadian Tourist Court, we found a delightful birding-ground. Here were fine trees, several irrigation ditches through which full-bodied streams flowed, and a pleasant stretch of riverbank. We were told of a spectacular canyon, some miles to the southwestward, through which wound the road to the old hill village of Galeana. Wherever we walked, the odor of orange blossoms filled our nostrils. In the trees overhead we saw several Rose-throated Becards. These pretty creatures behaved as if they were on their nesting-ground.

South of Linares, after crossing the Nuevo León-Tamaulipas state line, we entered a wilder, much more heavily wooded region in which birdlife was more abundant. Here the highway cut through the very heart of an extensive thicket. Slowing down, we watched the roadside carefully. Brown Jays frequently flew across the road just ahead of us, squawking loudly. Road-runners slipped off through the weeds, keeping their heads and tails low. The White-necked Raven, a species we had not seen for some time, was common. Often we passed one of the sedate

Roadside Hawk (*Buteo magnirostris*)
about 14 inches

birds perched in the top of a blooming *huizache* bush not far off the highway.

A new species for our list was the Roadside Hawk (*Buteo magnirostris*),[1] a middle-sized, somewhat chunky bird of prey which apparently found the highway a good hunting ground. It usually perched not on the very top of a tree, but down among the foliage on a fencepost or stub in the shelter of the thicket. When frightened, it flew off squealing, usually revealing the several dark bands on its light brownish-gray tail. It was dark brown above; white, barred with brown, below; and yellow-eyed when adult. Its general appearance was much like that of a Broad-winged Hawk (*B. platypterus*), a species which migrated through eastern Mexico but did not nest there and presumably did not winter there. Our first specimen of the Roadside Hawk we collected near the village of San Francisco. It was in oddly mixed, sub-adult plumage. Its eyes, which were of a beautiful shade of light brown, were apparently turning yellow.

Possibly the most noticeable bird of this section was the so-called "Mexican Eagle" or Caracara (*Polyborus cheriway*), a large bird which we frequently saw close to the highway. At a distance it appeared at first glance to be solid black with white head and neck; but closer scrutiny revealed the black cap and featherless orange-red area about the eye; the white barring of the upper back and irregular white patch in each wing; and the white basal part of the tail. We had seen this bird before, in Texas and Florida, but had never become well acquainted with it, and were therefore much interested in its rather uncertain, teetering flight; the negative dihedral, or bowed-downward position, of its wings in soaring; and the somewhat disproportionate largeness of the head and beak of the flying bird.

The Caracaras seemed to have about the same food habits as the vultures. At any rate they cruised up and down the highway with those less handsome birds, looking for carrion. They stood high, for their tarsi were long, and their bearing was regal. Since their claws were long and curved, they sometimes carried smaller animals away from the road in their feet. But we noticed that they did not fight very much with the vultures, despite the fact that the *zopilotes* had no talons. When the vultures were really hungry, the Caracaras, for all their fierceness of manner and visage, usually waited.

Near a large stream a few miles north of Victoria we had our first glimpse of the Red-billed Pigeon (*Columba flavirostris*), a species known to occur throughout wooded parts of eastern Mexico as far northward as the lower Río Grande valley. We saw only one bird, and caught no

[1] The common name "Roadside Hawk" has not, so far as I know, heretofore been used for this species, but such a name as "Large-billed Hawk" (based on the unfortunate scientific name *magnirostris*) is wholly inept; and the name "Broad-winged Hawk" should be avoided in view of the fact that the distinct (though admittedly similar) species, *Buteo platypterus,* has borne that name for more than a century. The northeastern Mexican race of Roadside Hawk, *Buteo magnirostris griseocauda,* has been called the Gray-tailed Hawk. This bird may well be known as the Gray-tailed Roadside Hawk.

Caracara (*Polyborus cheriway*)
about 24 inches

more than a flash of its red-brown chest and squarish, slaty-blue tail, but there could be no mistaking so large a species (it was about the size of a barnyard pigeon) and so swift a flier, and we knew we would have to be on the alert for it from now on.

At some cattle pens just north of Victoria we saw our first Mexican Crows (*Corvus imparatus*). They were handsome, glossy black birds, much smaller than the familiar Common Crow of the United States, with an odd, surprisingly feeble cry which resembled the syllables *gar-lic*. They were exceedingly gregarious at this season. Hundreds of them went about together in close-knit flocks, flying up in clouds, and settling upon the low trees or fences in such numbers that we might have slaughtered a dozen or so at a single shot.

As we moved southward we noticed that the shrubbery at either side of the road was in full bloom. The thorn-bearing mimosas and acacias were covered with small, fuzzy, golden balls, which had a dusty-sweet aroma. The blossoms on what had been pointed out to us as the *huizache* bush were cream colored. We passed great clumps of organ cactus—veritable forests of the majestic plants, all with fluted stalks which branched off symmetrically and reminded us of candelabra.

At quiet old Victoria we decided to put up at a tourist court which was just being finished at the north edge of the city. Here our first comment pertained to the luxuriance and beauty of the banana plants which stood in clumps about the building. Examining the broad, glossy leaves and huge, pendant buds, we recalled how wretchedly weatherbeaten the banana plants had been at Monterrey.

About these giant plantain lived several pairs of Inca Doves. Their spring song, a monotonous double hoot, was almost incessant. In some trees at the rear a flock of Great-tailed Grackles, Red-winged Blackbirds, and Red-eyed Cowbirds chattered and sang. In a tall prickly-pear cactus hedge at one side a flycatcher of some sort was calling in a high-pitched, strident voice. One of its callnotes resembled the syllables *fit-breer,* with the r's rolled. Noting this bird's clear yellow breast and belly, white throat, and slightly forked tail (which had no white either at the tip or along the sides) we decided it could be nothing but an Olive-backed Kingbird (*Tyrannus melancholicus*), another Mexican bird whose closest relatives were Central and South American, and whose breeding range extended as far north as the lower Río Grande valley of Texas. To refresh our memory, we reviewed the bird's species characters—the wholly unmarked and slightly forked tail, the dull olive back, the yellow breast and belly, and white throat. If it had been a Western or Arkansas Kingbird (*T. verticalis*) it would have had a gray back and square-tipped tail and white would have shown along the *edge* of the outer tail feathers. If it had been a Cassin's Kingbird (*T. vociferans*) it would have been grayer-backed; the gray of its chest would have separated the white of its throat from the yellow of its belly; and the square-tipped tail would more than likely have shown a light gray tipping.

After settling ourselves, we went to work. Semple skinned specimens,

I made a sketch of the Roadside Hawk which we had collected along the way, and Burleigh went hunting. In an hour or so he returned with a Red-billed Pigeon, an Eastern Phoebe, a Bewick's Wren, the race of which we could not determine in the field, and several Mexican Crows. The pigeon was simply but beautifully colored—the whole head, neck, breast, and a large patch on the coverts of each wing being rich reddish-chocolate, the back and scapulars olive, and the rest dark slaty-blue. There was not a hint of iridescence on the neck, but the eyes were bright reddish-orange; the feet were coral-red; and we found, on examining the bill closely, that only the soft basal portion was red, the hard, somewhat swollen tip being pearl gray.

XXI

Bird study in an entirely new country is thrilling, but it is also a bit hard on the nerves. One does not know where to start, which direction to turn, which road to take. Every prospect is bewildering. Birds are abundant on every hand; but one has no way of knowing which of these need most to be studied in life, which collected at once and preserved. Especially is one plagued by the suspicion that the commonest looking and most familiar sounding may be the least known of them all.

We carefully examined a map, perceiving thereby that Victoria was indeed well south of the border. The small, glossy Mexican Crows and scarlet hibiscus flowers had done their best to tell us this, but we had been so preoccupied with the problems of bird identification and so charmed by the colors and odors of the blossoming countryside that we had quite forgotten about latitudes and geographical zones. Looking round us with a new appreciation of our good fortune at being in so interesting a spot, we were more bewildered than ever. The dark sierra to the west fascinated us, but how could we reach those rugged heights without horses or burros and special guides? No, we were not equipped for tackling the mountains. How about the pretty rivers we had crossed fifteen or twenty miles north of the city? How about the low country which stretched off to the east?

At our conference beneath the blooming banana plants after early breakfast on the morning of February 16, we agreed that what we wanted more than all else was to get away from the main highway, to find a wild place in which there were no fences nor stone walls, no domestic animals, no people. How to reach such a place without walking miles from a road was the question.

Driving a few blocks southward, toward the city's principal square, we found ourselves at crossroads. The names on the signboards didn't help us greatly; but we chose what appeared to be the least improved of the four thoroughfares, turned east, and found ourselves on the famous old "Matamoros trail." As we moved toward the edge of town we were pleased that the road continued to be of plain dirt, less pleased with the assortment of ruts and puddles.

Just outside the city we entered a sisal-growing district. Here field after field of the formally set-out maguey lay along either side of the road, the huge clumps of glaucous green leaves rising to a height of six feet or more, each clump with a tall flower stalk growing straight up from its center. Parts of certain fields had been harvested, the fully developed leaves having been chopped or sawed off at the base and stacked neatly, ready for carrying in. Other areas apparently had just been cleared for planting. Not far from the highway a small mill was running full blast. Here the tough leaves were being pounded to pieces and the fibres extracted. An unpleasant, sourish odor permeated the air. A low cart, brimming with moist pulp and brown-skinned children, drove by. The sisal fiber itself, hanging on wires in the sun, looked like masses of hair. Some of it was wet, limp, and pale green; but most of it was dry, ready to be baled, and of a shade best designated as "peroxide blonde."

What of the birds of this treeless, thicketless, highly cultivated district? To our surprise, they were plentiful. Most noticeable of all were the Caracaras and Harris's Hawks, which perched on the high flower stalks, basking in the morning sunlight or watching the ground for prey. The flycatcher tribe was well represented. We identified both the Olive-backed and the Cassin's Kingbirds, the Say's Phoebe, and a new species for our list, the Ash-throated Flycatcher (*Myiarchus cinerascens*), which looked much like the familiar Crested Flycatcher (*M. crinitus*) of the eastern United States, but was somewhat smaller, grayer above, and much paler yellow on the belly. Golden-fronted and Ladder-backed Woodpeckers climbed about the maguey plants, pecking at the tough stalks exactly as they would have pecked at trees. Among the sprawling leaves lived Black-throated Sparrows, Ground Doves, Mockingbirds and Loggerhead Shrikes. The shrikes impaled their victims on the tough, sharp, terminal leaf spines.

Birds were not the only creatures which inhabited these sisal fields.

105

There were small, exceedingly agile lizards, upon which the hawks and shrikes must surely have been feeding. There were furry tarantulas and gaily colored butterflies. We saw a medium-sized rat and a small fox, which scampered swiftly off between the rows of stiff-leafed plants.

But we had not come to Victoria to make a biological survey of a sisal plantation. Through a fellow traveller we learned that by following the road on to the town of Güemes, then bearing right and proceeding a few miles farther, we would come to a river, the Río Corona. There would be no bridge, but the ford was safe. The woodland was heavy thereabouts. It would be a likely place for birds.

We reached the Río Corona that afternoon, finding it to be a beautiful, though not particularly large, stream of clear, cool water, flowing between well wooded banks. The sunlight poured in through the leaves and vines, obscuring rather than illuminating the farther shore and penetrating the water to its greenest depths. A grassy opening near the ford was guarded by huge cypresses. We got out of the car, glanced briefly about, and moved a step or two toward the river. How very quiet the place was, how utterly without wind! In vain we listened for a whistle, chirp, or alarm note. The only sound was the river's low soliloquy.

We might have stood there a long time enjoying the simple beauty of the scene. But ornithologists are innately, hopelessly restless. Some deep-rooted desire to interpret correctly each slightest movement of leaf or shadow, to identify each faintest bird cry, and, more than this, to let no sound or movement escape unnoticed, impels them to be alert, rouses in them a terrific, aggressive sensuousness, keeps them "on the go." We stood there beneath the cypresses, momentarily aware of a tranquility which was refreshing to our innermost souls. But a branch moved above us and our mood swiftly changed. The falling of a bit of bark brought us to attention, transformed us into a storm center of inquisitiveness. We looked upward hard and long, but saw nothing which had the shape of a bird or mammal. Presently we relaxed, rested our necks, and glanced at one another inquiringly.

As if in answer to an unspoken question, twigs crackled and wings flapped noisily a hundred feet overhead and a shower of bark flakes fell. Changing our position quickly and looking upward, we saw two birds, silhouetted against the sun's bright rays, flying close together upstream. They were short-tailed and blunt-headed, that much was obvious, and their wing-beats were rapid; but we could not tell what their color was. Altering their course, they wheeled toward the opposite shore, gave us our first look at their backs, and suddenly, in passing from shadow into full sunlight, became gorgeous, glistening green. They were parrots—the first wild parrots we had ever beheld! The clear yellow of their heads declared them to be of the species so well known commercially as the Yellow-head (*Amazona ochrocephala*).

For me this experience was nothing short of soul stirring. Tingling from head to foot, I found myself wondering whether I had not always been susceptible in some special way to the color green. Had I not, long years before, experienced a somewhat similar sensation at coming suddenly upon a stand of burgeoning tamaracks, fresh and dainty against the darkness of the spruce forest; at watching a newly emerged luna moth spreading and drying its wondrous wings? Had I not been thrilling quietly all my life at the color of young grain fields, of smooth lawns, of sage or willow tossing in the wind? Had I not been strangely roused by the sea-color in a cormorant's eye, the emerald glitter in a quetzal's flowing plumes? Not that all these passed in review as I stood there. Not that they entered even the outer fringes of consciousness one by one, to be weighed against this most recent sensation. It was only that, without need for recalling every detail from the past, I knew that this color of free-flying parrots had astonished and stimulated me, that a wholly new green had taken me unaware.

The parrots were only a beginning. A brilliant song burst through the wall of vines back of us. *Jay-hoo, choricky, choricky! Jay-hoo, choricky, choricky!* The bird seemed to shout. So clear, so loud, so thrown at us were the notes that we almost jumped—but we failed to discover the singer. A smallish hawk circled overhead, screaming in a high voice, but again we did not know what species it was.

Burleigh and I waded across the river, he going downstream, I up. Stealing through the matted undergrowth, watching now the shadowed forest, now the bright aisle through which the river flowed, I felt that very special joy which only the true adorer of nature can feel: joy at the small sounds of insects working; joy at the intricate patchwork pattern of light and shadow; joy at the yielding of the leaf mould underfoot. I stood suddenly still, as if transfixed. A small creature, perhaps a bird, perhaps a bat, perhaps even a beetle, had shot past me. I had heard the sound of its flight, a dull droning. Now I heard the sound again, above me somewhere, a low roar like that of a tiny electric fan turned on, then quickly off. It was a hummingbird, now perched on a slender twig not more than fifteen feet away. It appeared to be dark and colorless, for just back of it was a patch of brilliantly lighted leaves. Obviously watching me, it jerked its body excitedly. Now it darted toward me, squeaking shrill defiance, choosing a cubic inch or so of space in which to hang, wings whirring, at little more than arm's length from my very eyes! Scarcely had I noted the rich reddish-brown of its widespread tail, the glittering green of its throat, the less brilliant green of its upper parts, and the pale fawn-color of its belly, when it backed up, rose, and shot off through the trees. I kept it in sight for some time—a full second or so. How rapidly did it become smaller, smaller, smaller; with what finality did it vanish! I had had my first glimpse of the Buff-bellied Yucatán Hummingbird (*Amazilia yucatanensis chalconota*), a Mexican bird known to range as far north as the lower Río Grande valley.

Despite my happiness and feeling of elation, I was not quite at home in this woodland. Parts of it were awesomely dark. Much of the time I could not see any single object as a whole. Every tree trunk and branch was blurred with moss and vines and queerly shaped epiphytes. The sky was virtually invisible. Even the ground at my feet was hidden by a thick layer of loose dead leaves. The undergrowth was not really dense, however, for the larger trees had long since cut off the light supply from all vegetation growing beneath them.

A sharp thud sounded off to one side. If not a woodpecker, what then? Moving forward quietly, almost on all fours to avoid disturbing the vines, I saw, directly ahead of me, first the huge bole of an ancient tree, then the leaves and trailing root-mass of an odd orchid, then a curiously opaque patch of scarlet, which turned out to be not a flower but a bird's head. I could not identify the bird with unaided eye, but the binocular enlarged details and restored perspective. Motionless before me was a big woodpecker, a male Flint-bill (*Phloeoceastes guatemalensis*)[1]—a fine bird, considerably bigger than a flicker, with strikingly crested, large red head, white bill, pale yellow eye, thin neck, and black and white body. How fearless he seemed to be! In my approach I had been obliged to break vines and disengage myself from thorns, but he had remained where he was, motionless as the tree itself, watching me intently. Now he resumed his work, driving his powerful bill into the loose bark, scattering it in slabs. As he hitched upward I clearly saw the two white stripes on his black back and the black and brownish-white barring of his under parts. His gleaming white bill continued to be his most striking feature—that and the glossy red head with its ridicu-

[1] "Guatemalan Ivory-billed Woodpecker" is widely used as a common name for this bird, but the species is not by any means solely Guatemalan in distribution and the words "ivory-billed" inevitably lead to confusion with the larger Ivory-billed Woodpeckers of the genus *Campephilus*. The name Flint-billed Woodpecker is hereby suggested.

lous pipe-stem of a neck. Reaching a part of the tree from which the bark had long since fallen, he gave a sharp double rap with his bill. As he flew off, white flashed from the linings of his broad wings.

An instant after the Flint-bill had left, a medium-sized flycatcher darted down in front of me, snapped its beak loudly in capturing a moth, and returned to its perch. This too was a new bird for our list, a fact apparent not so much from its coloration as from the gentle, whistled *pee-oo* which obviously was its characteristic cry. It was about the size of a phoebe; indeed, it looked a good deal like that bird—but it did not wag its tail. It was wholly without a striking field-mark, its throat and chest being gray, its belly pale yellow, its upper parts brownish-olive— darker on the crown and slightly more rufous on the wing and tail feather edgings. It seemed to prefer shadowy places and was not quick in its movements save when snatching insects from the air. It was another member of that puzzling *Myiarchus* group, a distinctly Mexican form known as Lawrence's Dusky-capped Flycatcher (*Myiarchus tuberculifer lawrencei*).

Three gorgeous Black-throated Orioles (*Icterus gularis*),[2] again a species I had never before seen alive, flew to a branch directly overhead and scolded me harshly. They were somewhat larger than the well known Baltimore Oriole, but like that species in being golden-orange trimmed with black and white. The black was restricted to the wings, tail, back, narrow facial mask *and throat patch;* the white to one wing-bar and the tertial edgings. The orioles' scolding attracted a flock of small birds. Soon the trees about me were alive with Myrtle Warblers, a few Black-throated Green Warblers, a male Yellow-throated Warbler (*Dendroica dominica*), and several individuals of a little warbler which we had not so far listed. These were rich yellow below, gray-blue above, with two noticeable white wing-bars and a black area in front of and around the eye. Occasionally one of them broke into wiry, not very melodious song. They were Pitiayumi Warblers (*Parula pitiayumi*), a Central and South American species known to range as far northward as extreme southern Texas. The fact that certain of the males continued to sing indicated that they might even now be selecting their nest-territories.

[2] This oriole has been given the common name "Lichtenstein's Oriole," in honor of its describer. Lichtenstein himself, whose recognition of the black throat (in both male and female birds) as a diagnostic character is evinced by his choice of the name *gularis*, would, I feel sure, heartily approve of "Black-throated Oriole" as a common name. *Icterus gularis tamaulipensis,* the northernmost race of the species, may henceforth be known as the Alta Mira Black-throated Oriole.

Wondrous accounts of the day's doings were related that evening at the skinning table. Semple had heard a queer clacketty callnote, turned quickly, and seen a big Ringed Kingfisher (*Megaceryle torquata*) bearing down upon him. Shooting as it had flown past, he had been obliged to swim after the specimen. What a striking creature it was! Noticeably larger than the familiar Belted Kingfisher, it was dark bluish-gray above, with chestnut-brown breast and belly. It had a prominent crest, white collar and throat, one white spot in front of the eye and another on the lower eyelid, and a veritable spear of a bill about four inches long (measuring from the corner of the mouth to the very tip). Burleigh had seen more Yellow-headed Parrots, but they had eluded him. A band of Brown Jays had followed him constantly, making bird study difficult.

The stomach of our Ringed Kingfisher was packed with round-worms. The body (especially the pectoral muscles) of our Cassin's King-bird specimen was thickly studded with encysted white parasites of some sort. The eye-sockets of a wren which we had not yet identified were so crowded with minute, slender worms (thread-thin, but all alive, dozens of them!) that I could but wonder how the poor wren had been able to see at all. A world of beautiful birds was this Mexico to which we had come—but birds were not by any means its only inhabitants.

XXII

Eager to learn what we could about wild parrots, we returned to the Corona early the following morning. The parrots indeed were there, dozens of them. The place sounded like a madhouse.

As an observer of the Yellow-headed Parrot, I perceived that my first problem was one of mental adjustment and self-discipline. Here I was, at last, in the fine bird's home. Here at last I could watch it to my heart's content, learn what it was feeding on, observe its courtship behavior, perhaps ascertain what its natural enemies were. The day was before me. But what was I doing? What was my plan? So far I had not made a move toward a parrot. Instead I was laughing—laughing aloud!

There is nothing intrinsically funny about any sound, I suppose, sounds being funny only because they call amusing things to mind. This being the case, I must have been remembering—as I stood there chuckling to myself—a sort of droll-faced composite of all the caged parrots I had ever known—a dangerous-looking, utterly humorless Polly, which eyed me with coldly calculating eye, but looked with favor upon the sunflower seed in my hand, opened and lifted a foot in declaration of momentary truce, and sidled over to accept the miserable morsel; or my mother's almost embarrassingly faithful imitation of a parrot which had done its bit in a presidential campaign by yelling "Hurrah for Cleveland!" at everyone who passed; or the pet parrot our family once had had, whose chief joy was biting furniture to pieces, whose plumage was forever molting, and whose vociferous approval of the highest note in the song "Way Down Upon the Swanee River" made possible our finding it whenever it escaped.

I stood there laughing. Laughing at those cynical, *sotto voce* mutterings from the trees; laughing at those shrill *ow's*, which so reminded me of the yells of a small boy pinched suddenly and hard; laughing at those blood-curdling squawks, which were so shamelessly and so unnecessarily loud.

Heeding carefully the outcry, I could follow the wanderings of my companions. If, down the river a way, a terrific screeching sounded, I knew that Semple had put the parrots to flight. If, upriver, wild yells burst forth, I knew that Burleigh had routed a flock. My study of vocabulary did not progress very satisfactorily, however, partly because it was so difficult to ascertain what sounds were being produced by any given bird, partly because such a weird and comical variety of cries appeared to accompany the most ordinary of situations.

My laughter gave way in time to frank amazement at the parrots' cunning. Flocks perching in exposed dead treetops flew off the instant they saw or heard me approaching; but separate pairs, making eyes at each other beneath the canopy of leaves, sometimes let me walk directly beneath them, only to flap off squawking like demons as soon as they felt I had passed by far enough. Though most of the parrots apparently were mated, fair-sized companies assembled two by two in the tops of certain tall cypresses, leaving en masse when suddenly alarmed. The conversation of these neighborhood gatherings was pleasant to hear. Eavesdropper that I was, I regretted only that I could not understand the language. *Ork, ork, rook,* one bird would say, distinctly enough. *Rack, rick-ack,* another would reply. *Carrow, car-r-r-row!* still another would chime in, suddenly doubling the size of its head through the simple expedient of lifting all the plumage of its crown, neck, and face.

The parrots quieted down while feeding—an important fact which I did not know at first. Eventually I learned that the surest way of finding them at a meal was not through listening for their cries, nor yet by following them up and down the river, but by standing quietly beneath the ebony trees[1] waiting for the falling of a bean pod. An odd, unreasonable sound, that pop! on the dry leaves. No wind, apparently no disturbance in the treetop, yet down would fall the five- or six-inch-long seed container of the giant legume, ripped apart and dropped by an unseen Yellow-head!

I chanced to note a company of eight parrots flying quietly to a distant ebony. With the binocular I watched them climbing this way and that, each to a pod, as they set to work feeding. Presently I stalked them, approaching by a devious route so that they should not be able to see me. Not once did they chatter nor screech. Not once did they flap nor flutter. Being genuinely busy, they had no time for hilarity. Standing at last directly under them, I marvelled at my inability to see them. Bright, even gaudy creatures that I knew them to be, they were invisible. Nor did I hear so much as the briefest callnote. All that I heard was a low, steady, slightly breathy sound of munching, punctuated by sharp little clickings as pieces of pod hit leaves on their way to the ground.

An odd accident befell me as I listened to the parrots breakfasting above me. A big, dry, neatly chambered pod, tough as a piece of coconut shell and astonishingly heavy, dropped straight onto my head. For an instant I wondered if Semple, who was perfectly capable of such untoward behavior, might be playing a trick on me. At length, coming to my senses, I placed the blame on myself, where it belonged. Had not an old Mexican proverb warned us that he who sneaks under breakfast tables may well expect a crumb in the eye or a kick in the face?

The parrots finished their feeding at about half past ten o'clock and departed two by two, each of the four pairs keeping close together in flight, their wings beating rapidly, ibis-fashion, as they sought cool retreats in lower parts of the trees. The morning's work of filling up was done. The time had come for a period of peace and quiet in the shade.

Concealed in shrubbery, I kept my eye on two parrots which alighted in a big magnolia not far away. Obviously these two birds knew each other well. There was no fierce pursuit by the male, no squawking from the female—instead, only the gentle nuzzling, feather-nibbling and low conversation of two creatures who probably had long since accepted each other for better or for worse; who had, perhaps, been paired for years. Blissful, well-fed, serene, they sat side by side with eyes half-closed.

I observed this couple for a quarter of an hour or more. During this

[1] *Pithecolobium flexicaule,* a bean-bearing tree. Not a true ebony, but called "ebony" throughout much of its range.

PLATE VII
Chachalaca
(*Ortalis vetula*)

period they paid not the slightest attention to me. Indeed, they may not have seen me, even as I withdrew, though my guess is that they heard me when I turned to leave; that the plumage of their heads went down and the pupils of their orange eyes contracted suddenly as they watched me moving from the shadow out into the strong sunlight.

Surprised at having witnessed no courtship flights nor antics, I collected a Yellow-headed Parrot for the purpose of examining the reproductive glands. Picking the specimen up I discovered in the wings and tail partly concealed patches of red, blue, and orange which I certainly had not noticed in the living birds. The plumage was bloody, so, by way of saving work for myself later, I went to the river and proceeded to wash away the stains. Blood continued to ooze from the shot-holes; but what struck me far more forcibly was the fact that the wet bird was fast changing color, becoming an unlovely, sordid shade of brown. The phenomenon should not have taken me by surprise, for I had read that the green of parrot feathers was a "structural color," a refraction of light rays rather than pigment; but, as Gertrude Stein might have put it, this not-greenness of parrot plumage had never happened to me in a purely personal way before, and seeing my very first specimen turn brown in my hands was disturbing. So drastic, so apparently irrevocable was the change that I should not have been too greatly surprised at seeing green-colored water drifting off downstream. Not for an hour or so did the plumage lose its dampness, but as it dried out completely it became brilliant green once more.

Parrots were not the only birds we saw that day, of course. Brown Jays and Green Jays followed us about, threatening to raise a commotion at every turn, and a host of smaller birds moved restlessly among the trees which lined the river. Most of the visible little birds were Myrtle Warblers. There were literally hundreds of these fidgety, shy creatures, all of them molting, not one of them quite presentable. Chipping Sparrows were abundant too, and also in changing feather, but they were not timid. Noting their friendly acceptance of me, I could not resist a feeling which I had entertained many times before, that Chippies must have a profound understanding of, if not an innate liking for, the human race. They nest in well-kept orchards, trim cemeteries and formal gardens. They like towns and farmyards. They see human beings daily every summer of their lives. This being true, why should they view with alarm an ordinary looking man who chances to appear among them in their winter home?

A new wood warbler for our list was the Nashville Warbler (*Vermi-*

vora ruficapilla), a small winter visitant species with yellow throat and breast; olive back, wings, and tail; gray head (grayish-brown in the female); and a fairly conspicuous white eye-ring. Adult males which were just completing the spring molt were quite colorful, even the partly concealed rufous crown-patch being visible in strong light.

There were birds of brilliant plumage in the woodland too, a few of them new to us. In addition to the robust, showy Black-throated Oriole, which was common, there was the much smaller Hooded Oriole. The

Hooded Oriole (*Icterus cucullatus*)
upper, male; lower, female
8 inches

male was fiery orange with a black bib over the face and throat, narrow black saddle, black wings (marked with two white bars), and black tail; the female dull greenish-brown above, yellow below, without any black on the face or throat. The Rose-throated Becard was far more numerous here than it had been at Monterrey or Linares, but we listened in vain for its song. We recorded two transient or wintering members of the tanager tribe—the Western Tanager (*Piranga ludoviciana*), which was in rather dull winter plumage—the male yellow on the head, rump, and under parts, with a red smooch on the face, black on the back, wings, and tail, and with two distinct wing-bars (the anterior yellow, the other white), the female much duller throughout but with about the same pattern; and the Summer Tanager (*P. rubra*), in which the male was red all over, brightest on the head and breast, the female dull olive above, yellow below. Our attention was attracted to the latter species through its well-known *pit-i-cher* callnote. From the Western Tanager we heard no note of any sort.

As for the invisible birds, the most memorable was that which continued to sing *jay-hoo, choricky, choricky!* from the thickets. We must have heard this song a hundred times, but never once saw the bird. We fancied the singer to be small and dull colored, knew that it was terrestrial, and guessed it to be a wren, but somehow we failed to get a glimpse of it.

For me the morning's greatest thrill came just before noon, as I was walking back to the ford. Emerging from the forest to cross a thicketed opening, I found myself staring blankly at a poppy-red spot in a low tree three or four rods ahead. There was nothing subtle or indefinite about this spot. Of a bold, arresting shade, it stood out sharply against the gray-green of the thicket. It was, in fact, so obviously *unnatural* that I would have dismissed it from mind as a brightly labelled can had I noted any other indication of dwelling, road, or picnic ground close by. A plausible explanation occurred to me: my companions, having found a nest, had marked the general location with a can or piece of cloth.

I must have walked five full steps toward the poppy-colored spot before I realized that it was part of a living, breathing bird, a species I had all my life wanted to see—a Coppery-tailed Trogon (*Trogon elegans*)! It was perching upright, with tail straight down and underparts toward me. With the glass I could see the narrow snow-white band which separated that incredible red of the belly from the dark shining green of the head and upper chest; the short, conspicuously yellow bill and orange eyelids; the white outer feathers and square tip of the tail. Marvelling that I had not frightened it in approaching thus carelessly, I watched it turn its head deliberately as it eyed some object on the ground between us. Its bearing was sluggish, even drowsy.

The trogon must have perceived the collector in me an instant before I recognized the superb adult male specimen in him, for as I lowered the glass he sprang forward on thumping wings, banked sharply, flashed his white outer tail feathers, and darted off. As he changed course before disappearing, the copper color of his middle rectrices gleamed brightly.

Half-sick with disappointment and disgust at my blundering, I searched for the lovely bird in vain. The thicket had taken him and would not give him up. A red spot lingered before my eyes. So unbelievable had he been that the image which now followed my gaze seemed equally credible. No matter which way I looked I seemed to see a bird with poppy-red belly.

The afternoon was a busy one, what with notes to transcribe, an extremely tough parrot to skin, and two handsome woodpeckers to paint. Semple and Burleigh each had got a woodpecker, and the two birds were so much alike that even at second or third glance they appeared to be the same species. I was, however, fairly well acquainted with museum specimens of the commoner woodpeckers of Mexico and knew on comparing these two carefully that one was a Flint-bill, the species I had encountered on our first visit to the Corona, the other a Lineated Woodpecker (*Dryocopus lineatus*). The birds belonged, in other words, not only to different species but to wholly different genera.

Having been astonished and puzzled long since by the striking surface-similarity between these two woodpeckers, I was tempted to deliver a brief lecture on what some biologists call "convergence" or "convergent evolution," by way of explaining to my companions how two organisms, not closely related, could exist side by side (as in the present case) or at opposite ends of the earth (as in the case of the Great Auk of northern regions and the Adélie Penguin of the Antarctic), and respond so similarly to environmental requirements, or solve so similarly the vital problems of procuring food, escaping enemies, rearing their young, etc., as to become, during the long evolutionary process, very much alike superficially while at the same time retaining structural characters proclaiming a widely different ancestry. I was, as I say, ready to lecture, but as I compared the freshly killed birds—spreading the wings, opening the eyes, flexing the feet, pulling forward the odd tongues—the desire to explain yielded to a still stronger desire to keep still and wonder. Surely the two birds were very much alike—each about a foot long, each red-headed and strikingly crested, each black with white markings on the neck and body, each—and this was an especially striking feature—light-*billed*. Yet the most cursory direct comparison showed the two heads to be quite unlike in pattern, the Flint-bill's being wholly red, the Lineated's red only on the upper half and on the moustache-streaks, with a white line connecting the white of the bill with that of the neck-stripe; and careful parting of the back plumage revealed the significant fact that the white stripe in the Flint-bill was composed of feathers from the dorsal feather-tract, while in the Lineated Woodpecker it was composed wholly of scapulars, or *shoulder* feathers.

Discussing the problem of recognizing the two birds afield, we agreed that the Lineated Woodpecker could be identified by the long, pointed, somewhat flowing crest even if the white line across the head were invisible; that the Flint-bill's head was comparatively large and solid, even wooden in appearance, the crest feathers being firm and stiff. The cries of the two species we had not been able to compare directly; but the quick, incisive double-rap of the Flint-bill was distinctive. The Lineated Woodpecker pounded on dead wood too, occasionally, of course, but the performance wholly lacked the imperious quality which characterized that of the Flint-bill.

As we prepared the specimens, we found not greatly to our surprise that the Flint-bill was much the tougher-skinned of the two, particularly on the head. Someone even had had, we recalled, the audacity to suggest that "Thick-skinned Woodpecker" would make a good common name for the bird!

My Yellow-headed Parrot proved to be a male. The sex glands were very little, if at all, enlarged, so the nesting season probably had not yet started. The stomach was packed with chewed up, slightly digested beans from the ebony tree.

XXIII

There was little point in our searching for another collecting ground while the Río Corona continued to be so exciting. In the comparatively small area we had been visiting—a narrow strip of river edge two or three miles long—we had continued to find birds abundant, and our failing to identify several of these, or to discover which were responsible for certain songs and callnotes, lured us back despite our eagerness to investigate other places. Accordingly, we hurried to the Corona early on the morning of February 18, arriving there just after sunrise. As we got out of the car we noticed a chattering of Brown Jays across the river. We quickly separated, Semple electing to follow the road back a way, Burleigh going downstream.

The more I listened to the jays, the more certain I was that they were directing their intemperate outcry against some "enemy" wholly apart from ourselves. Our coming may have increased their excitement, to be sure, but the true object of their wrath, the primary cause of all this adverse publicity, was in their midst on the other side of the river—some owl which they had found half-asleep; some aboreal snake surprised in the act of swallowing its prey; or some good-sized mammal—possibly a lynx. Keeping a big tree between myself and the commotion, I walked straight to the water's edge and waded in. Although this course took me through a pool which was almost waist deep, I did not swerve. When I was within a few yards of the farther bank the volume of the alarum increased so noticeably that I knew I must be on the alert. Either "the enemy" had stirred, or the jays had become aware of my approach.

Above the raucous chatter rose a piercing squeal. Looking up, I saw a silvery gray hawk in the very top of a tall dead tree. The handsome creature was so luminous that it appeared to be a giver rather than a receiver of the morning light. Presently it squealed again, crouched, lifted its wings, and sprang forward. As it launched into flight the branch on which it had been standing snapped off and fell. The jays, beside themselves with excitement as the erstwhile perch crashed in their midst, scattered momentarily but promptly reassembled and followed the flying hawk toward the river, discreetly keeping beneath the cover of the trees.

As the hawk swung into clear view directly above me I noted that its wing-tips were somewhat rounded rather than sharply pointed, and that its proportions were those of a Red-tail rather than an accipiter. Lifting the gun, I took quick aim and fired. The hawk crumpled, fell, hit the water with a whack. The jays, which had stopped their outcry instantly at the sound of the shot, retreated swiftly into the forest.

The hawk was a Gray Hawk (*Buteo nitidus*),[1] a stream-loving spe-

---

[1] This hawk has long been known as the "Mexican Goshawk," but it is hard to imagine a more unsuitable name. Certain authors, literally translating the scientific name *nitidus,* have called it the "Shining Buzzard Hawk," a name which strikes me as being overly poetical. "Gray Hawk," which has been used by Coues, van Rossem, and others, is a good straightforward name which I feel should be adopted.

Gray Hawk (*Buteo nitidus*)
16 inches

cies which we had not seen along the highway nor in the sisal fields. About fifteen or sixteen inches long, it was a beautiful light gray, indefinitely barred with darker gray, above; and white, clearly but finely barred with gray, below. Its tail was of moderate length, and black, with white tip and three white bars. Its cere and large, strong feet were dull yellow, and its eyes rich brown, with glints and shadings which reminded me of agate. Its black beak and claws were smeared with dry blood.

Wondering whether the hawk had actually tried to capture one of the jays, I made my way slowly downriver, keeping to the mud and gravel of the bed itself, wading where the water was shallow, and clambering up to dry ground only where the channel was too deep or the bank too precipitous to negotiate. I had not hunted in just this way before and soon discovered a new dove for our list—a terrestrial species apparently, somewhat heavier bodied than the Mourning Dove, and with rounded rather than pointed tail. I must have flushed a dozen of these doves before getting a good look at one of them. They flew up from half-hidden pools, darted swiftly back into the brush, and alighted with a whirring of wings and rustling of dry leaves. Peering over the bank I sometimes saw two or three of them not more than a rod away, walking rapidly off with heads bobbing at every step, or standing on a fallen branch with bodies quite motionless, heads jerking as if in an effort to see me more clearly, and tails moving slowly up and down. This part of their habitat was thick with vegetation and dimly lighted, however, and I rarely saw more than about half of a given bird at any one time. They appeared to be plain grayish-brown above, pinkish-buff on the neck-front and chest, and white on the chin, belly and under tail coverts. The field-mark which I came to depend on in identifying them was the rufous of the under wing coverts which showed in flight, and the fan-shaped tail, the middle of which was of the same color as the back, the rest being darker, with broad white tipping on the four outermost pairs of feathers. These birds were Verreaux's or White-fronted Doves (*Leptotila verreauxi*). Not until I obtained a specimen did I clearly see the white forehead indicated by the name, or the delicate green and rosy-purple iridescence of the hind neck. A long-drawn-out coo, which sounded from the brush, was probably a callnote of this species; but I never actually saw one of the birds cooing. They were not paired, nor did the males seem to be paying much attention to the females. Probably their nesting season had not yet arrived.

The Red-billed Pigeons, on the other hand, were pairing everywhere. Large flocks of these robust birds were almost constantly in view, flapping noisily up from the water's edge, massed tightly in the top of a dead tree, or rushing swiftly overhead. Their ardent, openly amorous cries sounded near and far. So mixed and overlapped and run together were all these pigeon noises that it was difficult to ascertain what the callnotes of a single bird were. At length I stole up under a solitary male

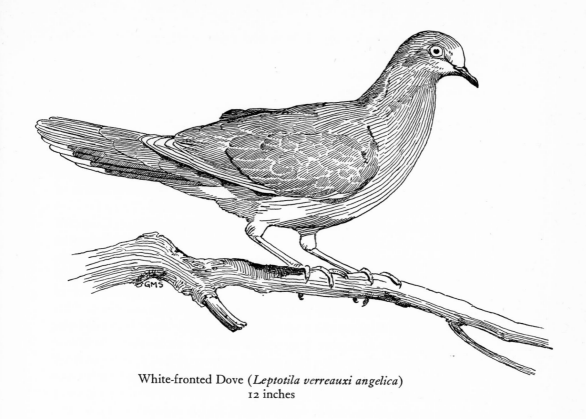

White-fronted Dove (*Leptotila verreauxi angelica*)
12 inches

which was performing on a leafless bough, and wrote on a piece of paper exactly what he called. *Cooooooo!* he began, his chest so inflated that I couldn't even see his head. Jerking all over, he continued: *Up, cup-a-coo! Up, cup-a-coo! Up, cup-a-coo!* This, then, was his song—a long, windy *cooooooooo,* followed by three *up, cup-a-coo's.* He sang it several times facing north. Turning a little, he sang it toward the northeast. Then he about-faced, in the manner of a baritone remembering the audience seated on the stage, and sang it straight to the south.

The Red-bills were feeding on mistletoe berries. Certain trees were fairly covered with this parasitical plant. Here the pigeons gathered by the hundred, hurtling down from the sky, swooping in and upward, alighting with adroit maneuvering of their wings and tails. They gobbled the berries noisily, walking up and down the branches, sometimes fluttering to keep their balance, sometimes sparring noisily for a choice position.

While the morning yet was cool, while still the sun's filmy rays slanted through the forest, I came upon my second Coppery-tailed Trogon. This time I was so well hidden by the brush that the gorgeous creature did not even know that I was there. He was perched on a dead branch in the open about fifteen feet from the ground. His posture was erect, his manner pensive. To my surprise he did not appear to be in the least interested in the insects which flew past him. How resplendent and fairy-bright he was, and how odd—with those black whiskers which curled up over his short yellow bill, that sleepy expression of his, and that long, square-tipped tail! He turned his head slowly, looking now up through the trees, now down toward the trail beneath him, with eyes half closed.

All at once he saw me. With a fillip of his tail, a surprisingly animated *chook!* of alarm, and a noisy *phut! phut!* of wings, he darted off. His long middle tail feathers, from which copper-color flashed, bent gracefully as he took a sharp curve.

Following him down-river a way, I came upon a whole flock of trogons, six or eight males and perhaps as many females, the latter dull gray-brown, with a noticeable white mark behind and below the eye, pure white chest-band, pink under tail coverts, and reddish-brown middle tail feathers. Listening to the songs of the male birds, I was reminded that a common Mexican name for this trogon was *qua,* probably an imitation of the callnote. To me these birds were calling not *qua,* but *co-ry,* repeating the syllables four or five times in giving a full song. What a queer performance it was—throaty, effortful, anything but melodious, a trifle like the plaintive calling of a hen turkey.

Slipping quietly into a clump of trees for a better look at the trogons, I surprised a company of coati-mundis, odd, somewhat raccoon-like mammals with long snouts, small eyes, and long, bushy tails. I say I surprised them. Probably I did. But surely I could not have surprised them half so much as they surprised me. They were in a tree, a dozen or more of them, snuffling, scratching, pulling at leaves, digging at bark, eating their breakfast. Their nonchalance astonished me. My presence must have been known to all of them, but they made no hasty move to depart. They looked at me insolently, with their bespectacled eyes twinkling and long noses wobbling up and down. They held their tails straight up part of the time as they moved along the branches. They sometimes clambered from one branch to another, but there was no monkey-like leaping, no swinging along from bough to bough, no squirrel-like frisking. They moved slowly, a little ponderously, but with grace and precision. I did not ascertain what they were eating. They drew bunches of leaves toward their mouths with their front feet, but they may have been eating insects rather than the leaves themselves.

One of them came down the main trunk headfirst straight toward me, turned when six or eight feet from the ground, trundled out a long branch and climbed across to another tree. Keeping my eye on this animal for a considerable time, I wakened to the fact that the others were nowhere to be seen. Slowly, without a sign of haste, passing quietly from tree to tree without descending to the ground, they had made off to "pastures new." Such a beast was the coati-mundi (*Nasua narica*). The Mexican name for it was *tejón*.

Not far from the tree in which I had encountered these entertaining creatures, I came upon a pair of Rose-throated Becards. Needing a specimen, I collected the male. To my great annoyance the dead bird struck a cluster of thorns about fifteen feet up and lodged there. Tossing sticks and stones was to no avail, since one of the wings had been securely impaled. The climb was difficult and painful, for parts of the main trunk were armed with huge thorns, some of them fully a foot long, and *branched* with thorns. I had to pick my way out to the specimen itself for I could not shake it loose. The noise I made attracted the Brown Jays and Green Jays, whose outcry in turn drew a host of warblers, gnatcatchers, tanagers, and other small birds. Scores of feathered beings hopped and chirped and squawked about me, voicing their curiosity or protest. Reaching the becard at last, I disengaged it from the thorn and dropped it carefully to an open spot beneath the tree.

At that instant all outcry ceased, and a burst of fluttering informed me that the birds had flown swiftly off through the woods. The stillness was almost startling. How dramatic, thought I—all those squawking jays shutting up and flying off the very moment the nature of my quest was revealed to them! The true reason for the hasty withdrawal became apparent presently. There, perched on a horizontal branch in the very next tree, with long tail straight down, and head lowered, was a big hawk of a species and genus I had never seen alive before—a Black and White Hawk or Collared Micrastur (*Micrastur semitorquatus*), which had slipped in quietly to see what the rumpus was about.

The newcomer and I regarded each other; but the hawk's interest in me was incidental and fleeting; what truly interested him was some object on the ground below me. He bobbed his head back and forth, as all hawks do, making it quite plain that he was giving his attention to something he could not clearly see. The truth dawned swiftly: he was eyeing *my* becard specimen! I could tell from his eagerness, from

Collared Micrastur (*Micrastur semitorquatus*)
about 24 inches

the keen look on his face, that he had already spotted the small carcass. More than likely he had watched it fall!

Quickly selecting a landing place, I swung from the branch and dropped. Nor was I slow about it. I had worked too hard already for that becard and had not the slightest intention of giving it to some miserable tramp of a hawk. I got there not an instant too soon. The micrastur swooped even as I dropped, his strong, rounded wings striking against vines; but my descent took him by surprise. With an astonishingly human cry, almost a moan, he turned and flew off through the forest. His manner called instantly to mind that of a Goshawk (*Accipiter gentilis*).

Semple got a Collared Micrastur that day, so I had a chance to examine and sketch this peculiar bird of prey. The facial ruff of the two-foot-long creature was something like that of a Marsh Hawk; but the bold color-pattern reminded me of no hawk I had ever seen. The upper parts were brownish-black, the lower parts buffy-white, the long, graduated tail black, barred boldly with white. About the neck was an almost complete white band. Plain to see, the Collared Micrastur was a tough bird, built for a tough existence. One of the slender, powerful, yellow tarsi had been gashed open from heel to hind toe, probably by a thorn. Had the hawk caught its prey that time, or had it missed? In the stomach we found a slender lizard, swallowed whole, and perfect enough to be preserved as a specimen. Part of the underside of this little reptile was a deep, rich lapis lazuli shade of blue.

An interesting new bird which we obtained was that thicket-dweller whose loud song had startled and puzzled us so frequently, that creature of mystery which we had nicknamed the "Jay-hoo Choricky." By dint of much thrashing about, a good deal of tearing of clothing, and a stubborn refusal to be led aside by even the most enticing of other songs and callnotes, we finally captured this bird, finding it to be the Spotted-breasted Wren (*Thryothorus maculipectus*). It was much like the Berlandier's Wren in size and proportions, but was olive-brown rather than chestnut on the upper parts, sides, and flanks; was grayish-white below, thickly speckled with black on the throat and chest; and had a white line over the eye, and black and white streaking on the sides of the head. It was a tropical species which probably did not range much farther north than Victoria. From what we had seen and heard of it we guessed that it was usually found not far from water.

To me the most memorable thing about this pretty wren was the way it had of singing *at* one. It was elusive, to be sure—elusive to the point of being utterly unseen and unheard most of the time; but one is not apt to remember the elusiveness of any creature whose song makes one literally jump with surprise; one is apt to remember, rather, its canny temerity, its ability to see without itself being seen, its almost psychic way of waiting by the trail until one is very close (and, of course, very much wrapped up in one's own thoughts) before hurling from the thicket its little bombshell of song.

Spotted-breasted Wren (*Thryothorus maculipectus*)
5¼ inches

XXIV

On our way to the Río Corona we usually drove through the outskirts of the village of Güemes as rapidly as the early foregatherings of cattle, burros, dogs, and chickens permitted. On the morning of February 19, however, a frantic squealing from the side of the street brought us to a full stop. Tied securely, back-down, to a crude table, its throat ready for the knife, a pig was employing the only possible means of defense left to it. Wriggling, twisting, kicking, threatening to bite—these had been to no avail. All it could do now was squeal—so squeal it did with all its mortal strength. What a terrifying, hair-raising, soul-baring sound that squealing was! A man stood near the unfortunate animal's head, knife in hand, ready to deal the death stab. Two younger men and a woman stood close by. Fascinated by the awesome spectacle, a dozen children gazed at a safe distance, the littlest of them with fingers stuck in their mouths. Back of the children slunk mangy dogs, so weak they tottered. And back of these, lined up on a fence, waited the vultures and caracaras, the only really happy looking element in the entire tableau. The pig's squealing did not embarrass them in the least; it only made their avid, knowing eyes the brighter.

The morning promised to be a noisy one. Scarcely had we left Güemes when a band of Chachalacas (*Ortalis vetula*) ran across the road ahead of us. Part of the covey—the older, more experienced birds probably—made off rapidly through the chaparral, half flying, half hopping, with crests raised high, tails fanned wide, and wings beating laboriously. The rest, bunched closely, stayed in the thicket. We could see their heads, high on their slender necks, only a few yards back from the roadside. The whole flock cackled loudly in alarm. The racket gave us the same uncomfortable, vaguely guilty feeling we had had in the presence of the doomed pig.

The Chachalaca is a kind of guan. It inhabits the brushy woodlands of drier parts of Central America and Mexico, being found as far north as southern Texas. It is lanky in appearance, is about two feet long, and looks something like a small, grayish-olive turkey with white-tipped tail. Its head is well feathered, however, only a small patch on the throat being bare.

The Chachalaca should, perhaps, be called the Chachalac, or Chick-arac, since the cry of the individual bird usually has only three syllables; but when a flock joins voices in that curious round of theirs, the word *chachalaca* is very clearly enunciated. Both males and females sing; or, if *sing* is not the correct word, they both cry, cackle, holler, or *chachalac,* as you will. The old males sing a full octave lower than the females and young males, and they all have a remarkable sense of, or instinct for, rhythm. When an old male starts his *Cha-cha-lac! Cha-cha-lac! Cha-cha-lac!* a pronounced beat is established almost at once because the pauses between the groups of syllables are each precisely as long as one of the syllables. As other birds join in, the syllable *cha* and *lac* become hopelessly jumbled and the pauses between *cha-cha-lac's* are filled, but these lesser performers never dominate; their shrill voices never change the beat established by the leader. When, presently, the chorus reaches full strength, the bass of the old males, the soprano of the females, and the scratchy falsetto of the young birds blend in a strange cacophony. *Cha-cha-lac-a! Cha-cha-lac-a! Cha-cha-lac-a!* sings the flock—on and on, on and on, pounding out the rhythm until the very branches seem to shake with it. Sometimes the racket becomes a rough *Ecuador! Ecuador! Ecuador!* or some word or phrase reflecting one's mood and thinking of the moment, but the beat is not lost. It is apparently just as natural for the birds to keep time while singing as it is for them to eat or sleep.

On and about our hunting ground along the Río Corona the Chachalaca was an abundant bird. We did not learn this until a morning or so later, however, when thirty or forty family flocks sang at the same time, producing one of the most remarkable bird choruses we had ever heard. I had waded the river as usual that morning, intending to make my way upstream. Barely had I entered the woods above the ford, when a deep-voiced male Chachalaca began calling directly across the river. I thought of wading back, for I knew we needed a specimen; but I surmised that Semple or Burleigh must surely be hearing the bird too, for neither of them had crossed with me. By this time every member of that particular male bird's flock was giving voice to its alarm, excitement, or abounding happiness. At least half a dozen birds must have been calling, every one of them keeping time with metronomic precision.

I was analyzing the queer chorus musically when a flock a hundred yards upstream started calling. What was responsible for this—had Semple disturbed one flock, Burleigh another? Now two more flocks started simultaneously some distance downstream, another started in the woodland far ahead of me, and, while I was trying to count the coveys which by this time were calling, a loud voice took up the cry in the brush only a few rods ahead of me. The clamor which presently rose kept me from hearing anything else very clearly. Listening, I could but feel that the birds were inciting each other to call. Surely I had not startled them. I had made no noise at all. I think they had not even seen me, save perhaps while I was crossing the river. The louder the volume of the combined voices the more the birds seemed to want to cry out. My head fairly rang with the uproar. A dozen or more birds comprised the flock near me, and scores if not hundreds of birds must have been calling near and far.

Occasionally, I noted, the bass voices dropped out, as if the old males

PLATE VIII
Cabanis's Tiger-Bittern
(*Heterocnus mexicanus*)

had decided that they had had enough. But on the round went, laughably shrill; and presently the bass voices returned, working gradually up to the fervor of the rest.

I managed to observe several flocks that morning, a total of perhaps a hundred birds, and not one bird was on the ground. They were all in low trees or bushes, moving slowly forward by walking along the horizontal boughs or leaping nimbly from twig to twig, balancing themselves by sticking out their wings, or by lifting, lowering, or spreading their broad tails. If I pressed a "singing" flock too closely, the rhythm of the chorus was lost and the *cha-cha-la-ca* round became a pandemonium of squawks and shrill *chreek's*.

An intermittent yammering of Chachalacas continued throughout most of the morning. A flock which we saw at eleven o'clock were silent, however, the birds being twelve or fifteen feet from the ground, each of them plucking off and gobbling ravenously the new leaves of a low-growing tree.

Skinning an adult male Chachalaca provided a great surprise for all of us. The bird's windpipe, after emerging from the body cavity, passed not directly forward along the neck, but backward the entire length of the breastbone, then, after a sharp U-curve, forward the length of the breastbone and up the neck to the larynx. This long extra loop lay close against the pectoral muscle, just beneath the skin. Equipped with a resonator of this sort, no wonder the male Chachalaca could sing such an impressive bass! The females and young males had no such loop in their tracheal apparatus.

These curious guans were not the only creatures we observed during those last few visits to the river country near Güemes. Among the most beautiful of them all were certain large arboreal squirrels, many of which were rich reddish-brown on the fore and under parts, and gray on the rump and tail. The more we saw of these animals the more puzzled we were by their color-patterns. Some of them were reddish-brown all over the head, neck, shoulders, and under parts; others had a red-brown band round the shoulders but were gray headed; others were somewhat piebald in appearance. Too, there was an occasional wholly black individual which obviously was the same in size, proportions and behavior, and which consorted with the red-and-gray ones in such a way as to make us feel that all were basically the same. We were not sure about the fact at the time, but all these squirrels *did* belong to a single polymorphic species, *Sciurus aureogaster*. They were quite common in the higher woods close to the river.

We saw much of the big Ringed Kingfisher, becoming acquainted with its low harsh rattle and grating *ke-rack,* but we never saw it plunge for a fish.

We obtained a fine fully adult specimen of the Roadside Hawk, finding that its eyes were a brilliant lemon yellow. Our nickname for this friendly little bird of prey was "Bunty Hawk," an appellative which described its comfortable, fluffed-up appearance peculiarly well. The bird obtained its food along the thicket-edge, hence frequented the roadside, especially in the early morning.

For the first time we heard the full song of the Olive Sparrow—a simple, deliberate series of unmusical chips, somewhat suggestive of the song of a Swamp Sparrow (*Melospiza georgiana*).

The Beardless Flycatcher was fairly common, though never very noticeable. Its *eee-yuck!* callnote we heard repeatedly, but what sounded more like its full song—a series of three to five high, unmusical, rather far-carrying notes delivered from the very top of a tree—it gave only occasionally.

We learned that trogons were extremely difficult to prepare as specimens. The skin was so delicate that it tore easily, particularly when it became at all dry, and the feathers came out in handfuls. The safest method involved moistening the skin frequently while carefully cutting (rather than pulling) it away from the flesh.

Among the birds we collected were three which were new for our list. One of these was the Louisiana Water-Thrush (*Seiurus motacilla*), a winter visitant species which we encountered along the river's very edge, February 20. It was easily recognizable from its loud, ringing song, its metallic alarm note and dashing flight, and the wagging of its tail. It sang only infrequently.

Another new bird was a curiously flimsy, tropical bird of prey which was considered to be rare throughout its range—the Blackish Crane-Hawk (*Geranospiza nigra*). Burleigh collected a female specimen not far below the ford. About twenty inches long, it was small-skulled and rather weak-billed for a hawk that size, and had bright reddish-orange legs and feet, and geranium-red eyes. Its long, slender tarsi instantly reminded us of the famous Secretary-bird (*Sagittarius serpentarius*) of Africa, and, despite the vast discrepancy in the size of the two forms, we could not help wondering in what respects their habits might be alike. Our specimen's plumage was loose and fluffy, with a purplish-white bloom which came off with shaking or rubbing. Narrow white tipping on each belly feather gave the under parts a delicately laced-over appearance. The rather long tail was marked with three broad white bars and a narrow white tip, and there was indefinite white mottling on the face, throat, and under surface of the wings. The most curious feature of all was the tiny outer toe, almost a vestigial digit really, but armed with a neat little claw which doubtless was effective enough when it came to capturing frogs, snakes, and lizards. We found a small green lizard in the bird's stomach.

The third new bird was a Cabanis's Tiger-Bittern (*Heterocnus cabanisi*)[1] which we secured about half a mile above the ford. It flew up from the bank and alighted, somewhat awkwardly, in a tree. Nothing about its behavior or habitat at all suggested the American Bittern (*Botaurus lentiginosus*), which belonged of course, to a wholly different genus. What a bizarre mixture of black, white, buff, chestnut, gray, and clay-color the plumage of this tiger-bittern was! How like a fish's eye was its eye! Since I did not carry paints with me while hunting, I was obliged to sketch this eye in pencil a moment after I had shot the bird. The pupil was roughly diamond-shaped, the iris pale yellow about the pupil, silvery-black at the periphery. The featherless gular patch was a wonderful pale apple green—a shade one might expect to find on the belly of a reptile.

XXV

What I have said thus far about the birdlife of the Victoria region has so accented the new species we were finding that a false impression may have been created. We were seeing new birds on every hand, to be sure— species which naturally demanded our first attention—but wherever we went we continued to see Cardinals, Kiskadee Flycatchers, Olive Sparrows, Green and Brown Jays, White-eyed Vireos, Berlandier's Wrens, and mixed flocks of winter visitant wood warblers, blackbirds, and the like. Parts of the region were truly wild. We saw a white-tailed deer; a freshly killed lynx which some men were carrying to Güemes; a coyote, feeding with some vultures. Along the main highway, which was sometimes noisy with traffic, we occasionally had the feeling of being in a metropolitan district; but a few rods off the pavement, in thicket so

[1] This species ranges southward to Panama, hence the common name "Mexican Tiger-Bittern," which has been used widely, is misleading. A good common name should, if possible, be descriptive, but since such a name might in this case suit equally well one of the South or Central American Tiger-Bitterns of the genus *Tigrisoma,* the distinctive (though admittedly not descriptive) name "Cabanis's Tiger-Bittern," which has been used by van Rossem, is hereby offered.

Black Vulture (*Coragyps atratus*)
about 24 inches

dense that it was all but impossible to move forward without the help of a machete, we quickly sensed the essential wildness of uncleared parts of the countryside.

We continued our work at Victoria until February 27, going afield daily despite the chilly mornings and almost continuous drizzle, visiting principally the flat country five to twenty miles north of the city. Driving to the Arroyo de la Presa, the Río Caballeros, the little village of San José de las Flores, or the Río Santa Engracia (a tributary to the Corona), we left the car just off the main highway and struck out after birds.

On the morning of the twenty-second we were detained at the outskirts of the city by a weird roadside carnival—a company of Black Vultures devouring a horse carcass about ten feet off the highway. Stopping the car, we watched from a distance then backed toward them, a maneuver which did not disturb them in the least. Getting out, we walked still closer. When we were within about thirty feet, a few of them eyed us dubiously, as if pondering the disadvantage of being caught, and returned to their meal. Having torn their way into the abdomen and consumed the soft visceral mass, they were now working at the tougher parts, pulling and tugging away at the thick skin and tendons. What a restless, combative, violent company they were! They resembled a swarm of gigantic black bees—jostling, shoving, and biting each other, thrusting and parrying, leaping into the air, hovering awkwardly just above the moving mass of wings, eventually dropping into and merging with it again. The carcass was completely hidden most of the time, but we had a glimpse of it when an over-eager bird caught its head between ribs, extricated itself with a violent wrench and much wing flapping, and fought the crowd off with savage jabs of its beak. Occasionally a newcomer, alighting on a convenient hoof, was mobbed and driven off. A gruff, puppy-like *woof, woof* rose intermittently above the incessant undertone of hissing, the rustling of coarse wing feathers, and the moist snapping of mandibles. At attention the birds stood erect. As they flew in they put their feet far forward and alighted with a bounce. Walking, they took long strides, sometimes limping or hobbling, often with wings half raised.

To one side stood the motionless, hunched up, surfeited few which presumably had arrived first. Beyond these moped ragged, rusty black young birds, some of them with patches of filthy gray baby-down still clinging to their heads. Plainly enough they were hungry, but they had been bitten and whacked and driven away so repeatedly that they had given up all hope of dining with the elders.

133

We counted sixty-seven *zopilotes* in all. Garbage disposal system that they were, they were respected and looked upon with a kind of affection by the *paisanos,* the country folk of the district. They were afraid of no one, for no one ever bothered them. They were all Black Vultures. There was not a single Turkey Vulture in the lot. But amongst the bystanders, on fenceposts along the opposite side of the highway, were two frowning Caracaras.

There is no point in calling a Black Vulture beautiful. He has no use for what human beings call beauty. Beauty of that sort would be in his way. That he is admirably built for carcass hunting and carrion consuming no one can deny. Featherless head, tail stiff enough and square enough to serve as a prop, big feet, strong muscles: these are what he needs. Examining a Black Vulture closely—scaly toes, coarse plumage, musty smell, and all—we find it hard to fathom even his mate's admiration. What *does* a Black Vulture do to make himself attractive when the season of courtship and nesting rolls round?

He may strut, lifting and spreading his feather in some display. He may, for all I know, perform some strange *danse macabre*. I have witnessed nothing of this sort. But I have seen his masterful and impressive courtship flight, high in air. Now, forgetful of carcass hunting, he shows off, plunging, swerving, veering upward, following the object of his affections closely. How the air rushes past his heavy wings! What a roar his plunging makes! Standing beneath him and his *compañera*-to-be, I have marvelled at the ease and grace with which he manages his heavy body in flight. Magician indeed is love!

Leaving the hippophagous company at the highway's edge, we drove a mile farther on and stopped to look at large mixed flocks of blackbirds milling about some deserted shacks. We chanced to see far to the west of us a line of large, heavy-bodied, black and white birds flying slowly toward the north. Obviously they were not herons, for their feet did not stick out behind. As they settled, apparently among some large trees, the white patches on their wings flashed like signals from a heliograph. We felt that they must have flown down to a body of water.

Having decided to go after them, we walked westward a mile or more, eventually coming upon a narrow lagoon, possibly a dammed-up stream, five or six feet deep, with sedge-choked, tree-lined banks. This we followed cautiously, pushing through the rank vegetation to the water's edge, looking for the big black and white birds. At length they flew up. They were wild Muscovy Ducks (*Cairina moschata*), splendid creatures as big as geese, with big broad tails. We did not get a close look at them, for they were wary; but we noted that only one of the seven sprang from the water, that the others whirred majestically out from the lower boughs of an oak.

New birds every day, new birds wherever we went! On February 23, in a thick wood along the Río Santa Engracia, we saw our first motmot —that strange, tropical bird which was famous for its racket-tipped tail. As if transfixed, it sat upright on a dead branch, watching us solemnly. Even without the binoculars, we saw that its general color was dull green, that its pointed bill was almost as long as its head, and that its tail was long. Lifting our glasses, we saw the turquoise blue of the forehead and crown, the narrow black mark through the eye, the black pendant-shaped spot on the chest, even the serration on the cutting edge of the beak. It was over a foot long, with body considerably larger than a robin's, and small, inconspicuous feet. How sober the beautiful creature's mien, and how erect its posture! To our regret it neither reached back to pluck a barb from its tail (the racket-tipping was alleged to result from such plucking) nor opened its mouth to reveal the tiny brush at the tip of its tongue. It was one of the most northward-ranging of all the Momotidae, a family peculiar to the New World tropics. Its full name was the Blue-crowned Motmot (*Momotus momota coeruliceps*).

Not far from the motmot's vine-hung retreat we came upon a Yuca-tán Hummingbird cutting capers in a nook back a short way from the river bank. Flashing the green of its back and reddish-brown of its tail, it paused to probe some pale orange bergamot blossoms, dipped to snatch up a minute spider, sped off to nag a female trogon which had flown in too close, and rushed back to stand guard from a slender twig. This was presumably the tiny bird's individual feeding territory, a sort of sylvan room ten yards long, two yards wide, and three yards high, walled with rain-spangled foliage.

In a strangling fig close by, we saw a Gray's Robin (*Turdus grayi*). It had a pale tawny breast, olive-gray upper parts, greenish-yellow bill, and orange-brown eyes. Even its callnote, a low *cup, cup, cup,* brought to mind the dooryard robin which we knew so well.

In thickets well away from the river we discovered a small, dark purplish-blue finch, with forget-me-not blue on the top of the head, fore-cheeks, lesser wing coverts, and rump—a relative of the buntings obviously, since it was like them in size, proportions, behavior and song. It was a tropical species which did not range much farther north than this—the Blue Bunting (*Cyanocompsa parellina*). The female was rich woodsy brown all over, without markings of any sort.

135

The brightly colored Painted Bunting (*Passerina ciris*) also inhabited the drier thicket-lands, but it was, we believed, a winter visitant rather than a breeding species. The fully adult male was unmistakable with his bright red under parts, purplish-blue hood, and yellow-green back; but the females and subadult males were inconspicuous, being plain dull green above and dull yellow below. The Varied Bunting (*P. versicolor*) we failed to find, though we knew that it nested in, or at least migrated through, the district. The male was a strangely colored confection—dark purplish-plum color on the body, with blackish face, blue crown, red nape, and blue rump. The female was brownish-gray all over, with a hint of blue on the tail. The well-known Indigo Bunting, which migrated through the region, we did not see. Female Indigo and Varied Buntings would have to be identified with great care, for they looked much alike, the former being brownish-gray, the latter dull brown.

An interesting warbler which was new for us also inhabited these drier thickets. It was an active little bird with somewhat the manner of a Wilson's Warbler and a lively, noticeable song. It stayed close to the ground, almost never exposing itself to clear view. Its alarm note was a weak *chi-chit*. The male was olive-gray above, bright yellow below, with partly concealed dull orange crown-patch bordered at either side by a distinct black stripe. The female was less colorful, with yellowish-olive rather than orange crown-patch. This bird was Brasher's Yellow-crowned Warbler (*Basileuterus culicivorus brasheri*)[1], the northernmost race of a species which ranged throughout Central America and northern South America. We were to find it fairly common about Victoria and in more southerly parts of Tamaulipas, especially in the dense beds of *huapilla* or wild pineapple (*Bromelia pinguin*).

A large black hawk which we obtained along a dry stream bed near the village of San José de las Flores, and managed to sketch before nightfall, proved to be an adult Urubitinga. It was a comparatively short winged though lanky creature with long, powerful legs and feet. Its eyes were dark brown, its cere, supraorbital shield, and mouth-corners dull yellow. In its stomach we found the remains of a rodent, probably a cotton rat (*Sigmodon*).

Burleigh had an experience on February 23 about which he talked for days. While making his way along the riverbank he was astonished to see a rabbit making for him full speed down the trail. The little beast did not avoid him in the slightest, but dashed between his legs and went

[1] Hellmayr has called the nominate race of this species the "Golden-crowned Warbler." "Yellow-crowned Warbler" seems preferable as a species name.

136

straight on, obviously covering the ground as fast as it could. Burleigh did not keep his eyes on it long, for a considerably larger, slender-bodied, short-legged animal suddenly bounded past him, hot on the rabbit's trail. Having no time to change cartridges, he fired away with a futile load of dust shot. The carnivore, possibly a jaguarundi cat, continued its pursuit, wholly undaunted.

That day we parked the car close to a thatch-roofed house. The tiny yard, which was perfectly bare, was enclosed by huge organ cactus plants, now in full bloom. Here the gorgeous Black-throated Orioles fed, moving slowly among the waxy flowers. Here, perched on the tops of the fluted columns, Inca Doves basked, one plump little dove to a column. Near the house, at noon, we met a huntsman fresh from the thicket, rifle in hand, three filthy dogs at his heels, a gutted *jabalina,* or peccary, slung over his back. He flung the *jabalina* to the ground with a grunt, and the dogs moved forward to sniff. What an unlovely creature it was, with its tusked, gore-smeared face, and a huge swelling—caused, possibly, by the larva of some bot fly—showing through the thin bristles of its back.

On February 24 I had a glorious time with the birds along the Río Santa Engracia about twenty kilometers north of Victoria. Early that morning I was fortunate enough to collect from the top of a tall dead cypress our first specimen of White-throated or Bat Falcon (*Falco albigularis*), a trim, firm-bodied male about nine inches long. It was slaty-black above; white on the throat and sides of the neck; black, finely barred with white on the chest; and chestnut throughout the rest of the under parts. The tail was marked with four or five narrow gray bars. The cere, eyelids, and feet were yellow. The eyes were very dark brown, almost black. In the stomach were the remains of several large beetles, a dragon fly, and a Beardless Flycatcher.

Along that stretch of the river one of the commonest plants was a shrubby nightshade (identified subsequently as *Solanum verbascifolium*) which grew in dense, five-foot-high clumps close to the water's edge, especially on certain gravel bars. Its leaves were large, soft, and mullein-like. As I forced my way through these vile-smelling clumps, I noticed that small flocks of dull olive-colored birds frequently flew out ahead of me. They were black-headed, somewhat yellowish below, and about the size of Black-headed Orioles, so for a time I actually thought they belonged to that species; but when I chanced to see that their bills were blunt I suddenly realized that they were wholly unknown to me. The more I saw of them the more puzzling they became. Not for the

137

life of me could I decide whether they were finches or tanagers. Some individuals were blacker-headed than others, and these same birds seemed to be brighter throughout, especially on the belly. The only sound I heard from them was a thin squeal—a cry quite unlike anything I had ever heard from either a grosbeak or tanager. They were not easy to observe, for once they settled in the shrubbery they became virtually invisible. The only good looks I had at them were from considerable distance. Training the binocular on nightshade clumps across the river I sometimes picked them out as they sat there quietly feeding.

While thus watching a distant company of these birds, which actually bit off and chewed pieces of the nightshade leaves, swallowing the juice and letting the crushed portions fall where they might, I chanced to note that a good-sized heron was heading directly toward me, flying just above the water. The heron proved to be an immature Cabanis's Tiger-Bittern. It glided slowly past, obviously without detecting me, and alighted not more than twenty feet away just behind the bole of a huge cypress. A plan quickly resolved itself in my mind: I would lay aside gun, collecting basket and binocular and creep up on the bird just to see how close I could get to it.

Stealthily I moved forward on hands and knees. Completely hidden by the trunk of the great tree, and presently blocked by it, I crawled round to the right. There, only four or five feet away, on a root or "knee" which stuck up from the water, stood the bittern, busily preening a wing. Obviously I could not leap at the unsuspecting bird, for I could not get my whole body, especially my feet, suddenly into the position of my right eye. Content with smiling inwardly at the scene the bird and I must have presented, I reached my right hand slowly forward. The bittern saw first the tips of my fingers, then my arm, then the glitter of my eye. Drawing itself in, it flapped clumsily off, squawking as if in mortal agony. So terrified it was, and so determined to get away, that it almost struck the water. Its wings and legs were a jumble. For an instant it looked as if it might fall completely to pieces. Very funny it all was. Very funny indeed! But suppose I had been an ocelot or a jaguar, or even a little ring-tailed *cacomixtle!*

We left the car headed the wrong direction at the side of the road that day, thus bringing the highway police force down upon our heads. He was a fierce and capable looking police force indeed, but he did not make a scene, and when we showed him our bird specimens he led us to a truck (which was parked correctly), opened the door, and pointed to the prettiest baby coati-mundi imaginable, curled up between the gearshift and an oil can. *"Tejón,"* said the police force, with a winsome smile, tickling the soft little beast until it chippered, rolled over onto its back, and kicked its hind feet ecstatically, kittenwise.

The twenty-fifth we spent on several sorts of problems. First, there was a female Bat Falcon to collect. The specimen proved to be much bulkier, and almost three inches longer, than the male, but its coloration was the same. As in the male, its eyelids and cere were bright lemon yellow, its feet the yellow of ripe field corn.

As for the olive-colored, heavily billed birds which ate the "stink bush" leaves, we ascertained that they were wholly uncrested and that their bills were bluish-gray at the base. We continued to see them along certain stretches of riverbank. We enjoyed watching them as they sat quietly among the leaves, fluffed out their body feathers, turned their heads slowly from side to side, leaned forward to bite off a mouthful, then settled back blissfully and started chewing. We spent a good deal of time following them, finding it difficult to get close enough for a shot with the auxiliary barrel.

Among these leaf chewers suddenly appeared a glossy black bird with bright red ring round its neck and dull red breast and belly. The superb creature was of exactly the same size and shape as the others; had the same sort of thick, seed-cracking bill; and to our great surprise promptly settled down to nibbling and chewing. The problem was solved: all these "stink-bush birds" were Crimson-collared Grosbeaks (*Rhodothraupis celaeno*), the red and black one a fully adult male, the others females and subadult males. We doubled our efforts and collected some of them. For a time we feared we should not be able to preserve a perfect specimen, for the plant juice caused the skin of the throat to decompose so rapidly that patches of feathers slipped out soon after the birds were shot.

A third problem which continued to puzzle us was a doleful, far-carrying moan which we had been hearing, usually at dusk. Today, during the gentle rain, the sound rose from a thick patch of trees along the Río Caballeros. Burleigh and I, each quite unaware as to what the other was doing, he on one side of the river, I on the other, started off in pursuit. Inevitably our paths converged. How startling it was, down in that netherworld of nettles and vines and thorns, to hear a twig snapping, to turn with gun half raised, to see Burleigh creeping forward, stalking the very creature I was after! Startling it was, to be sure; more than this, it was deeply revealing, for in my friend's movements there was something of a jaguar's self assurance and poise, something of a great snake's supple noiselessness, something of a deer's sensitivity to things underfoot. Had I not been so deeply interested in the unknown creature we both were after I should gladly have given up the chase and observed primitive, predatory man.

Burleigh and I smiled foolishly at each other for an instant, then resumed our stalking together. The weird sounds continued to issue from thick branches fifteen or twenty feet above ground. How solemn, how startlingly human were those loud, slightly quavering moans! We were almost directly beneath the creature now, whatever it was. Presently a branch moved, leaves rustled, and out flapped a Collared Micrastur, the same kind of hawk which had tried to steal my Rose-throated Becard. The lugubrious moans had probably been its love song!

Among the most interesting organisms we saw that busy day were great colonies of leaf-cutting ants which were gathering food for their young. Long lines of the tireless insects marched back and forth along well defined trails, each homeward-bound worker holding firmly in its mandibles a neatly cut piece of leaf. In sheltered places the ants had no trouble, but where wind struck their trail the pieces of leaf heeled over like sailboats with gunwales awash, some of the ants could not keep their feet, and others lost their precious cargo entirely. Most of the colonies were gathering pieces of willow leaf or the tiny, new, composite leaves of acacia; but one colony was specializing on beautiful little four-petalled yellow flowers, which they carried upright, precisely as if to keep the highly prized nectar from spilling out. The flowers were just large enough to hide the ants which carried them, so, looking at them from afar (that is to say, without kneeling or bending over) we easily imagined them a long line of little golden-yellow flowers moving gracefully off through the forest under their own power.

On the twenty-sixth we obtained our first specimen of Muscovy Duck. The Mexican name for the great glossy creature was *Pato Real,* or "Royal Duck." I spent four hours making a sketch of its head. How well do I remember the bizarre tubercles and papillae, the fine wrinkles, the rows of coarse pores on the face, the crest which curled so jauntily to the right, the brown eye with its elliptical pupil, the rich iridescence of the dark plumage, the pristine whiteness of the wing-patches, the broadness of the eighteen tail feathers, the sharp, heavy, strongly curved claws and muscular feet! Never had I handled a duck like this. Never would I forget it now!

We discovered two hummingbirds new for our list on February 26 in the brushy woodlands along the Arroyo de la Presa. These tiny *chuparosas* we found about certain trees which had just burst into snowy bloom. Both species were well known in the United States and we had no way of ascertaining, at the moment, whether they nested in the vicinity. One of them was the Black-chinned Hummingbird (*Archilochus alexandri*), the other the Broad-billed Hummingbird (*Cynanthus latirostris*). We failed to see the female of either species. The male Black-chins appeared to be solid black on the throat save when they turned their bills directly toward us, revealing a narrow band of shining purple at the lower edge of the gorget. The Broad-bills were dark in general appearance, but in proper lights their throats became glittering blue and their bellies brilliant green. Their bills were noticeably red at the base. In both species the females were known to be much less brilliantly colored than the males, and their outer tail feathers were tipped with white. The female Black-chin was green above, plain grayish-white below; the female Broad-bill green above, ashy-gray below. Female Black-chins were almost impossible to identify positively in life, for they looked very much like female Ruby-throats (*Archilochus colubris*).

A familiar United States bird which we recorded for the first time on February 26 was the Yellow-breasted Chat (*Icteria virens*). Even as it skulked in the thicket we could see that it was too large for a Thick-billed Yellow-throat. On the twenty-seventh we collected another winter visitant which would shortly be returning to a far more northerly nesting ground—the Yellow-bellied Flycatcher (*Empidonax flaviventris*). Finding these *exotic* birds, these species which in a sense belonged somewhere else, reminded us that at the height of the spring migration, a few weeks hence, bird study in these wooded lowlands would be a lively, time-consuming, patience-trying business indeed.

On Sunday, February 27, we lingered at the main square in Cíudad Victoria to hear the church bells. At the appointed hour the boy bell ringers appeared, climbing the ancient and beautiful towers, and prepared for work. From their high stations they looked down upon us, smiling. All at once, as if at some signal which only they had seen or heard, they started. Pulling, pushing, heaving, straining, they turned the bells completely over. The lads with the biggest bells had no easy time of it. We could hear them grunting. But they laughed along with the others, even as they struggled. What a jangling! What a clangor! By the time every ringer had struck his stride a pronounced and compelling rhythm had asserted itself. I could not resist the feeling, as I stood there listening, that keeping time must be a thing of instinct, possibly even of physiology, with all of us, whether we happened to be Chachalacas or merely human beings.

141

XXVI

In Victoria we became acquainted with Mrs. Bensel, an interesting lady, English by birth, though with considerable experience in America, who was now in charge of the principal hotel's dining room. Mrs. Bensel regaled us with an account of her life in various parts of Mexico; gave us the local names of certain birds; told us about the Rancho Rinconada, an estate owned by her husband, located sixty kilometers to the south of Victoria, on the Río Sabinas; and at our request wrote down the names of the five sorts of ticks known to live in Tamaulipas.

This interest in ticks was not wholly impersonal, for we had already encountered the pests. Most of them were no bigger than the head of a common pin, but they could bite, attach themselves, and sink their heads into one's skin, making themselves thoroughly objectionable. Mrs. Bensel assured us that we were not really suffering from them, named various substances we might us in discouraging them, and informed us that if we really wanted to find out what ticks were like we would have to go down to the Rancho.

On the slip of paper Mrs. Bensel handed us were these words: *niguas, airedores, conchudas, garrapatas, pinolillos.* These, she explained, were the five kinds of ticks, and worst of all was the first. This *nígua,* which was practically invisible, could completely bury itself in one's flesh, causing indescribable misery. She was peculiarly qualified to discuss *níguas* at the moment, since one of them had crippled her foot for days. She brought us the creature itself, wrapped carefully in several layers of paper, when at last she had succeeded in extricating it. It was a little smaller than a radish seed, and was grayish-white, semi-transparent, and marked with two dark spots. Having no hand lens, we could see neither its legs nor its mouth-parts. The smallest of the ticks, and apparently the most abundant, were the *pinolillos,* infinitesmal animals which hatched out in dense masses on low-growing plants, and which one knocked onto one's clothing literally by the hundred as one walked through the brush. Some persons believed these *pinolillos* to be merely young *garrapatas,* and not a different species.

Every word we had heard about the Rancho Rinconada—especially the vivid descriptions of a big black and white fowl known as the *Faisán Real,* or "royal pheasant," which inhabited the woodland there—had increased out desire to see the place; so when, on February 27, Mr. Bensel returned from Texas, we persuaded him to go down with us for a few days. We started on the morning of the twenty-eighth. In our equipment was sulphur enough for starting a small match factory. This we were to dust on ourselves, shake into our clothes, eat if necessary. If it did no good we were to us alcohol, kerosene, gasoline, or carbide. How we laughed as we discussed the various measures we would employ in outdoing those ticks—stupid, blithering idiots that we were!

About thirty kilometers south of Victoria a sign at the side of the road made our hearts leap high:

TRÓPICO DE CANCER

The Tropic of Cancer! In a fragment of time too brief for easy computation we had passed from one of the world's broad geographical belts to another—we were in the Torrid Zone! Into my mind rushed picture after picture from my old "grade school" books—drawings of tapirs and anteaters, of native huts and dugouts, of rubber trees dripping milk into little buckets. These pictures had been very real to me. They were still real. In a certain sense they were more real than the Torrid Zone itself, which I now could *see* lying everywhere about me.

Still farther south, beyond the Cuesta de Llera (Llera Hill), the appearance of the countryside definitely changed. Here the tall, slim, well-leafed-out trees were hung with thousands of lianas which resembled gray ropes thrown about at random. Once more we were in the foothills of the Sierra Madre. Narrow, verdure-choked valleys furrowed the steep slope to our right. Occasionally we glimpsed a thatched roof, a neat, square corn patch half hidden in the forest, or a burro standing in a tiny pen. In leafless trees at the side of the highway we frequently saw large, pendant, straw-colored nests which looked like oriole nests. They appeared to be about a foot and a half long and were invariably in an exposed position as if the birds had purposely avoided hiding them. We later learned that they were the nests of the Black-throated Oriole. The species obviously was not colonial, for we never saw more than one nest in a tree.

At the foot of a long, gradual descent we slowed up, turned right, and left all signboards behind us. After fording a small stream and climbing a steep bank we began dodging stumps and boulders as we followed a dirt road through the thicket. Repeatedly we were obliged to open gates and take down bars in order to move forward. Complacent cattle refused to be hurried out of our way. Eventually, a low, gray, flat-roofed house appeared ahead, then a clearing, a cactus fence, and a shed or two. We had reached the Rancho Rinconada.

143

As we got out of the cars, a great flock of parrots left the tree above us, circled briefly, and returned, screeching at the tops of their voices. The din was downright annoying. The phrase the birds most frequently used was a clearly enunciated *heel-o, cra, cra, cra!* so, despite our efforts at disregarding it, this "parrot talk" dominated all other sounds, even our conversation. We observed that the birds did not have yellow heads. They were Red-crowned Parrots (*Amazona viridigenalis*). There were literally hundreds of them.

Red-crowned Parrot (*Amazona viridigenalis*)
12 inches

At the edge of the shed's roof, the picture of loneliness and dejection, perched a white domestic pigeon. The poor thing looked as if it had forgotten how to coo. Rousing itself with effort, it flew down to meet us, walked silently about our feet, then fluttered back to its place on the roof. Surprised at seeing it, Mr. Bensel explained that it was the only bird left of a flock he had brought down from Victoria. The rest had been "killed by hawks."

We yanked our belongings out of the cars, glanced at the cool, tidy house which was to be our base, and prepared to go afield. "The ticks," warned our host, smiling blandly, "may bother you a little. If you notice them on your clothes just brush them off. They'd be easier to see if you had white pants."

PLATE IX
Lineated Woodpecker
(*Dryocopus lineatus*)

Consulting my watch, I found that it was eleven o'clock. Though not a particularly good hour for birds, I started out, heading straight for the Río Sabinas. Finding an open stretch of bank, I paused to enjoy the tranquil beauty of the scene. Fine dust in the air and minute particles of silt and vegetation in the water imparted a bright haziness to everything I saw, giving me almost the sensation of looking through a golden veil. Gigantic cypresses, hung with moss, reached upward into the warm clear blue, and downward into a reflection as immeasurable as the sky itself. Tall stalks of dry cane moved, but did not rustle, in the slight wind. A sound of water slipping down a shallows was faintly audible.

A partly dead cypress at the water's edge was alive with birds of seven species—every blessed one of them with bright yellow under parts. From below, the effect was bewildering, not alone because the birds were active, but also because I could not seem to free myself of the feeling that a yellow floodlight was playing on the whole tree. The largest of the company I took at first to be Kiskadee Flycatchers, but I soon perceived that there were two species instead of one—the true Kiskadee, which we had first seen at Monterrey a month earlier, and an astonishingly similar but heavier-billed bird which was olive on the back, wings, and tail, and wholly without reddish-brown in its plumage. The new bird was the Boat-billed Flycatcher (*Megarynchus pitangua*), a South and Central American species which ranged northward into tropical parts of eastern Mexico. All these big flycatchers were noisy and quarrelsome—so noisy in fact that I could not be sure which species was responsible for certain cries; but I noted that the Kiskadee stayed very low in the tree, watching the water kingfisherwise, whereas the Boat-bill kept to the topmost branches. I heard no *geep!* nor *wheep!* from the Boat-bill. Its most characteristic cry seemed to be a rapidly repeated *ki-zi'dick*. Even at considerable distance it appeared to be more bull-headed than the Kiskadee, and its bill was not only heavier but also much more decurved. In color-pattern, size and proportions the two birds were amazingly alike. Though they belonged to different genera the casual observer would probably have called them the same species. As with the two large black, white, and red woodpeckers which we had had a chance to compare in life for the first time in the vicinity of Victoria, these flycatchers were not closely related, but the process of evolution had brought them *convergently* to so much the same point that they resembled each other superficially.

Four somewhat smaller and proportionately longer-tailed flycatchers, which perched in the tree's very top, were Olive-backed Kingbirds.

Still smaller were numerous querulous flycatchers which spent most of their time flying about in a loose flock above the tree, capturing insects. Smallest of all were five Dark-backed Goldfinches, which were drying out after a bath; and a company of stub-tailed, blunt-billed birds of about goldfinch size which were not finches at all but little tanagers known as euphonias. These euphonias belonged to two species.

Of all this diverse, yellow-breasted company the middle-sized flycatchers were the most noticeable, for they were considerably the most active. Hawking for insects high in air they were as gentle and almost as graceful as swallows; but the instant they returned to the tree they became disputatious over perches, set up a loud cheeping, and waved or

Boat-billed Flycatcher (*Megarynchus pitangua*)
10 inches

146

GMS

Social or Giraud's Flycatcher (*Myiozetetes similis*)
7 inches

fluttered their wings excitedly whenever another bird alighted close by. Their cheeping was oddly like that of distressed barnyard chicks. Their most noticeable field-mark—aside from the strong yellow of the breast and belly—was the bold white superciliary line which separated the gray crown from the blackish-brown facial mask. The chin and throat also were pure white; the back, wings, and tail, olive. As for the brilliant orange crown-patch, I did not see it at all until I had collected a specimen and parted the gray feathers of the top of the head. These petulant but pretty creatures were Social Flycatchers (*Myiozetetes similis*), a tropical species which did not range much farther north than this.

I made no attempt to cross the river, though I perceived that the water was quite shallow. Moving slowly upstream under a canopy of

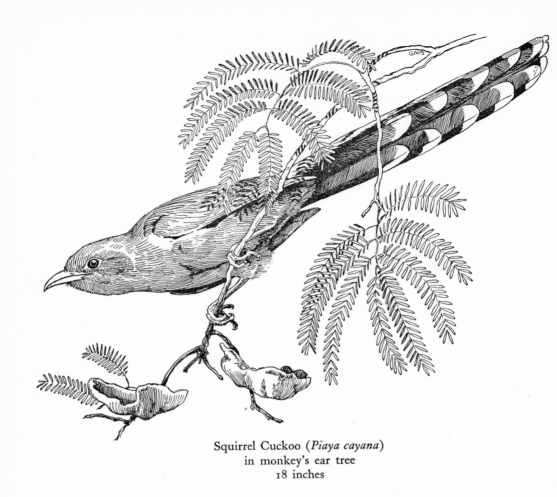

Squirrel Cuckoo (*Piaya cayana*)
in monkey's ear tree
18 inches

sapodilla and kapok trees, I came to a little clearing and trifurcation of the trail. Here instinct bade me stop, keep myself hidden, and look about with care. A branch fifteen feet above me suddenly moved, a leaf fell, and out into plain sight slipped a slender Squirrel Cuckoo (*Piaya cayana*). It was about eighteen inches long; was reddish-chestnut above, pale pinkish-brown on the throat and chest, gray deepening to black on the belly; and had a ten-inch-long tail. As it fell easily into flight, I noted that its tail feathers were broad and that the outer ones were black, boldly tipped with white. It alighted in a thinly leafed monkey's ear tree, giving me a chance to note its apple-green bill and crimson eye. Its facial expression was not particularly alert, but its ability to hop and run along the branches justified completely its common name.

A muffled tapping attracted my attention to a tree just across the trail. There, clinging to a horizontal bough, was a streaked, brown bird somewhat smaller than a flicker, busily investigating a tangle of orchid roots. Dismissing me with a glance and the roots with a jab of its beak, it hitched along toward the main trunk, using its tail woodpeckerwise, as a prop. Had I not known that the various members of the creeper family all were smaller birds, I should certainly have called this bird a big Brown Creeper, for its behavior instantly called that bird to mind. It was, in fact, an Ivory-billed Woodcreeper (*Xiphorhynchus flavigaster*), the first member I had ever seen of the large neotropical bird family known as the Dendrocolaptidae. Using the glass I could see the buffy-white throat, the whitish streaking on the head, back, and underparts, the unmarked reddish-brown wings and tail, and the long, light-colored, very slightly decurved bill. It was not a noticeable bird. Nothing about it clamored for attention. Watching it as it crept round the mossy trunk, I could not help wondering what its callnotes might be. I was to learn later that its song was strikingly like that of the Canyon Wren.

Before changing my position I decided to see what birds I could squeak up. Green Jays, Brown Jays, and Cardinals flew in to investigate almost immediately. With them was a thrush which had a conspicuously buffy eye-ring. On collecting this bird, I sensed at once that it was a winter visitant from more northern parts of the continent. It was a Russet-backed Thrush (*Hylocichla u. ustulata*).

Moving along the trail which led to the right, I was fairly awed by the splendor of the butterflies. A narrow-winged black and scarlet one glided swiftly past, its wings set horizontally. A larger, rounded-winged one, pale brown and avocado-flesh green, flopped erratically about as if dodging invisible vines. A black, peacock-blue, and emerald swallow-tail fluttered daintily above a sprawling mass of lantana, dipping downward as if in search of a leaf on which to lay an egg. Large pale yellow sulphurs darted to and fro, heeding neither leaves nor flowers, bent only on pursuing other sulphurs. On the bole of a gigantic *higuerón,* or strangling fig, a bit of gray bark moved, flashed deep bluish-purple, and revealed itself as four slowly opening wings.

It was now almost noon, so I started back to the ranch house. Two Yucatán Hummingbirds shot across the path, missing me by inches. A Blue Mockingbird (*Melanotis caerulescens*), dull grayish-blue all over, a bit brighter on the throat and crown and with black face-mask, scolded from a tangle of poison ivy. A trogon called *coo-ah, coo-ah, coo-ah, coo-ah* back in the woods. In the top of a cypress down stream,

Ivory-billed Woodcreeper (*Xiphorhynchus flavigaster*)
10 inches

150

four Military Macaws (*Ara militaris*) sat sedately. They were about three feet long, green, with blue on the outer parts of the wings, blue and dull red on the tail, and plush-red forehead. Yellow flashed from the under side of their wings and tails as they made off, squawking hideously.

At luncheon we swallowed food perfunctorily while tossing off descriptions of birds we had never seen before, firing questions at our host, and scratching noisily. At the table there were four of us—four, that is, not counting the ticks.

Semple described great flocks of green parakeets which he had seen. Burleigh's account was of shy terrestrial doves he had followed through the brush; of a Blue-headed Vireo he had carefully identified; and of two species of euphonias which he had collected. Both of these little tanagers I had seen in the big, bird-filled cypress near the river, but I had not fully sensed the difference between them. One was somewhat larger than the other, though the same in proportions. The male of this larger species was golden-yellow throughout the under parts and on the forehead, glossy blue-black otherwise save for white on the inner webbing of the outer tail feathers. The female was olive above, grayish-white on the throat, breast, and belly, and yellow on the sides, flanks, and under tail coverts. This was Bonaparte's Euphonia (*Tanagra lauta*). In the smaller species the yellow of the male was restricted to the breast, belly, under tail coverts, and forehead. The whole head, aside from the forehead, was glossy purplish-black, the upper parts otherwise glossy blue-black save for the white at the base of the outer tail feathers. The female was olive, brightening into yellow on the flanks and under tail coverts, and into gray with a faint blue gloss on the crown, hind neck, and upper back. This was Lesson's Euphonia (*Tanagra affinis*). The two species went about in mixed flocks, feeding principally on the orange-colored berries of a mistletoe which grew in great bunches in opener parts of the brushy woodland back from the river's edge.

I reported my brief encounter with the Ivory-billed Woodcreeper, Blue Mockingbird, Russet-backed Thrush, and four Military Macaws. The last-named birds roused a good deal of interest; but inevitably the talk swung round to the subject which was uppermost in our minds— the big black and white game bird, the *Faisán Real*. We had plied Mr. Bensel with query after query concerning this creature, but still could not quite picture it in our minds. What part of its plumage was white, what part black? Was its head feathered or bare? Did it gobble, or was its cry a wholly different sort of sound? To our growing bewilderment,

Bonaparte's Euphonia (*Tanagra lauta*)
above right, male; above left, female
4 inches

Lesson's Euphonia (*Tanagra affinis*)
below left, male; below right, female
3¾ inches

the answers to these questions seemed to vary somewhat, but we all realized by this time that the bird was huge, very good to eat, and not easy to capture. "You just *might* get one," Mr. Bensel finally conceded. "But they're not very common, remember. They live way up among the red rocks, and they're shy and hard to get close to."

After our meal Mr. Bensel led us to the front of the house and pointed out some light-colored spots high on the mountain beyond the river. "That's the *faisán* country up there," said he. "Those are what we call the 'red rocks.' The big *jobo* trees up there are the place where the birds feed and roost." Our host's skepticism concerning our ability to get one of these "royal pheasants" was almost more than I could bear.

Three hours later, after skinning the specimens I had collected during the morning, I started after a *faisán*. My companion was a youth named Pepe, son of Mr. Bensel's chief farm hand. Pepe led me through a cluster of thatched huts amongst which were bee hives, sorry looking dogs, and tethered pigs; out a good trail half a mile; then straight up the mountain. Pepe was friendly. That I judged from his ready smile as well as from the eagerness with which he called to my attention the *perdiz* (partridges) which were whistling everywhere about us, the squawks of the big *guacamayos,* or macaws, and the shrieking of the innumerable parakeets. Pulling at a shrub, he warned me against eating the glossy leaves. Though glad enough to have this bit of advice, I was completely at a loss to understand why I should need it.

Along the foot of the mountain the vegetation was brushy and dense. Indeed, it was almost impenetrable where the tough, jagged-leafed *huapilla,* or wild pineapple, covered the ground. After half an hour's climb, however, we entered a dark, spacious woodland where there was scarcely a bramble underfoot nor vine before the eyes. We had reached the *jobo* (pronounced *hobo*) plums, the biggest trees on the mountainside. To these the *faisán* would come to feed, to sound his love call, perhaps to spend the night.

Making our thoughts known by signs (it would have been the worst sort of tactical error to talk), Pepe and I moved slowly up the slope. The woodland was very still. Far below us sounded faintly the wistful cries of the *perdiz,* the jabber of parrots in the cornfields, the barking of dogs. The light was dim, the sky visible only in tiny patches between the leaves. The sun had long since disappeared behind the mountain, though yellow light still flooded the valley.

A rustling of leaves far overhead stopped me short. I gathered instantly from Pepe's animated gestures and lit-up face that the cause of this disturbance was some interesting or desirable creature, but his whispered comment I could not understand. Moving forward cautiously, I saw on a high bough a large, dark, turkeylike bird with small head and long slender neck. There was no clear patch of white in the plumage, none whatever, so it obviously could not be the much-talked-of *faisán*. But what was it? Sensing danger, the lanky bird peered downward, lifted its big tail, turned, and strode sure-footedly along the branch. *Whuff, whuff, whuff* came the sound of its wings as it flew to a higher branch, ran to the outermost twigs, and leaped into the next tree. Whatever this agile creature might be, it was perfectly at home far above ground. Since it was wholly new to me, I decided to try for it. Aiming at the long neck, the part I could see most distinctly in the dim light, and leading a little, I fired. The dead thing tumbled heavily to the ground. Running forward, I picked up a gallinaceous bird about the size of a hen turkey, but slighter in build, a tropical species known as the Crested Guan (*Penelope purpurascens*).[1]

"Ajol!" cried Pepe joyously, pronouncing the fowl's Mexican name exactly as we would pronounce *a hole*. He insisted on carrying it, so, snipping a length of thin vine with his machete, he tied the broad wings in close against the body, fashioned some deft knots and an extra loop, and grasped the bird not by the head or feet, but by this improvised handle. His wholly unexpected appreciation of a preparator's problems surprised and delighted me. An average "guide" would have slung that specimen over his shoulder or lugged it home by the head.

The Crested Guan was, as I have just said, a bird I had not expected to encounter. It was a big, forest-inhabiting cousin of the Chachalaca, and I was pleased indeed to have it. But shooting it had spoiled our chances for a *faisán* that evening. When Pepe waved his hand toward the mountain top, saying *"Faisán muy lejo,"* I agreed with him perfectly: the *faisán* was indeed very far away by this time. Being an intelligent bird, it would not come to feed on the *jobo* plums after hearing the shot I had just fired.

Somewhat disappointed despite our success in getting the big guan, I indicated to my companion that we would not yet go down the mountain, but that we would see what else we could find. Soon we were out of the *jobo* plum forest, stumbling over a vine-strewn, cactus-studded

[1] This species, which ranges southward well into South America, has long been known as the "Purplish Guan," but since some of the races are not at all purplish, the name "Crested Guan" (as used by Herbert Friedmann in his recently published volume on the galliform birds of North and Middle America) seems much more suitable.

outcropping of rock. A loud, clearly enunciated song, which suggested a wren's, burst from a thicket close by. A handsome dark gray squirrel bounded along a ledge above us. A pair of trim Long-clawed or Singing Quail (*Dactylortyx thoracicus*), about the size and shape of Bob-whites, but with a good deal of reddish-brown on the head and neck, ran a short way ahead of us, stopped to watch, ran on again, refusing to take wing. Pepe had a special name for these birds—a word I should have written down.

Having failed to obtain so much as a glimpse of the great *faisán,* we made our way back through the lofty plum trees, and began the descent. Dark clouds were gathering. The atmosphere had grown close. A terrific clamor of parrots rose from the lowlands.

Pepe left me at the thatched village, giving me directions as to how to reach the Rancho. I reached the river about seven o'clock, noticing as I looked out from the trees that the western sky was lurid. As I waded the shallows a flock of Muscovy Ducks swept by. Hardly had I reached

Singing Quail (*Dactylortyx thoracicus*)
about 10 inches

the opposite shore when a weird chorus of Chachalacas began. Upriver, down-river, to the left, to the right, near and far, flocks of the noisy birds gave their agitated cries. Every tangle along the Sabinas must have sheltered at least one clamorous covey. Every Chachalaca in the whole valley must have been calling. By the time all the birds were sounding off a remarkable rhythm had been established—a rhythm as subtle and compelling as that of an Eskimo crane-dance. "That," sententiously commented Mr. Bensel at the house, "means rain."

XXVII

Even as our host predicted, it rained—slowly, steadily, all night long. Less slowly, less steadily, but all night long nevertheless, we three ornithologists scratched tick bites. Sulphur did no good, kerosene did no good, alcohol did no good. The flashlight passed from sufferer to sufferer, and many a tick was caught red-handed. Not infrequently Burleigh would report on his findings: "Just got eighteen more!" or "Twenty-six more that time, all in a row!"

It rained while we dressed next morning. It rained during breakfast. At breakfast we ate sulphur. We didn't mind the taste of the stuff so much, but hated the looks of it as it floated on the coffee.

Mr. Bensel took our minds off our troubles with talk about parrots. We had been hesitant to shoot these birds for fear of offending someone. We knew they were kept as pets, and guessed that they might be a source of revenue. Mr. Bensel assured us that no one would care how many of the accursed creatures we took away with us. "Why," he went on, "you can't raise anything around here for the *papagayos*. There are four or five kinds of them—these noisy red-headed ones that keep flying over, the yellow-heads, the little green parakeets, and the big *guacamayos,* or macaws. They're all bad. The natives are too poor to buy ammunition, and they don't have shotguns anyway, so they frighten the birds out of the cornfields any way they can. The parakeets fly up screeching when someone yells at them or throws rocks. But the macaws take their time. They know they don't need to hurry. When someone starts yelling at them, they all grab whole ears of corn, and fly off with the ears sticking out at each side of their beaks!"

I was glad enough for the rain, for it gave me a chance to finish some inside work. First came a sketch of the head of the Crested Guan, the *ajol* which Pepe had helped me get. Now that I had a chance to examine the bird in good light, I found it an interesting, though scarcely a handsome creature, with high, ragged, somewhat squarish crest. Its throat was practically featherless, the skin there being warm pomegranate-red. Its plumage was dark olive-brown, the feathers of the neck and under parts being edged with grayish-white. Skinning it, I found a dozen or more *jobo* plums in the crop and gullet. These were a little smaller than crab apples, some being ripe and yellow, others green.

At ten o'clock the rain stopped. Laying aside paints, brushes, and skinning tools, I walked rapidly to the river, then upstream to the forking of the three trails. Here the birds, as if rejoicing over the dripping leaves and drenched air, were clamorous and active. A few feet above ground four Blue-crowned Motmots flew noisily from vine to vine, perching carelessly. Their disyllabic callnotes, which seemed to originate near my ears rather than in their throats, and which suggested the *hoot-hooting* or *poot-pooting* of small owls, might, I surmised, have been the basis for the word *motmot*. An orange-red tanager, whose dark wings were marked with two pinkish-white bars, and whose tail, when spread, showed white at the corners, I identified as an adult male Flame-colored Tanager (*Piranga bidentata*), a Mexican and Central American species whose scientific name, *bidentata,* called attention to the two notches or "teeth" on the cutting edge of the upper mandible. Both male and female Flame-colored Tanagers had two white wing bars. In subadult males the head and body were yellow-orange; in females the head and under parts were dull yellow. The only other members of the tanager family which I encountered were euphonias. Restless flocks of these little birds bounded hither and yon in the manner of goldfinches. So fond were they of mistletoe berries that I could observe them closely whenever I wished simply by hiding under a tree in which mistletoe grew profusely. Their cries were not noticeable. Bonaparte's Euphonia had a callnote which sounded like *pidgel-eece*. I did not hear either species give a song.

In the very top of a high tree a band of parakeets were feeding. I had to shoot twice in getting a specimen. Each time I shot, the birds flew out, screeching wildly, but they did not depart. They seemed to be feeding on flowers and buds.

All through the woodland certain small trees had blossomed during the night. Here, fanning the white petals and glistening stamens with their wings, Buff-bellied Yucatán Hummingbirds fed. There were flowers aplenty and to spare, yet the hummers wrangled incessantly, squeak-

Masked Tityra, male (*Tityra semifasciata*)
8 inches

ing, chittering, driving each other about, or, if at peace amongst themselves, working off their surplus energy on some luckless motmot or
trogon, attacking from behind or below, sometimes obliging the much
larger, though comparatively phlegmatic bird to open its beak in self-
defense.

Noticing fresh chips on the trail, I paused, heard a dull *puck, puck,
puck-puck,* and traced the sound to a dead stub about twenty feet overhead. It was a Flint-billed Woodpecker at work on a nest cavity. At first
only the tail and wing-tips were visible; but presently the bird backed
up, spit out a mouthful of chips, and preened its wing. The fact that

the head was not wholly red, but shining black on the fore part of the crest and on the throat, told me that this was the female. Rapping the stub imperiously, she summoned her mate, acknowledged his coming with a quick bow, and flew off. The male now took his turn at excavating.

The birds which Pepe had called *"perdiz"* were calling everywhere along the river's broad flood plain. I wanted very much to see one of these; for despite their Mexican name, which meant "partridge" or "quail," I felt they could not be a close relative of the Bob-white, since their callnote was so wholly different. Stalk them as I might, however, I could not get a glimpse of one. Their mellow whistling was the more tantalizing because it frequently sounded only a rod or so off the trail. The true Bob-white was, incidentally, a fairly common bird of the low-lying farmlands along the river. We frequently heard its clearly enunciated, onomatopoeic call.

While I was observing a band of euphonias, trying to discover differences in the callnotes and mannerisms of the two species, a thick-billed, gray and black, shrike-like bird moved slowly down a slender branch, shaking the leaves with each hop. Using the binocular, I identified it as a Masked Tityra (*Tityra semifasciata*), another member of the Cotingidae, the family to which the Rose-throated Becard belonged. It was a beautiful light gray, with black all over the front of the head, black and gray wings, and broad black band on the tail; but a striking field-mark was the featherless, raspberry-red area about the eye. Presently a second tityra appeared—a dusky-headed, brown-backed, less definitely patterned individual, the female. The pair were dignified, unhurried, and laconic, their only callnote being a dry *quert*. Watching them, I listened for other cries which might justify the name *chatterer,* a term sometimes applied to cotingas in general. So far as these tityras were concerned, *chatterer* was the worst sort of misnomer.

At noon Semple gave us a full account of a Brown Jay which he had observed carrying sticks to a partly built nest about fifteen feet from the ground in a thinly leafed tree; of the whistling *perdiz* which he had tried in vain to see in the wild pineapple beds; and of Groove-billed Anis (*Crotophaga sulcirostris*) which he had encountered along a trail. These strange members of the cuckoo family the Mexicans called *garrapateros* or "tick-birds." They were solid black with bronzy, blue and green reflections; appeared to be rather loosely put together; and were given to going about in small companies. Their long, rounded-tipped tails flopped from side to side in the wind. Their beaks were strikingly thin and high, and distinctly grooved. Semple had secured two specimens. These we

Groove-billed Ani (*Crotophaga sulcirostris*)
12 inches

PLATE X
Bat or White-throated Falcon
(*Falco albigularis*)

examined with great interest, noting first the well developed eyelashes, then the odd, musty smell.

Semple's most exciting capture of the morning was an immature male Blackish Crane-Hawk—an incredibly long- and slender-legged bird, black above, mixed black and white below, with broad white tail bands and buffy-brown under tail coverts. Its eyes were red, but less intensely so than those of the fully adult specimen we had obtained along the Río Corona, near Güemes.

Among large trees near the river Burleigh had collected a new fly-catcher for our list—a Greater Pewee or José Maria (*Contopus pertinax*), the latter common name a Mexican interpretation of its customary callnote. It was a trim bird about the size of a phoebe, olive-gray with buffy-white belly, a faint suggestion of wing-bars, and triangular wisp of crest. Burleigh had got a parakeet, too, but it was only about half as bulky as mine, nine as against twelve inches long, dull olive on the under parts, and blue at the tips of the wing feathers, whereas mine was a bright shade of green all over. Despite the similarity in proportions, the two birds belonged to wholly distinct species, the smaller being an Aztec Parakeet (*Aratinga astec*), the larger a Green Parakeet (*A. holochlora*). Certain individuals of the latter species had scattered yellow, orange, or orange-red spots on the crown, face, neck and throat. These markings were usually so small as to be invisible in the free-flying birds.

We were busy all afternoon sketching and skinning. Our laboratory was in a shed a rod or so back of the house, a low, cool, though rather poorly lighted room with screened openings at the end and along one side. Here we peeled off our shirts and scratched away to our hearts' content. Fearful that mice or ants might destroy our specimens, we put the finished skins inside big fibre panniers or on shelves suspended by wires from the ceiling. It was strictly against the rules to leave anything edible on the table or floor, for this might attract the ants.

Toward evening a plaintive yammering started on the mountainside beyond the river. This continued without interruption, although varying from time to time in pitch or intensity, until dusk. It seemed to come from the dark forest of *jobo* plum trees just below the red rocks. It was, we were told, the lonely crying of the mate of the Crested Guan which I had shot.

After dinner I wrote notes for an hour or more. The best place for this work was the dining room table, close by the big kerosene lamp. Here a horde of minute insects gathered. On the table, on our notebooks, on our hands and arms, in our very hair they hopped, crawled, and ran. Flying, they dashed against the lamp's hot chimney or straight downward into the flame. Some drowned in ink. Some courted, displayed, or sparred with rivals. Some lurked in the shadows, lying in wait for, pouncing upon, and devouring others. Some were caught when we closed our notebooks, never to move again.

Through the window came the soft trilling of a toad and stridulation of tree crickets. On the screen sounded the incessant tapping of moths, beetles, cockroaches, and jewel-eyed lacewings. A goatsucker of some sort called. At this weird sound I stuck the cork in the ink bottle, snatched up gun and flashlight, and hurried from the house. Out in the blackness of weeds and brush, out somewhere beyond the shed and horse corral, I heard the strange bird of night four times more. Then silence, complete silence, save for the harmonics of the tree crickets and the trilling of the toad.

XXVIII

Next morning I was to make another try for the *Faisán Real*. Rain or shine, I was to start for the big trees on the mountainside early enough to be there by daybreak. Following an arrangement made by Mr. Bensel, I was to call for Pepe on my way through the little village, just beyond the river.

Glad to have something to do aside from scratching tick bites, I rose in the darkness at about five o'clock, shook my damp clothes and shoes as a precaution against scorpions, and dressed. Determined to travel light, I took neither flashlight nor the fisherman's creel I usually carried for specimens. All I would need, I decided, were the binocular and gun.

The atmosphere was close, the fog heavy. Despite the semidarkness I had no trouble following the path past the horse corral, between the patch of tall cane and the palmetto thicket, and thence down a steep and slippery bank to the river bed. This route I knew fairly well. As for the other side of the river, the cart lane which led through the innumerable cornfields, the side road to the little village, and especially the path to Pepe's house, I could not be so certain.

As I waded the shallows a flock of Muscovy Ducks sprang from the water, wheeled heavily, and passed directly overhead. Though I was wholly unable to see them in the fog, I could actually feel the wind from their wings. Reaching the opposite shore, I kept to the water rather than trying to climb the precipitous bank, soon found the cut through which livestock were driven down for a drink, and made my way up to the cart lane. As I approached the village, I wondered how tolerant the dogs would be at this hour. Recalling that the dog at Pepe's house had been small and dirty and so nondescript as to be useless as a means of identifying the place, I cut a stout stick.

The fences, hedgerows, and thatched houses at either side of the lane were vague and two-dimensional. A monstrous apparition which loomed directly ahead turned out to be a bull. So placid was he that I did not even brandish my stick at him. I acknowledged his right to the middle of the thoroughfare, however, and walked around him discreetly. A dog barked. Three more dogs took up the cry. The canine population of the village, now thoroughly roused, welcomed this opportunity to voice its interest, alarm, and protest. Clutching my stick, I whacked at the grass and weeds. Let them come, the wretched curs, let them come!

Arriving at a sharp turn in the road, I thought I recognized the path leading off to the right. A pile of bamboo poles and a tethered pig assured me that I had chosen correctly. But nowhere did I see Pepe. Walking toward the hut, I looked closely for a small dog, but no dog appeared. Surely this was the place Pepe had pointed out! The more carefully I scrutinized the bare yard, the rows of bee hives, and the broken-off tree at one side, the more confident I became. But where could Pepe be? The noisy barking should have roused him by this time.

"Hi, Pepe!" I shouted, hoping to sound Mexican rather than American. My voice rang out through the fog, inciting the dogs to greater out-cry, but no answer came from the hut. Realizing that it was growing late, that Pepe might be waiting for me elsewhere, above all that it was wholly up to me to find him, I called again. This time there was a grunt in response. "Now I've done it," I thought. "I've awakened the wrong household. These people won't know me, nor Pepe, nor Mr. Bensel, and they'll wonder what I want with anybody at this hour of the night." As for the *faisán* and my interest in getting one, the less said the better.

A hanging over the doorway moved slightly as a girl's solemn face peered out and a little hand waved. I waved back, hardly knowing whether I had been greeted or motioned to go away. Presently a bare-foot man came forth, straightened up, and tightened his belt. On his head was a broad hat, in his hand a huge machete. I was so surprised that I failed to say good morning. The man, whoever he was, certainly was not Pepe. The only word which came to me, I spoke—*"Faisán!"*

At this the man smiled good-naturedly, motioned toward the mountain, shoved his feet into flimsy canvas-topped sandals, and started out the path. I followed, not knowing whether it was Pepe or the *faisán* we were going after. In either case, I thought, we were heading in the right direction. If necessary, I could dismiss the man and go on by myself.

Though it was now past six o'clock, and considerably lighter, the fog had not lifted nor become less dense. My companion, who was not a young man, appeared to me to be inadequately dressed. Although a person of few words, he obviously knew what he was doing. I was glad enough to follow him, the more so when, turning directly right from the trail, we started up the mountain toward the forest of giant plum trees.

The sweet-voiced *perdiz* had wakened by this time and were whistling far and near throughout the river's flood plain. My guide seemed to realize that I was not after these birds, for he paid no attention to them. A gorgeous male trogon which flew up he dismissed with a brief *"Pajarito!"*—Mexican for "little bird." Recalling my hunt with Pepe, I said "Ajol, no!" by which I hoped to convey the idea that I did not want another Crested Guan. My companion seemed to understand me perfectly.

Within half an hour we had reached the great plum trees. Here we moved less rapidly, not only because we wanted to reduce the noise but also because the going was difficult. So dense was the fog that we could not see the treetops above us. Knowing that I might have to shoot at any moment, I stepped ahead of my companion. Frequently we paused to listen.

A low, throbbing *oomh!* sounded straight ahead, off in the fog. So indistinct was this dull booming noise that I had scarcely noticed it. My companion touched my arm and pointed up the slope. *"Faisán Real!"* he whispered. Then giving a faint whistle and a low *quit, quit,* he imitated the cries of the female bird. This he did not to attract the male, which was repeating his *oomh* about once every ten seconds, but to acquaint me with other callnotes which I soon might hear.

The *faisán's* booming was a variable sound, sometimes loud, sometimes scarcely audible. Listening, I recalled how the hoots of Prairie Chickens on the Saskatchewan plains had varied with the direction and strength of the wind. Here, however, there was no wind. The heavy, wet leaves hung utterly motionless, as if they had been dipped in wax.

Slowly, as quietly as I could, and breathing hard from the excitement as well as the exertion, I picked my way over the rocks, wet vines, and slippery roots upward toward the booming sound. If only the fog would lift! If only the gray shapes about me would become less vague! Pausing to make certain that I was heading in the right direction, I wondered how far away the bird could be.

Suddenly, in a tree only a short way up the slope, a long bough shook, leaves swished and rustled, and a shower of big drops fell noisily. Though unable to see any part of the tree distinctly, I knew that some large-sized bird or beast had moved, was moving now. Taking a few steps forward, I sank to my knees. From this position I watched the gray ghost of a branch sinking lower, lower, lower, as if pulled earthward by invisible wires. Toward its tip some heavy creature was deliberately moving.

A projection at the end of the silhouetted branch attracted my attention. A slow movement there suggested power and muscle rather than the shaking of mere leaves. More clearly now I perceived that the projection resembled a grotesque, almost a malformed, bird with oddly humped back and erect, fantastically plumed tail. I looked at it with the glass, but the image became no clearer. If bird at all, it certainly could not be the *faisán,* for it appeared to be no larger than a pigeon.

Oomh! The sudden, sensuous sound beat at my eardrums as the fantastic projection wobbled, shook, sank lower, merged with the silhouetted leaves. The truth dawned at last: before me at the end of the sagging bough was the great *faisán* himself. The oddly shaped projection, which had called to mind a bizarre bird with plumed tail, was the *faisán's* incredibly crested head! There was no point in denying the sensation—I was tingling from head to foot. There we were, the *Faisán Real* and I, face to face at last, and my job was to kill the creature. The longer I deliberated, the more cordially I hated the thought. This opportunity to observe one of Mexico's most spectacular birds was, perhaps, an opportunity of a lifetime. The *faisán* probably had not the faintest notion that I was close by, for no jay nor squirrel had sounded a note of warning. Were I to wait and watch, might I not see some wonderful plumage display, some courtship dance, perhaps the arrival of the female bird? The *faisán* suddenly moved again. The whole branch shook. Instantly sensing that my duty was to collect the specimen, to ascertain, at least, exactly what the *faisán* was, I raised the gun and fired. The heavy body plunged from the thrashing bough, struck the ground, and flopped down the slope.

Stumbling over the vines and wet rocks, I found my prize, a heap of black and white among the leaves. Fairly shaking with excitement, I lifted it from the ground. It was a Great Curassow (*Crax rubra*), a mag-

Great Curassow or *Faisán Real,* male (*Crax rubra*)
about 36 inches

nificent gallinaceous bird with big, broad tail, strong legs and feet, and
muscular, powerful head. It weighed as much as a turkey.

I put it carefully down, and knelt to examine it. It was about three
feet long. The prominent yellow knob, or wattle, at the base of the bill,
the tousled crest of stiff, recurved plumes, the short, velvety feathering
of the face: how striking all these were! Truly the bird was regal in size
and beauty, truly it was a *Faisán Real!* Its plumage was blue-black all
over, except for the pure white of the belly and under tail coverts.

Hearing a rustle I looked up, and there stood my Mexican friend, smiling diffidently. Rising, I shook his hand. *"Bonito!"* he said, expressing his admiration for the bird.

Hoping to see a female curassow, we walked a considerable distance along the foothill's rock-girt flank. Once we thought we heard a low *quit* and rough beating of wings ahead of us, but that was as close as we came to finding one. The female was known to be brown rather than black and white; and though she possessed no knob at the base of her bill, her head was adorned with a crest of stiff, recurved black and white feathers even more showy than the male's.

Proudly I carried my specimen through the village, across the river, back at last to the Rancho. My friends there had not yet finished their breakfast. How their eyes shone as they examined this, by far our largest and most spectacular bird! How good that breakfast tasted! My mind was on the sketch I wanted to make of the *faisán's* tousled head, but I told my story with proper regard for the importance of every detail.

My guide, I learned, was Maclovio Rodríguez, Pepe's father. As for Pepe himself, and Pepe's nondescript dog, nobody seemed to knew why they had failed to show up.

XXIX

The ticks were getting us down. The excitement of collecting such birds as the Great Curassow helped us to forget our troubles, to be sure, but the daily grind of picking the *pinolillos* off, eating sulphur, shaking and hanging out clothes, and applying iodine to the bites was nerve-racking and fatiguing. Semple's legs and back were so covered with bites that we were downright alarmed. Burleigh was given to dropping work, jerking off his clothes, and going after the pests with jackknife and forceps. I spent one utterly wretched night because of sulphur which I rubbed accidentally into my eyes. We derived small comfort from Mr. Bensel's statement that this was the height of the tick season, that the worst would soon be over, that tick fever was a rare malady, perhaps not caused by ticks at all.

March 3 started off with a goatsucker hunt. Early each morning I had heard the peculiar, rasping cry of some creature which I thought must be a Pauraque, Nighthawk, or Whippoorwill. Hearing the sound again, half an hour before dawn, I dressed quickly and went afield, flashlight in one hand, gun in the other. This time I kept to the paths.

Specimen or no specimen, I intended to eat breakfast in peace. The "goat-sucker" called intermittently during the twilight period, but I did not get close to it, did not once see it, and was never dead certain even that it was a bird. As the light grew stronger its cries became less fervent and frequent, and finally they stopped altogether.

The sun rose as I was returning from the river. As I walked along the path, my attention was attracted by a loud squeaking which I thought must be that of a hummingbird, but which issued not from any clump of flowers, nor from branches overhead, but from a palmetto thicket to one side. So earnest was the sound, which I at once interpreted as battlecry, that I crossed the fence and walked toward it. When about thirty feet away I saw a Buff-bellied Yucatán Hummingbird, perched on a dead weed about four feet from the ground. It bobbed its head, jerked its body, and squeaked loudly, as if trying to attract attention or elicit help. Presently it flashed from its perch, returned, alighted an instant, then darted repeatedly toward the base of a thick, low-growing palmetto, backing up swiftly after each dart downward. I noticed to my astonishment that a small brown knob which seemed to grow out of one of the thick leaf stems shrank perceptibly each time the hummer attacked. Hardly believing my eyes, I inspected this knob with the binocular, to find it a hunched-up, golden-eyed Ferruginous Pygmy Owl (*Glaucidium brasilianum*) about six inches high. So ludicrously small did it appear to be that I seriously considered the possibility that I was seeing one owl with the naked eye, and a second, more distant one, through the glass.

While watching developments, I noted that the owl's eyes were piercingly bright, and that the hummingbird was beside itself with animosity. The owl was not tucked in for the day, as orthodox owls should be by sun-up, but was out for a hunt and hungry as a tiny bear. Why it did not try to catch the hummer I do not know. Possibly it was too intelligent for such a waste of energy. Its incredible smallness made the hummer seem unnaturally large and fierce. When, with roaring wings and flashing gorget, this thimbleful of fury bore down in attack, the owl cringed visibly.

The Ferruginous Pygmy Owl is a diurnal species. After breakfast I was fortunate enough to come upon another one downriver a mile or so, in a big cypress at the water's edge. Attracted by the *pit-i-cher!* of a Summer Tanager and the alarm cries of other small birds above me, I looked up, saw that the agitated company were directing their protests at something in their very midst, and presently perceived that this some-

168

thing was another tiny owl. This time the owl was sitting in the sunlight, in full view, on a leafless twig sixty feet or so above the river. Since we needed the specimen, I shot it at once, little realizing that it would fall into water ten feet deep several yards from shore. Observing that it was drifting downstream very slowly, I decided to swim for it, backed out of the tangle of poison ivy in which I was standing, and started to take off my clothing. At that instant a silver flash beneath the floating owl attracted my attention. At the second flash I grabbed a rock and hurled it with all my might. When the fish attacked the third time the owl disappeared momentarily, then bobbed up again. Hardly knowing how to deal with a rival of this sort I lifted the shotgun, waited for another disturbance of the water, and shot at the poor owl again. Then, yanking off my clothes, I plunged in.

The owl was a sorry-looking specimen by the time I had it safe on

Ferruginous Pygmy Owl (*Glaucidium brasilianum ridgwayi*)
6 inches

the bank. A few feathers had been torn out by the fish, but no part of its skin or flesh had been bitten away. After blotting it carefully with my shirt, I flopped it gently about in the warm air. From experience I knew that it would not do to let so wet a specimen dry without fluffing out the plumage repeatedly. Furthermore, since the atmosphere was humid and hot, the abdominal region might decompose and the valuable bird be lost unless it was thoroughly dried at once.

Half a mile farther downstream I saw a Snakebird or Water Turkey (*Anhinga anhinga*) circling gracefully with head and neck drawn in and paddle-shaped tail fanned. At the same place I frightened from the trees a great flock of Military Macaws. This time I was close enough to see the narrow black lines on their light faces. As they flew off I noted again the brassy-yellow color of the under side of the wings and tail.

In a cavity near the top of a forty-foot stub a pair of Bat Falcons had a roosting- or feeding-place which was possibly their nest as well. As I walked toward this stub, the trim male came forward to meet me on rapidly beating wings, screaming shrilly. When I rapped on the stub, his mate flew out and circled, scolding in a slightly deeper voice. Choosing a hidden spot, I sat down to watch. Both birds soon stopped their screaming. The female, which was conspicuously the larger, disappeared for a time, then flew straight back to the cavity. The male continued to perch on the topmost snag of the stub for ten minutes, preening vigorously, then made off upriver.

Two Red-crowned Parrots flew into the tree above me. Watching them with the glass, I decided they must be hunting a nest site. They stayed together constantly, gave only the gentlest cries, and moved up and down the middle part of the tree, investigating every crevice. Making their way out a slender branch, they walked or sidled; on the broad boughs or leaning trunk, however, they waddled comically, supporting themselves with their beaks as a man uses a cane.

With a piercing squeal the male Bat Falcon returned, flying low, carrying a rather heavy-looking, limp object in his talons. Struggling upward with his burden, he made straight for the cavity near the top of the stub. The female came out with lifted wings and a low cry. What happened from this point on I cannot fully report, for I was not able to see much; but bunches of small feathers began floating or zig-zagging to the ground, and when the female lifted her head I could see that she was swallowing. Annoyed by feathers which clung to her beak, she shook her head, finally scratching the offending bits off with a claw. Occasionally, just after swallowing a mouthful, she looked about with her bright dark eyes. Once she looked straight at me, hidden though I was.

All this while the male bird was invisible, but he must have been standing close by, and perhaps he shared the meal. Curious as to what species of bird he had captured, I walked forward and gathered some of the feathers which had fallen. They were from a Gray's Robin.

The heat had become oppressive. Examining my Ferruginous Pygmy Owl specimen, which was still somewhat damp, I decided that I could not afford to risk losing so valuable a specimen, so headed back for the skinning room. Two Gray Hawks flew out as I moved between some tall, ragged clumps of bamboo. They spiralled quickly, drifting toward the foot of the mountain. Half a mile off they began to scream. Now the smaller of the two, presumably the male, devoted itself to a beautiful courtship display. Swooping gracefully upward, it turned a backward flip, plunged deeply and again shot upward, letting momentum carry it to a position in front of the other bird before flipping backward or sideways again. The performance, which continued for several minutes, strongly suggested the Marsh Hawk's "looping the loop."

The stomach contents of the Ferruginous Pygmy Owl I examined carefully. If the owl had caught a hummingbird, I wanted to ascertain that fact. I found nothing but insect remains.

Barely had I finished work on the owl specimen when Burleigh returned from clambering about the vine-covered ledges halfway up the foothill directly west of the Rancho. The most interesting bird he had found there was the Fan-tailed Warbler (*Euthlypsis lachrymosa*), a species none of us had expected to encounter. It was an inhabitant of well-shaded ravines, and it stayed so close to the ground among the fallen logs and tangled vines that it was exceedingly hard to see. Like the Louisiana Water-Thrush it was a *walker*. It fanned its tail frequently, flashing the white tip conspicuously. It was dark slaty-gray above and yellow below, with an orange-brown wash over the breast and sides, a partly concealed yellow crown-patch, and three small white spots on each side of the head—one in front of, one just above, and one just below the eye.

When Semple came in, he brought with him two very interesting birds. One of these was an adult male Flame-colored Tanager, a species we had seen but not collected, the other that much talked of denizen of the *huapilla* tangles, the *perdiz*. Most of the morning he had waited quietly along a trail, and he had seen and captured the whistling "partridge" at last.

171

Delighted beyond words, but still not realizing what a thrill was in store for us, I examined the specimen. Surely this bird was dull-colored and thin-necked for a quail. It was larger than a Bob-white, too, had no clear-cut white or buffy lines or patches on its head, and was almost comically blunt at its tail end. Since part of its head had been shot away, I didn't for a time realize how long and slender its bill was.

The fact became suddenly apparent that this was no quail, nor Bob-white, nor true partridge of any sort. It did not even belong to the Order Galliformes, the great, widely ranging group of fowl-like or chicken-like birds. It was a *tinamou!*

There I perched on the gasoline drum which served as my seat at the skinning table, examining this strange and lovely bird. Of course these whistling *perdiz* were not true quail. Not once in our thrashings through the brush had we put up a covey. Not once had we observed one of them on a rock, fence post, or low branch, announcing through song his desire for a mate.

Alas, the specimen had been damaged badly. In order to secure it

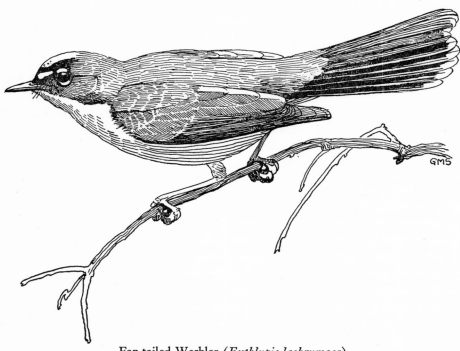

Fan-tailed Warbler (*Euthlypis lachrymosa*)
6 inches

172

at all Semple had been obliged to shoot at close range. The upper mandible had been shot away completely. The lower mandible dangled by a shred of skin. With these riddled remains as a model, I should not be able to make the sort of portrait I wanted, though we would preserve what we could, of course.

Sewing the skin of the chin and throat together with silk thread, I finished this, our first specimen of the Rufescent Tinamou (*Crypturellus cinnamomeus*). Knowing that it could never be perfect, since parts of it were completely missing, I resolved to get one of my own on the morrow.

XXX

Although we heard tinamous whistling in all directions we soon discovered that they lived within clearly defined ecological boundaries. Close by the river, where large trees had shaded out the shrubbery and the ground was comparatively bare, they apparently could not survive; but in less impressive, scrubbier woods, especially those which had an "understory" of *huapilla,* or wild pineapple, they were numerous. This *huapilla* grew in a dense, three- or four-foot-high jagged-leafed mat so tough and crisscrossed that no man in ordinary garb could walk through it without scratching himself badly. The tinamous throve in this *huapilla.* In a sense, the plant was their habitat. Wherever the mat was extensive they fed, walked about, and whistled even within a few feet of its outermost edge.

It was March 4. According to our plan we were to remain at the Rancho two more days. One of these I was prepared to devote principally to tinamous. Not only was I eager to obtain a perfect specimen and water-color sketch, but the more I thought about the birds the more fully I realized the importance of learning what we could about them. These Rancho *perdiz* belonged to the northernmost species of tinamou known. They were the northern "frontiersmen" of the entire Order Tinamiformes. How did such adventuresome tinamous behave? What were the chances of their pushing northward across Tamaulipas into the United States? Did their very existence depend wholly on the food and protection afforded them by these *huapilla* beds?

Before breakfast I walked out the lane leading north from the ranch-house. Here, at exactly the same spot in which I had heard it time after time, a tinamou was calling. *Whoo-ee-you!* rose the gentle, slightly querulous whistle from the depths of the tangle. The bird was only a few rods off, but it might as well have been ten miles away for all I could see of it. Following an old trail, I walked a short way toward it and crouched. For a full minute it did·not whistle. When it started again I judged it to be not more than five or six yards from me. I clearly heard its footfalls on the dry leaves. It must have been feeding, for occasionally I saw one of the tall seed-bearing stalks shaking slightly while a *tap-tapping* of bill sounded. For a time it moved toward me, whistling once about every fifteen seconds; then it turned and walked slowly away. Since the crouching position was uncomfortable, I sat down. After waiting almost an hour I rose to check my observations. During that period the bird had moved about in an individual feeding territory roughly thirty feet square. No other tinamou had joined it or shown the slightest interest in it so far as I had been able to observe. It had made no obvious attempt to cross the trail. Crossing the trail was, of course, precisely what I had hoped it would do.

On my way back to breakfast I passed two more tinamous, each occupying the same spot it had occupied day after day. I was not the only member of our party who knew these two birds. All three of us had watched and waited for them, hoping in vain to see them.

After breakfast I crossed the river and walked straight to the base of the foothill where, at either side of the trail, the *huapilla* thicket was unusually dense. Here I set about counting the birds as best I could, at the same time taking special note of those which were nearest to the trail. Along a stepped-off 150-yard stretch I heard nine birds on the foothill side (the *huapilla* mat, though dense, was comparatively narrow there), and fifty-two birds on the other side. There was no way for me to determine precisely how far away the farthest of these were, since the *huapilla* growth on that side continued to, and ended abruptly with, an extensive cleared area about a quarter of a mile to the east. Not knowing whether these whistling birds were males or females, not being sure even that a whistling bird represented a pair, I gave up trying to estimate the density of the tinamou population. It was interesting, nevertheless, to listen, to note how sedentary the birds appeared to be, and to speculate on what was happening in that shadowy, latticed-over world of theirs. Eager to obtain a specimen before the fervor of the morning singing period should ebb, I seriously considered shooting *at a whistle*. What saved me from this foolishness I do not know, for I was admittedly close to being desperate.

174

It was impossible, of course, to keep my mind wholly on tinamous. A fearful squawk, which echoed from the foothill, attracted my attention to a flock of sixty Military Macaws, flying abreast down-river, and I stood there spellbound, like a country boy watching the fast freight go by. When a band of euphonias appeared I couldn't help listening to them in hope of discovering callnotes by which to distinguish one species from the other. Especially was my interest diverted by a small, short-tailed wren, which was new for our list, and which appeared to resemble the tinamou in that it inhabited only the *huapilla* tangle. This bird was the White-bellied Wren (*Nannorchilus leucogaster*), a species considerably smaller than either the Berlandier's or the Spotted-breasted Wren, plain brownish-gray above, grayish-white below, with a noticeable white line over the eye. Its song bubbled and spilled over but was so fragile and soft-throated as to sound far off even when the wren was only a rod or so away.

Not wholly forgetful of the tinamous, which continued their whistling all morning, I decided that I ought to collect one of these wrens. The midgets were invisible most of the time, though I could determine their whereabouts from their songs. When finally I glimpsed one down among the dagger-lined shadows, I lifted the gun and fired, sensing as I pulled the trigger that the target had moved to safety a split second before. Failing to hear the bird's song again, I picked my way through the tangle, discovered on certain leaves a cluster of tiny fresh shot scars, and began wondering if I had not got the wren after all. Using great care lest I snag my hands, I pried a tough leaf up with the gun. No wren was underneath it but the idea of looking further appealed to me, so I laid aside the gun, lifted the leaf again, held it back while lifting another, and thus went on gathering the whole sprawling rosette into my left arm, while looking carefully for the specimen. The lowest leaf of the plant was partly dead and quite tough. I lifted it and there, crouching on the ground not more than four feet from my very face, looking at me with wide-open grayish-yellow eyes, was—a tinamou!

What opportunity had I for letting the armful of *huapilla* go and grabbing up the gun? The opportunity, perhaps; but not the impulse. Out shot the brown bird as if catapulted from the thicket. Straight through the tangle of vines it flew on roaring wings, barely clearing the sharp tips of the *huapilla* plants and coming noisily to earth thirty yards off. The whole performance—the take-off, the panic stricken bolt through the vines, the awkward landing—all this was the escape of a creature which knew nothing of steering a course or putting on brakes

175

in flight; the getaway of a bird so essentially terrestrial that it quite possibly had never in its whole life flown before!

The rest of the morning I sat at trail crossings, climbed trees, crouched behind rocks, even tried cutting fresh trails through the *huapilla* on the chance of seeing a tinamou. Toward noon the sounds of walking and pecking ceased as the presumably well-fed birds quieted down. Leaving the scene of my fruitless labors, I walked back to the Rancho, scraped off the ticks, and lunched on roasted *faisán*.

Shortly after two o'clock I returned to the base of the foothill. The tinamou population was comparatively silent now, though here and there a bird whistled drowsily. A band of Aztec Parakeets flew into a bare tree directly above me. Not even suspecting my presence, since a thick vine shut me from sight, they fell to chattering and arranging themselves two by two. With a terrific screeching they flew off, tightly bunched, as a Collared Micrastur shot into the tree, alighted an instant, and sped on. Peering through the woods in the direction the slim hawk had taken I heard the sudden scream of a stricken bird. Twice the mortal cry rang out, then stopped as if snipped off with scissors. This was too much for me. Running down the trail, I saw the hawk in a dead tree, watched it fly off, saw feathers floating midair beneath the perch on which it had stood. The feathers were black and brilliant orange. The Micrastur had caught a Black-throated Oriole.

All afternoon I walked back and forth watching for a tinamou. I did not return to the Rancho at supper time for I had food with me. Hopeless though my quest appeared to be I felt it my duty to stay in the *huapilla.* Eating my supper a trifle disconsolately, I thought about these shy, baffling creatures for which I had been so doggedly searching. How wonderfully secure they were, back in their armored sanctum! How my ideas about them had changed during the past forty-eight hours! Had someone, a week or so before, asked me to discuss tinamous, I probably would have mumbled something about "chicken-like birds with compact plumage, short tail, small head, and slender bill." I would probably have described the fowl as "primitive." I might have remembered that their eggs were among the incredibly, even shockingly beautiful things of earth—some blue or blue-green, others leaden-purple, blackish-gray, or pinkish-buff, those of certain species so highly glossed as to look like polished ball bearings or pool balls fresh from the factory. I might even have recalled W. H. Hudson's description of a tinamou frightened from cover, borne swiftly upward by the wind, and dashed to earth because of the stub-tailed bird's utter inability to direct its flight. Sooner or later

PLATE XI
Coppery-tailed Trogon
(*Trogon elegans*)

I would have recalled that tinamous were found only in the New World. "South American," I almost certainly would have called them, not even remembering that there were tinamous in Mexico!

A week, a day, a few hours at the Rancho and lo! I had become something of an authority on tinamous. Had I seen one? Well, I had had a glimpse of one. Had I handled one? Yes, I had skinned a badly mutilated one. Two tinamous: not much on what might be called the tangible side; yet by this time I knew a very great deal. Not through seeing and handling, but rather through *not*-seeing and *not*-handling had I learned what manner of creature was the tinamou!

The sun had long since slid down behind the mountains. Cool air crept up from the river as dusk enveloped the woodland. A gentle brightness lingered along the trails. I moved homeward reluctantly, still watching, still listening, still hoping.

At a right angle turn in the trail I paused. How many more hours would I have in tinamou country? When, ever, would I be in tinamou country again? Resolving to make one more try, I about-faced. Off through the trees led the trail, a darksome tunnel now, with light at the other end, light here and there where the trees were thin. I had gone a hundred paces when a dark object appeared along the trail edge ahead. Looking closely I thought I saw the object move. "Shoot, shoot now!" spoke an inner voice. "Don't shoot! Wait till you see it clearly!" spoke another. "Go ahead, maybe it's your bird. *You've got to take a chance now and then!*"

The gun was at my shoulder. The dark thing vanished. But at that instant the shot rang out. I had aimed correctly, not at the object itself, but a little to one side of it. Sensing that the bird or beast, whatever it was, would return to cover by the quickest route, I had made this allowance automatically.

I ran forward. At the base of a small tree lay my tinamou. A split second more and the bird would have been safe back of the heavy trunk. My first impression, as I lifted the specimen from the ground, was of the smoothness of its feet. They were warm and smooth—as smooth as wax candles. They were an odd, pale shade of coral-red. Examining the eye, I found it to be surprisingly large, the iris an indefinite yellowish-gray. The clearly defined patch of ear coverts reminded me of a small, flat, plush-covered button.

It was dark when I got back to the ranch house, much too late for making a sketch. I skinned the tinamou out, all save the head. The flesh was a peculiar light blue or green, firm and slightly translucent. In the

177

crop was a small handful of hard little balls—seeds of that all-important plant, the *huapilla*.

XXXI

Beside the Rufescent Tinamou and White-bellied Wren concerning which I have just written, our party obtained on March 4 two other interesting bird species about which very little is known. One of these was, we saw at a glance, a close relative of the well known Evening Grosbeak (*Hesperiphona vespertina*), and the more we thought about its occurence along the Río Sabinas in early March the more strongly we felt that it must be a Temperate Zone species which nested high in the mountains but descended to the foothills in winter. It was a chunky, rather short-tailed bird with strikingly heavy, pale greenish-yellow bill. The male was black-headed, olive-backed, olive yellow below, and largely black on the wings and tail. There was a bit of white at the tips of the outer tail feathers, and the tertials and adjacent wing coverts were ashy-gray. The female was duller throughout, the black of the head being restricted to the crown and fore part of the face. These birds went about in loose flocks, feeding on berries in certain leafless trees. White spotting at the base of the primaries occasionally showed as they flew. They were Abeillé's Grosbeaks (*H. abeillei*), a distinctively Mexican and Central American species.

The other new bird was the White-winged Tanager (*Piranga leucoptera*), a tropical species with the proportions of the Summer Tanager and Flame-colored Tanager but much smaller, being only about the size of an English Sparrow. The male was a beautiful rose-red, with black mask just enclosing the eyes; two distinct white bars on the black wings; and black tail. In the female the head and under parts were yellow, the rest olive save for the two clear white bars on the wings. We did not hear this beautiful little bird's song. It probably was rare along the Sabinas. We subsequently ascertained that it had never before been recorded so far north as Tamaulipas.

March 5 was to be our last day in this land of tiny brown owls, great arboreal curassows and guans, and crepuscular phantoms which called in a goatsucker's voice. A few hours more and all this would be memory—the gentle whistling of the tinamous from the *huapilla* beds, the painted *papagayos* above the quiet river, even the forlorn white pigeon which sat on the roof of the shed so silently hour after hour, waiting for the hawk which had carried its companions off one by one.

At five o'clock that last morning I was up and off after the "goat-sucker." Stubborn fool that I was, I continued to believe that that weird cry had been made by some bird, that I was the chosen tool of Fate through which it would be obtained. Weary of the ticks, but wearier still with acknowledging their hateful supremacy over us, I plunged into the moisture-laden thicket in a mad, final drive. Alas, my quest was futile. Soaking wet, I returned to breakfast empty handed. To this day I do not know what that "goatsucker" actually was.

The tinamou's portrait in water color came next. I gave myself to this delightful work for more than an hour. The startled expression on the face of the crouching bird under the *huapilla* plant was fresh in my mind. The thrill of encountering tinamous so unexpectedly still was upon me. As I recorded the proportions and feather arrangement of the head, and the delicate colors of the eye, eyelid, and bill, I lived again the hours I had spent in pursuit of this interesting and beautiful bird. As stroke after stroke of the brush transformed the white paper into a tinamou portrait, a feeling of triumph and accomplishment possessed me. Here was proof such as no other tangible thing could furnish that I *knew* something about tinamous—proof stronger than the spoken or written word, proof stronger than a photograph, proof far stronger than the specimen itself. For he who re-creates a bird with pencil or brush comes to know his subject peculiarly well. He realizes as the average observer does not and cannot, what a bird's markings truly are: how a narrow bar across the crown or forehead may be made up of the dark tips of literally hundreds of small feathers; how the richest and most exciting plumage colors may be the result of the way in which feathers lie over one another; how the patterns of certain feathers may, for all their intricacy and delicacy, be completely hidden most of the time. He must know how his bird is built, how the bones articulate, how the vertebral column, windpipe, and esophagus occupy the neck side by side, how the whole expression of the face may depend upon the correct placing of the highlight in the eye. More than all this, he must know how the bird behaves, how it feels, how it uses its brain. Realizing that its very existence bespeaks an adequate mental and physical equipment, he must acknowledge that it possesses intelligence somehow akin to his own. Far short though his drawing may fall of what he sees before him, or of the image of the living creature in the back of his mind, a vital fact is nevertheless established—the fact that a human being has carefully studied and tried to understand a bird.

Next on the program was the preparation of a male Hooded Oriole specimen. While working with this elegant little bird we noticed a screaming of hawks in the thicket to the north of us. So loud did the outcry become that we finally ran out to investigate. After a short search along a little used trail we came upon two Collared Micrasturs, the male on the ground with a living three-foot-long snake in his talons, the female looking fiercely on from a low tree close by. The screaming had attracted a company of smaller birds—Brown Jays, Green Jays, Cardinals, Black-crested Titmice, and Yucatán Hummingbirds principally, all of which added their own voices to the outcry but made an obvious point of keeping at a discreet distance. As we watched, the female micrastur flew to the ground, hobbled forward, and clutched at the writhing reptile with one long, powerful foot. As if at an unspoken command all the small birds now closed in a little. There could be no doubting the intensity of their interest. They looked on as if they did not want to miss a single detail. The micrasturs, observing us for the first time, apparently, screamed more loudly than ever, leaped into the air, and made off, the snake continuing to wriggle in the outstretched feet of the male. The band of small birds followed. The incident was of great interest to all of us for several reasons, the principal one, perhaps, being that the snake was the first *living* snake any of us had ever actually seen in Mexico.

About the middle of the morning Burleigh went out for a brief final excursion and returned with a male Prevost's Mango (*Anthracothorax prevosti*), a beautiful, dark-colored hummingbird new for our collection. It was definitely larger than the Buff-bellied Yucatán Hummingbird, had a slightly decurved bill, and was shining green above and below, with peacock-blue lights on the sides of the neck and breast, a velvety black chin and throat, wonderfully irridescent reddish-purple tail, and a fluff of pure white resembling the tiniest of powder puffs at the base of each foot. The female, which we did not see, was said to be quite different in color, being shining green above and on the sides, and white beneath, with an irregular line of black down the middle of the throat, breast, and belly. We handled the male specimen carefully and at the same time proudly, bearing in mind that not a day had passed on this fine adventure of ours without our coming upon some new and beautiful bird.

The Prevost's Mango finished, we wrapped or fastened down our most recently prepared specimens. Packing the collection was not an onerous task for we had worked out a system of drying the birdskins rapidly and packing them away finally day by day. By eleven o'clock our guns, skinning and painting outfits, damp, dirty clothing and tents (which we had not used) were ready for the trip north.

Mr. Bensel informed us that putting the cooking utensils away and boarding up the house would require an hour more, perhaps longer, so I decided to take one last walk along the river. I knew exactly where two Blue-crowned Motmots would be, upstream a few rods from the tree in which I had seen my first woodcreeper. I knew exactly where Rufescent Tinamous Nos. 7, 8, 9, and 10 would be, whistling along a certain stretch of trail. I had had these *perdiz* spotted and numbered for days, though I had not actually seen one of them. I knew exactly where a certain pugnacious Buff-bellied Yucatán Hummingbird would be, zooming back and forth across a shadowy opening which it obviously considered its own. I knew where each and every one of these new-found acquaintances would be, for I had encountered them repeatedly day after day as I had gone to or returned from our collecting grounds. I wanted to look at them all one by one, to let their cries, colors, and postures flow directly into my mind once more through my ears and eyes. How satisfying would be the thought of them on the long drive northward! Even facing the hot highway with its glare and dust would not be so bad with the image of a Coppery-tailed Trogon, or an agile, slender Squirrel Cuckoo in my innermost mind.

The river could have been gayer with colors of sunset or sunrise, or more animated with the reflections of Muscovy Ducks or Military Macaws flying over; but it could not have been more serene. So perfect were its cypress images and drifting cloud images that I could easily have believed myself hanging upside down but for the flies which occasionally dipped, sprinkling thin circles of light where the reflections were darkest.

A motmot hooted. A tinamou whistled. A male Vermilion Flycatcher, carrying the sun's fire in its crest, darted downward to snatch a gnat from the shining water.

XXXII

Before leaving Mexico we had one more day afield—a memorable day high in the mountains of southern Coahuila. Here the scenery was not comparable to the snow-capped Orizaba or Popocatepetl, and we saw no montane bird quite so spectacular as the Imperial Ivory-billed Wood-pecker (*Campephilus imperialis*); but the vegetation and animal life were so dissimilar to anything we had encountered even on the heights above the Mesa de Chipinque, that we realized as never before how amazingly diverse Mexico was. Over and over that day, we recalled what Frank M. Chapman had written of his climb by train from the city of Veracruz to "the great central plateau"—of the changes which had so impressed him as he had risen from the arid coastal zone (*tierra caliente seca*) first to the humid tropical zone (*tierra caliente húmeda*) at some 900 feet elevation; then to the temperate zone (*tierra templada*) at about 2,700 feet; then to the humid alpine zone (*tierra fría húmeda*) at some 5,500 feet; and finally to the arid alpine zone (*tierra fría seca*) at 8,000 feet—all within six hours![1]

Our birding ground that day (March 6) was about eleven miles south of the city of Saltillo—the steep slopes above, and the rough, shallow gullies just below, Diamante Pass. An excellent road took us to the pass proper, which proved to be a comparatively open flat or saddle at 7,800 feet elevation. The woods immediately surrounding this open area reminded us somewhat of the shinnery oak thickets of Oklahoma. They were not, in other words, an impenetrable tangle of thorny branches and vines like that which we had encountered in the foothills below the Mesa de Chipinque, but a tough, thickset growth of low trees, most of them oaks, probably, some of them bearing spiny green leaves, with here and there a clump of glaucous green weeping juniper, or a fine large pine. A thousand feet or so above the pass, just beyond the upper limits of the mixed woodland which I have just described, grew tall, dark green firs or spruces. Some of these majestic conifers seemed to spring directly from solid rock.

At the side of the road we paused to listen, conscious first of a slight light-headedness, then of the clear, gentle beauty of the morning, then of the vast distances which seemed to make themselves felt all about us. We were astonished at our ability to hear the chattering of birds on slopes far below us. Directing our glasses that way we saw tiny spots of grayish-blue moving in rapid succession from one gully to another. The birds were somewhat long of tail. They moved through the air in swoops, and had a way of plunging into the shrubbery at the end of a flight. They were jays of some sort, of that we were instantly certain; and from their general proportions, even as observed at that distance,

[1] "Notes on Birds Observed at Jalapa and Las Vigas, Vera Cruz, Mexico," *Bulletin of the American Museum of Natural History*, Vol. X, Article 2 (February 24, 1898), 15.

we felt sure they belonged to a species different from that which we had seen on and about the Mesa de Chipinque.

Securing a specimen required a determined chase from gully-head to gully-head back and forth across the pass. Instinct seemed to inform the birds that we were after them, and they warned each other of our whereabouts by screeching loudly especially just after alighting at a perfectly safe distance. All three of us concentrated on them for a time— a procedure which was not easy because we were so conscious of the shortness of our stay and of the need for identifying numerous other birds. Finally, with a long wing shot, we collected one. It proved to be, even as we had expected, a Scrub Jay (*Aphelocoma coerulescens*), the very species we had become familiar with long since in peninsular Florida, in the Big Bend Country of Texas, in the Black Mesa section of the Oklahoma Panhandle, and in California. It was, as compared with the Mexican Jay, a short-winged, long-tailed bird, and there was one other point of difference: in the Mexican Jay the throat and breast were of about the same light shade of gray, but in the Scrub Jay the throat was noticeably whiter than the breast. The callnotes of the two species were alike in being harsh, unmusical, and expressive of varying moods. We continued to encounter Scrub Jays wherever we went. While climbing to the lowest of the tall firs above the pass we heard and saw a troop of them following some mammal through the brush. We caught no more than a fleeting glimpse of this harassed, overpublicized creature, but could see that it was of about the size, color, and shape of a lynx.

Another noticeable bird of the pass proper was the Phainopepla (*Phainopepla nitens*)—an elegant creature about the size of a bluebird, with conspicuous crest and white marks on the inner webs of the primary wing feathers. The males were glossy blue-black, the females gray, and in both sexes the eyes were red. They went about in scattered flocks. Often, in looking across the pass, we saw fifteen or twenty of them at one time, but rarely more than one bird to a treetop. They were busy hawking for insects. In flight they were graceful, particularly when, after a successful capture, they wheeled abruptly midair, fanning their long tails wide and revealing the white markings of their wings.

Spotted Towhees were common in the brush. They were easy to identify in flight because the white tail-corners showed so plain. The Brown Towhee was less common, and it appeared to inhabit only the more heavily eroded parts of the gullies below the pass. This species we had not seen since our trip westward to the Laguna de Mayrán in late January. It was a very plainly colored bird, grayish-brown in general effect, lighter below than above, with a reddish-brown tinge on the crown, lower belly, and under tail coverts; light buff throat; and sparse dark streaking where the buff of the throat faded into the light gray of the breast.

A brush-inhabiting species which we momentarily confused with the Brown Towhee proved to be a wholly new bird for our list—the Crissal Thrasher (*Toxostoma dorsale*). It was grayish-brown and long-tailed and we recognized it as a thrasher the instant we saw its long, slender, sickle-shaped bill. Its principal marking—the reddish-brown under tail coverts or crissum (from which the word *crissal* is derived)— were visible enough once we had the specimen in hand, but they did not serve very well as a field-mark. Somewhat to our surprise we saw a few Curve-billed Thrashers also in the openest part of the pass. We could not help wondering whether this species actually bred there, for we saw nothing which resembled at all closely the cholla cactus in which we had many times found its nest in arid parts of the south-western United States.

Ground-inhabiting finches with strikingly white outer tail feathers proved to be Red-backed Juncos (*Junco phaeonotus*). Specimens which we obtained were in beautiful, fresh plumage. A striking feature was their golden-yellow eyes, which were the more brilliant because of the narrow, dark facial mask surrounding them. The gray head, reddish-brown back and white outer tail feathers all were good field marks. These juncos were common, but we did not hear them singing, hence supposed that they had not yet started to nest.

One of the more noticeable birds was the Red-shafted Flicker, a species we had failed to see in the Monterrey region although we had found its feathers there in the lining of a Verdin's nest. It was given to sitting in the very tops of the trees. Occasionally we saw it flying below us. The orange-red wing and tail linings were distinct enough, but the most conspicuous field-mark was the white rump patch. We saw no Bronzed Woodpeckers anywhere. As for the Hairy Woodpecker, we saw it once—apparently a much whiter-breasted individual than those we had seen on the Mesa de Chipinque, hence probably of a different geographical race.

Closely bunched flocks of small birds which swung restlessly from pine to pine almost certainly were Red Crossbills (*Loxia curvirostra*), but we did not see them very clearly and did not collect one. Another bird about which we were uncertain, for we saw it only at great distance, appeared to be a trifle smaller than a crow, was gray, black, and white, and looked disquietingly like a Clark's Nutcracker (*Nucifraga columbiana*). Since that mountain-inhabiting species had not, at the time, been recorded from any part of Mexico aside from the San Pedro Mártir range of Lower California, we did not feel justified in listing it without having a specimen as proof, but Clark's Nutcracker it indubitably was. The species has recently been recorded as far south as the Cerro de Potosí, near Galeana, Nuevo León.[2]

Bluebirds which we saw all were more or less blue-throated and brown-backed, hence belonged to a species we had not so far recorded—the Mexican Bluebird (*Sialia mexicana*). The so-called Western Bluebird and Chestnut-backed Bluebird of the western United States were races of this species. We did not see either the Eastern Bluebird or the Mountain Bluebird anywhere about the pass.

We found that it paid to scan the sky carefully now and then, for certain birds which we did not see at eye level or below us sometimes passed overhead. Among these were the White-throated Swift, which was common and noisy but often fed so high in air as to be scarcely visible; the Band-tailed Pigeon, which must have had a feeding ground somewhere to the north of us; and the Pine Siskin, which we identified by its harsh, drawled callnotes as it swung along in undulating flight.

Before climbing to the higher slopes, we happened upon a company of Black-eared Bush-tits (*Psaltriparus melanotis*) feeding on mistletoe berries in a small, isolated clump of oaks. When first we saw these lively midgets we thought they must surely be mobbing an owl. They bustled in and out of the oak clump, scolding, squeaking, fluttering their wings noisily, darting outward as if to depart, then suddenly turning in midair and diving back into the branches. They were fluffy and long-tailed, and resembled tiny chickadees. They were gray above, white below, with pinkish-brown sides and black face and ear coverts. The eyes of those which we managed to see at all clearly were startlingly white. We counted about seventy of them in that one small clump of oaks.

On our way up the mountain from the pass we recorded only three species which we had seen before in Mexico—the American Raven, Ruby-crowned Kinglet, and Hutton's Vireo. None of these was at all common. A sibilant cry attracted our attention to a Brown Creeper which spiralled its way up a trunk, flew to the base of another tree, climbed upward a few feet, then paused stone-still for several seconds, watching us.

[2] "Clark Nutcracker in Nuevo Leon, Mexico," A. Starker Leopold in *Condor*, Vol. XLVIII, No. 6 (November, 1946), 278.

The great scarcity of wood warblers struck us more and more forcibly the longer we looked for them. The only individual of the family which we recorded that whole day was a female Olive Warbler (*Peucedramus olivaceus*). It had a dull yellow head with dark facial mask (including the ear coverts), plain gray back, grayish-white under parts, and two not very noticeable white wing bars. The male, which we did not see, was known to be a considerably brighter bird, the head in particular being of a rich shade of yellowish-brown, set off by the black mask. The species ranged northward beyond the border into the mountains of New Mexico and Arizona.

Among the great firs at last, and a trifle weary from the hurried ascent, we had a real surprise in the form of a small, energetic bird which flew down to greet us with a slightly drawled, slightly husky *chick-a-dee-dee-dee-dee!* There it perched, only a few feet away, giving us as good a look as we could have wanted at a Mexican Chickadee. Its cap and throat were black, and it had that inquisitive, take-me-at-face-value manner which all chickadees have, as it started pounding at a small object held tightly in its feet.

We could not watch it without being struck by its forthright, unequivocal chickadee behavior. For all the grandeur of this mountain setting, for all the wildness and remoteness of this political unit known as the State of Coahuila, the chickadee was our little friend, no less.

It was the last "new bird" we were to see on our expedition. Something about its manner, something about the way in which it stopped its busy pounding long enough to give us a second's undivided attention, reminded us suddenly and powerfully of faces and sounds and smells which belonged to us but which were fifteen hundred miles or so away—to the northward.

APPENDIX

As has already been stated, this book does not pretend to be a complete field guide to, or handbook of, Mexican birds. It would hardly be fair to bird students visiting Mexico for the first time, however, not to mention certain common species which we did not happen to see on this trip; and describing these additional northeastern Mexican forms leads easily and naturally to a consideration of the birds of the rest of the republic.

In the following roughly phylogenetic résumé I have endeavored to name first in each group the species most easily identified or most likely to be seen. For detailed descriptions of all these birds and information concerning their distribution, the reader is referred to the several-volume work, *The Birds of North and Middle America,* by Ridgway and Friedmann. *Catalog of Birds of the Americas,* by Cory, Hellmayr, and Conover, is devoted primarily to distribution, but the footnotes are full of information concerning the characters by which certain subspecies can be recognized. The first volume of a much-needed *Distributional Check-List of the Birds of Mexico,* by Friedmann, Griscom, and Moore, has recently appeared. This does not describe the birds, but it gives important ecological information concerning their ranges. Material obtained directly from this *Check-List* I acknowledge with the initials FGM. A complete field guide to Mexican birds, illustrated with pen and ink drawings, is being prepared by Emmet R. Blake of the Chicago Natural History Museum. Edward L. Chalif is preparing a field guide with numerous plates illustrating all Mexican birds in color. Meanwhile, the present list will be helpful.

Persons studying birds in Mexico must bear in mind that a great many United States species are Mexican to some extent (i.e., they actually breed in Mexico, or are found there in winter or during migration), hence a thoroughgoing knowledge of United States birds is indispensable. Take, for example, the herons. The problem of identifying this group in Mexico is only slightly more difficult than it is in the southern United States, for almost all North American herons are found in both countries. In higher and drier parts of northern Mexico many birds are the very same as those of the southwestern United States. But wherever one may be in Mexico one must be on the alert for the unexpected; and when one is as far south as Tabasco, Michoacán, or Chiapas one may expect to see wonderful and unfamiliar birds no matter what the season.

In preparing the following summary, I have turned repeatedly to certain persons, or to their publications or collections, for information. In many cases I have mentioned these sources parenthetically, but I wish to list here several persons who have helped, at the same time naming the areas concerning which they are especially well informed: Alexander Wetmore, Veracruz; the late A. J. van Rossem, Sonora; Ludlow Griscom, Guerrero; Robert T. Moore, Sinaloa, Sonora, and the republic in general; Pierce Brodkorb, Chiapas, Tabasco, Campeche, and Veracruz; L. Irby Davis, the lower Río Grande valley, Tamaulipas, San Luis Potisí, Veracruz, Zacatecas, Chiapas, and the republic in general; Emmet R. Blake and H. C. Hanson, Michoacán; George H. Lowery, Jr., San Luis Potosí, Veracruz, and Coahuila; Thomas D. Burleigh, Coahuila, Hidalgo, Veracruz, Puebla, and Guerrero; Robert J. Newman, Veracruz and San Luis Potosí; Ernest P. Edwards and Robert B. Lea, Chiapas, Michoacán, Oaxaca, Durango, Veracruz, San Luis Potosí, Hidalgo, Nuevo León, and Tamaulipas; Melvin A. Traylor, Jr., Veracruz; William B. Davis, Guerrero and Veracruz; William H. Burt, Michoacán, southern Sonora, the Revilla Gigedo Islands, and the west coast in general; Arthur E. Staebler, Chiapas; J. Van Tyne and Milton B. Trautman, Yucatán; Stephen W. Eaton, Tamaulipas, Veracruz, and Oaxaca; Helmuth O. Wagner, Chiapas, México, and Tamaulipas; Robert W. Storer, Guerrero; Allan R. Phillips, Sonora; Dwain W. Warner and Robert M. Mengel, Tamaulipas and Veracruz; Dale A. Zimmerman and G. Bryan Harry, Jalisco; Paul S. Martin, Tamaulipas, Michoacán, and Durango; William B. Heed, Richard S. Robins, E. K. Miller, James Poppy, and Byron Harrell, Tamaulipas.

I wish to thank Roger P. Hurd for his faithful assistance during our field work in Michoacán, México, the Federal District, Hidalgo, Querétaro, Guanajuato, Nuevo León, and Tamaulipas in 1948 and 1949; Frank Harrison for his wonderful hospitality to us at the Rancho del Cielo; and Everts W. Storms, for making Pano Ayuctle, along the beautiful Río Sabinas, seem so much like home during our several visits there.

Family Tinamidae: TINAMOUS

The Rufescent Tinamou (*Crypturellus cinnamomeus*), which I have described and figured (pp. 173–78), is considerably the best known tinamou of Mexico. It ranges northward to Linares, Nuevo León, in the East (Irby Davis), and to Nayarit and Sinaloa in the West, breeding chiefly in the low country and the foothills. The Little Tina-mou (*C. soui*), Slaty-breasted Tinamou (*C. boucardi*), and Great Tinamou (*Tinamus major*) are found only in southern Mexico. The largest of the four is *T. major*, the smallest *C. soui*. They are all plain-colored, wholly terrestrial, and ordinarily very hard to see. Wetmore has listed all four species from southern Veracruz.

Family Colymbidae: GREBES

The Least Grebe (*Colymbus dominicus*), described on page 67, is local and resident throughout low parts of Mexico. The Eared Grebe (*C. caspicus*) breeds sparingly in Chihuahua and northern Baja California and winters probably through-out Mexico. The Western Grebe (*Aechmophorus occidentalis*) breeds on the prairie lakes of Zacatecas and on Lake Chapala (Irby Davis) and winters in western Mexico. The Pied-billed Grebe (*Podilymbus podiceps*) winters widely and breeds locally.

Family Diomedeidae: ALBATROSSES

The Black-footed Albatross (*Diomedea nigripes*) and Laysan Albatross (*D. immutabilis*) are to be seen off the west coast of Baja California. They are said to be less common than formerly. See Alexander's *Birds of the Ocean* for descriptions.

Family Procellariidae: SHEARWATERS

Shearwaters and petrels are very rare off the east coast. The Black-vented Shearwater (*Puffinus opisthomelas*) breeds on the west coast of Baja California; the Townsend's Shearwater (*P. auricularis*) on Clarion, San Benedicto, and Socorro Islands of the Re-villa Gigedo group; the Pink-footed Shearwater (*P. creatopus*) on San Benedicto. The Sooty Shearwater (*P. griseus*) is common off Baja California from March to August (FGM).

Family Hydrobatidae: STORM PETRELS

Among the Mother Carey's chickens likely to be seen off the west coast are the Leach's Petrel (*Oceanodroma leucorhoa*), Black Petrel (*O. melania*), and Least Petrel (*Halocyptena microsoma*). The last breeds abundantly on islands in the northern Gulf of California and on the San Benitos. See Alexander's *Birds of the Ocean* for descriptions.

Family Phaëthontidae: TROPIC-BIRDS

The Red-billed Tropic-bird (*Phaëthon aethereus*) breeds in numbers on islands off the west coast of Mexico. Its long, slender middle tail feathers are white. The Red-tailed Tropic-bird (*P. rubricauda*) visits waters off the west coast of Mexico occasionally. Its long middle tail feathers are deep red.

Family Pelecanidae: PELICANS

The Brown Pelican (*Pelecanus occidentalis*) breeds along both coasts. The White Pelican (*P. erythrorhynchos*) winters throughout Mexico, in the interior as well as along the coast.

Family Sulidae: Boobies

Four boobies are to be encountered off both coasts: the Blue-footed (*Sula nebouxi*), Blue-faced (*S. dactylatra*), Red-footed (*S. sula*), and White-bellied or Brown (*S. leucogaster*). The adult Red-footed is white with black wing-tips. The adult Blue-faced is white with black remiges and rectrices. The Blue-footed is brown (more or less mottled with white) on the head, neck, breast, and upper part of the body, white on the lower breast and abdomen; immature birds are mottled brown all over. The White-bellied or Brown Booby is solid brown except for the white of the breast, belly, under tail coverts, and under wing coverts.

Family Phalacrocoracidae: Cormorants

Most likely to be seen is the Mexican Cormorant (*Phalacrocorax olivaceus*). Adults are purplish black on the head, neck, and under parts and the gray feathers of the back and wings are black-edged. In the breeding season thin white feathers sprinkle the neck and a white line borders the gular sac. Young birds are brown (lighter, sometimes white, below). The somewhat larger Double-crested Cormorant (*P. auritus*) is resident along the coasts of Baja California, Sonora, Sinaloa, and Guerrero. Its status in eastern Mexico is doubtful, but it is to be looked for there along the sea-coast and also on lakes well inland. The Brandt's Cormorant (*P. penicillatus*) is common on the coasts of Baja California. The Pelagic Cormorant (*P. pelagicus*), is a "rare and local" resident on the west coast of the northern half of Baja California (FGM).

Family Anhingidae: Snake-birds

The Snake-bird or Darter (*Anhinga anhinga*) inhabits low parts of Mexico, breeding locally. I have seen it in southern Tamaulipas (p. 170).

Family Fregatidae: Frigate-birds

The Magnificent Frigate-bird (*Fregata magnificens*) nests along both coasts of Mexico. Adult male black all over, with red gular pouch; female black with white lower foreneck, breast, and sides, and whitish collar across back of neck. The Lesser Frigate-bird (*F. minor*) nests on the Revilla Gigedo Islands. In this species there is a brown band on the wings, and in the female the band across the back of the neck is brown, not white.

Family Ardeidae: Herons

All herons found in the United States and Canada are also found in Mexico, some of them only as transients or winter visitants. The Great White Heron (*Ardea occidentalis*) has been reported from Yucatán, Quintana Roo, and Chinchorro Bank, near Cozumel Island (FGM). The Chestnut-bellied or Agami Heron (*Agamia agami*), which has been reported from Chiapas, Veracruz, and Tabasco, is a beautiful South and Middle American species almost three feet long, grayish-blue on the crest, lower back plumes, and curled foreneck feathers; dark glossy green on the back and wings; rich chestnut on the breast and belly. The Cabanis's Tiger-Bittern (*Heterocnus mexicanus*), inhabits low country from Colima, Jalisco, Nuevo León, and Tamaulipas southward (p. 131). The Banded Tiger-Bittern (*Tigrisoma lineatum*), a large, boldly marked Central and South American species, has been recorded once in Chiapas.

Family Cochleariidae: BOAT-BILLED HERONS

The Boat-billed Heron (*Cochlearius cochlearius*) has been recorded from the Río Soto la Marina in Tamaulipas (Harold F. Mayfield), Sinaloa, and Nayarit southward. It is unmistakable at close range, but at a distance looks much like a Black-crowned Night Heron (*Nycticorax nycticorax*).

Boat-billed Heron (*Cochlearius cochlearius*)
about 24 inches, with neck stretched out

Family Ciconiidae: STORKS AND WOOD IBISES

The Wood Ibis (*Mycteria americana*) is to be looked for anywhere along the coast and also inland. The Jabiru (*Jabiru mycteria*), which stands almost five feet high, has a very heavy, straight bill, and is white all over except for the naked black head and neck and red band of skin on the fore-neck. It has been seen several times in Chiapas (Miguel Alvarez del Toro) and reported once from Veracruz.

191

Family Threskiornithidae: IBISES AND SPOONBILLS

The Glossy Ibis (*Plegadis falcinellus*), White Ibis (*Eudocimus albus*), and Roseate Spoonbill (*Ajaia ajaja*) have been recorded in many parts of Mexico. The White-faced Glossy Ibis (*Plegadis mexicana*) has been seen in San Luis Potosí (Irby Davis).

Family Phoenicopteridae: FLAMINGOS

The American Flamingo (*Phoenicopterus ruber*) has been reported from Campeche, Cozumel Island, and Quintana Roo. A colony may breed somewhere in the Yucatán Peninsula (FGM).

Family Anatidae: DUCKS, GEESE, AND SWANS

The Muscovy Duck (*Cairina moschata*), which I have discussed (pp. 134, 135, 140, 162, 181), inhabits the low country from Nuevo León, central Tamaulipas, Nayarit, and Sinaloa southward. It is the only anatid found in Mexico but not in the United States also. The Mexican Duck (*Anas diazi*), which looks very much like the Black Duck (*A. rubripes*), ranges from central Mexico northward into the southwestern United States. The Fulvous Tree Duck (*Dendrocygna bicolor*) and Black-bellied Tree Duck (*D. autumnalis*) are widely distributed but local. The little known Masked Duck (*Oxyura dominica*) has been reported from Nayarit, Jalisco, Colima, Tamaulipas, and Veracruz (FGM). Many species of ducks winter in, or migrate through, Mexico.

Family Cathartidae: NEW WORLD VULTURES

The Turkey Vulture (*Cathartes aura*) and Black Vulture (*Coragyps atratus*) are widely distributed, the former at all elevations, the latter chiefly in the low country. The bizarre King Vulture (*Sarcoramphus papa*), with its boldly buff and black plumage and oddly ornamented head, has been recorded northward as far as Veracruz, Puebla, Campeche, Quintana Roo, and Sinaloa (FGM).

Family Accipitridae: HAWKS, EAGLES AND ALLIES

Kites and allies

All Kites found in the United States inhabit Mexico also. The Mississippi Kite (*Ictinia misisippiensis*) is a transient and winter visitant. The White-tailed Kite (*Elanus leucurus*) breeds locally in Tamaulipas, Nuevo León, Veracruz, Tabasco, and Campeche. The Swallow-tailed Kite (*Elanoides forficatus*) has been reported from several states and is especially common in Chiapas (Irby Davis). The Snail or Everglade Kite (*Rostrhamus sociabilis*) inhabits marshes of eastern Mexico. There are additionally:

1. Plumbeous Kite (*Ictinia plumbea*). Looks like a Mississippi Kite, but tail crossed with several white bars and much chestnut shows in spread wings. Southern Tamaulipas and Oaxaca to Argentina.

2. Gray-headed Kite (*Odontriorchis palliatus*). 20 inches. Found locally, about marshes, from Bolivia and Brazil to Tamaulipas, Oaxaca, and Yucatán. Adults pearl-gray on head and neck; slaty-black on back and wings; white below. The tail, which is rather long, broad, and rounded, is black, crossed with two or three light gray bars. Some immature birds dark-crowned with white forehead and nape, and plain creamy-white below; others dark brown throughout upper parts and creamy-white below, streaked with black in middle of throat and on chest, belly, and flags.

3. Hook-billed Kite (*Chondrohierax uncinatus*). 16–18 inches. Large, noticeably hooked bill. Some adults bluish-slate all over, others brownish-slate, others slaty-black, but tail always marked with one to four light gray or white bands. In some individuals (possibly subadult) under parts narrowly barred with white. Immature

PLATE XII
Rufescent Tinamou
(*Crypturellus cinnamomeus*)

Gray-headed Kite (*Odontriorchis palliatus*)
adult (right) and immature
20 inches

birds often (perhaps always) white below, dark brown above, with white collar. Found locally, about marshes, from Argentina to Tamaulipas, the Federal District, and Sinaloa.

4. Double-toothed Kite (*Harpagus bidentatus*). 12 inches. Adults dark bluish-gray above; chin and throat creamy-white, with blackish midline; breast, sides, and belly barred with gray or russet and white, the dark bars strongly rufescent in some individuals; under tail coverts buff. Young birds dark brown above, with partly concealed white markings, and buff below, with blackish midline down chin and throat and fuscous streaking on breast,

sides, and belly. Forested lowlands from Brazil and Bolivia to Oaxaca and Veracruz. To be looked for in southern Tamaulipas.

Accipiters

The accipiters most likely to be seen in winter are the well-known Cooper's Hawk (*Accipiter cooperi*) and Sharp-shin (*A. striatus*). The former breeds widely, though sparingly, southward to Nuevo León and Michoacán (Edwards). Sharp-shins seen in winter are apt to be the familiar, much-barred-below race, *velox,* but breeding birds and some winter birds are of the plain-breasted race, *suttoni* (see color plate). The Bicolored Hawk (*A. bicolor*), which looks like a Cooper's Hawk with gray breast and belly and solid chestnut flags, is a tropical species breeding from Argentina to Oaxaca and Yucatán. It has been taken in southern Tamaulipas (Martin and Heed). The Goshawk (*A. gentilis*) breeds sparingly in the mountains of western Mexico southward as far as Jalisco.

Buzzard Hawks and allies

Almost all buzzard hawks which inhabit the United States and Canada winter in, or migrate through, Mexico, and several of these breed there. Species apt to be unfamiliar to the visiting bird student are the confiding Roadside Hawk (*Buteo magnirostris*) (pp. 100, 101, 130), which breeds in lowlands from Argentina and Paraguay to Yucatán, central Tamaulipas, Nuevo León, and Colima; the Gray Hawk (*B. nitidus*), which breeds in lowlands from Bolivia to southern Texas and southern Arizona; the White-tailed Hawk (*B. albicaudatus*), described on page 40, which breeds from Argentina to southern Texas, and which is especially common in the Autlán district of Jalisco (Zimmerman and Harry); the Short-tailed Hawk (*B. brachyurus*),

Hook-billed Kite (*Chondrohierax uncinatus*)
middle bird immature; the others adults in brown (left) and slaty phases
18 inches

Double-toothed Kite (*Harpagus bidentatus*)
adult (right) and immature bird
about 12 inches

which occurs in eastern Mexico and probably breeds locally; the unmistakable White Hawk (*Leucopternis albicollis*), which is white both above and below (with a black subterminal tail-band and much black in the wings), and which breeds from Brazil to Oaxaca and Veracruz; and the three puzzling "black hawks"—the Zone-tail (*Buteo albonotatus*), the Mexican Black Hawk (*Buteogallus anthracinus*), and the Urubitinga (*Hypomorphnus urubitinga*). Despite alleged differences in shape, flight, habits, etc., between these three birds, they can be very difficult to distinguish. All are black when adult and have yellow cere and feet. All perch low at times, and are somewhat sluggish in manner. Young of the three species are alike in being mottled with brown, black, buff, and white, and in having several tail bands.

The flying Zone-tail has the proportions of the Turkey Vulture, for its wings are rather long and narrow. The Mexican Black Hawk and Urubitinga are not nearly so long-winged proportionally. The Zone-tail and Mexican Black Hawk are about the size of a Red-tail, the Urubitinga considerably larger.

The adult Zone-tail has three light tail-bands (gray above, white below), and the light barring of the under-wing is extensive. The adult Mexican Black Hawk's tail has a broad, noticeable white bar and white tip. Seen from below, the spread wing shows much light barring and a whitish area at base of primaries. Upper tail coverts, though narrowly tipped with white, at a distance appear to be black. The Urubitinga is a lanky, muscular bird with long legs, two broad white tail-bars, and *conspicuous white upper tail coverts*. Its wings are rounded and appear quite dark beneath

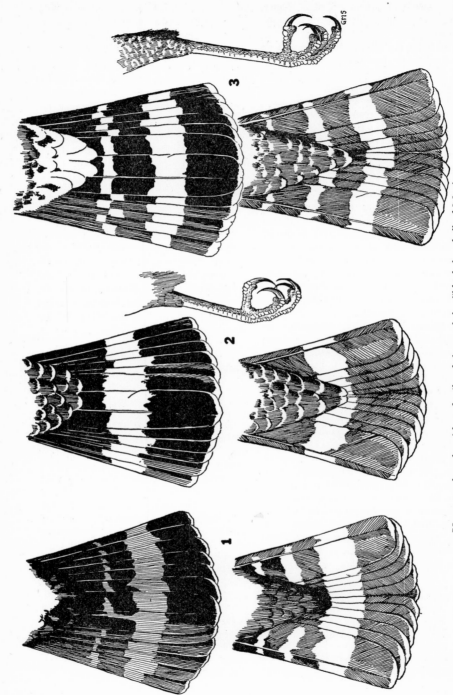

Upper and under sides of tails of three of the "black hawks" of Mexico
1. Zone-tailed Hawk (*Buteo albonotatus*) 2. Black Hawk (*Buteogallus anthracinus*)
3. Urubitinga (*Hypomorphnus urubitinga*)

when spread. Feathers of tibial region usually rather noticeably tipped with white (see drawing).

The following allies of the above-named species must be described in detail:

1. Fishing Buzzard (*Busarellus nigricollis*). 18 inches. A wide-winged, short-tailed, heavy-footed bird found about marshes and along rivers. Flight resembles that of Osprey (*Pandion*). Chestnut with light buff head and neck, black lower throat, and many black bars on the tail. Head and body plumage narrowly streaked with dark brown. Argentina and Paraguay to Veracruz and Sinaloa.

2. Black and White Eagle-Hawk (*Spizastur melanoleucus*). 24 inches. Rather small occipital crest. Tarsi fully feathered. White below and on head except for black of crown, lores, and narrow circle about eyes; upper part of body black; tail black, crossed by several gray bars. Breeds in lowland forest from Argentina to Oaxaca, Veracruz, and Yucatán.

3. Ornate Eagle-Hawk (*Spizaëtus ornatus*). 30 inches. Occipital crest, sometimes conspicuous, may be fanned widely or compressed until it appears to be a single feather. Tarsi fully feathered. Dark brown above; white, boldly barred with black and rufous, below. Tail long and broad, crossed by several gray bars. Breeds in tropical rain forest from Argentina to southern Tamaulipas, Oaxaca, and Yucatán.

4. Black Eagle-Hawk (*Spizaëtus tyrannus*). 30 inches. Occipital crest. Tarsi feathered to toes. Adults blackish-brown all over, but under parts, back of head, and tarsi more or less spotted and barred with white. Tail long and broad, crossed with gray bands. Breeds in tropical rain forest from southeastern Brazil to Oaxaca, San Luis Posotí, and Yucatán.

Eagles

The Golden Eagle (*Aquila chrysaëtos*)

and Bald Eagle (*Haliaeetus leucocephalus*) have been recorded in Mexico, the former rather frequently in the mountains, the latter in Baja California. The powerful, spectacularly crested Harpy Eagle (*Harpia harpyja*) has been reported from Oaxaca, Chiapas, Veracruz, Tabasco, and Campeche (FGM). The Solitary Eagle (*Urubitornis solitaria*), which is much like the Urubitinga but still larger, breeds locally from Chile to Oaxaca, Jalisco, and extreme southeastern Sonora. It is slaty-black with a narrow white tip and broad gray band on the tail.

Harriers and allies

The well known Marsh Hawk (*Circus cyaneus*) is found throughout Mexico in winter. The rare Blackish Crane-Hawk (*Geranospiza nigra*) breeds in lowland forest from western Ecuador to Sonora, central Tamaulipas, and Yucatán (see pp. 130, 131 for description of adult; p. 161 for description of young).

Black Hawks of Mexico

The black hawks present a knotty problem in identification. The Zone-tail, Mexican Black Hawk, Urubitinga, and Blackish Crane-Hawk are regularly black when adult. Melanistic Western Red-tailed Hawks (*Buteo jamaicensis calurus*) are sometimes black, with vague brown and gray markings. The Swainson's Hawk (*B. swainsoni*) is sometimes black. The dark phase of the Short-tailed Hawk is brownish-black. Not to be forgotten are the Solitary Eagle, Black Eagle-Hawk, Snail Kite, and Hook-billed Kite (all briefly discussed above) which are virtually black when adult or in dark plumage phase; and the Harris's Hawk which, despite the bold red-brown of its wing coverts, often appears to be solid black.

Family Pandionidae: Ospreys

The Osprey or Fish Hawk (*Pandion haliaëtus*) may be encountered along any watercourse, especially during winter or the migration season.

Family Falconidae: FALCONS AND ALLIES

The Peregrine (*Falco peregrinus*), Prairie Falcon (*F. mexicanus*), Pigeon Hawk or Merlin (*F. columbarius*), Aplomado Falcon (*F. femoralis*), and Sparrow Hawk (*F. sparverius*) are found in Mexico. The beautiful Bat Falcon or White-throated Falcon (*F. albigularis*), which I have discussed (pp. 137, 139, 170–71), breeds from Argentina to central Tamaulipas, Nuevo León, Durango, and Sonora (van Rossem).

The Caracara (*Polyborus cheriway*) and

Laughing Falcon (*Herpetotheres cachinnans*)
about 19 inches

Collared Micrastur (*Micrastur semitor-quatus*) I have discussed and illustrated. The latter breeds in lowland forest from Argentina to central Tamaulipas in the east and to Sinaloa in the west. The very much smaller (13 inches) Barred Micrastur (*M. ruficollis*), which breeds in tropical forest from Argentina to Puebla, Veracruz, and Oaxaca, is dark gray above (brown-backed in the female), and finely barred with dark gray and white below. The tail is blackish-brown, tipped with white and crossed by three narrow white bars. Young birds usually have a collar of buffy-white, and their under parts are buff, sometimes sparsely barred with dark brown.

The Red-throated Caracara (*Daptrius americanus*) breeds in tropical forest from Brazil to Chiapas. 24 inches. Glossy blue-black except for white of belly, thighs, and under tail coverts. Legs and bare skin of face and throat red; bill yellow, eyes deep red.

The Laughing Falcon (*Herpetotheres cachinnans*) is about 19 inches long. Buffy-white on crown, collar, and under parts; crown narrowly streaked with black; large black patches on sides of head meet on nape. Wings and back dark brown. Tail black, crossed by buff bars. Usual cry a loud, far-reaching wail. The "laugh," which sometimes precedes the wail, is not very loud. Argentina to southern Tamaulipas in the east and Sonora in the west, in forests principally of coastal lowlands.

Family Cracidae: CURASSOWS, GUANS AND ALLIES

The Great Curassow or *Faisán Real* (*Crax rubra*), which I have discussed and figured (pp. 151–52, 162–66), breeds in tropical forest from Ecuador to southern Tamaulipas, Yucatán, and Oaxaca. The Crested Guan or *Ajol* (*Penelope purpurascens*) inhabits tropical forests from Colombia and Ecuador to southern Tamaulipas and Sinaloa. The well-known Chachalaca (*Ortalis vetula*) seems to be partial to thicketed, dry lowlands. In the east it ranges northward through Tamaulipas into southern Texas, in the west to Guanajuato and Jalisco. The Rufous-bellied Chachalaca (*O. wagleri*), a western species, ranges from Jalisco to Sonora and southern Chihuahua. It has chestnut-rufous belly and chestnut-tipped outer tail feathers. The Black Chachalaca (*Penelopina nigra*) breeds from Nicaragua to Chiapas. Adult male: glossy blue- or green-black with red bill, red feet, naked red throat, and bare purplish area about eyes. Female: dark brown, spotted, mottled, and barred with black. The remarkable Horned Guan (*Oreophasis derbianus*) of Chiapas and western Guatemala has an upright knob on top of the head. Male and female alike in color —glossy blue-black with white band across middle of tail and vaguely streaked light gray area on foreneck and chest. The species is about three feet long.

Family Phasianidae: QUAILS, PARTRIDGES AND ALLIES

The Bob-white (*Colinus virginianus*) ranges widely in Mexico. In 1949 I was surprised to find it at 8,000 feet above Lake Pátzcuaro, in Michoacán. It varies in color or geographically and several Mexican races are quite different from those of the eastern United States. Other quails found both in the United States and in Mexico are the Mountain Quail (*Oreortyx picta*), Scaled Quail (*Callipepla squamata*), California Quail (*Lophortyx californica*), Gambel's Quail (*L. gambeli*), and Harlequin Quail (*Cyrtonyx montezumae*).

No bird student in Mexico should miss the wonderful Singing Quail (*Dactylortyx thoracicus*), a species known also as the Long-clawed or Long-toed Partridge. It is an inconspicuous forest bird, but its song is loud and unforgettable. Gaumer said of it: "At nightfall it sings a very pretty song, beginning with a low whistle, is three times repeated, each time with greater force; then follows the syllables *che-va-lieu-a* repeated from three to six times in succession. The tone is musical, half sad, half persuasive, beginning somewhat cheerfully, and ending more coaxingly." I have heard the bird singing at various times of the day, and I wrote down the phrase as *pitch-wheeler*. The species ranges from El Salvador and Honduras to Yucatán, southern Tamaulipas, and Jalisco, in the mountains.

In the high country from Puebla west to Colima, Michoacán, and Guerrero lives the trim little Banded Quail (*Philortyx fasciatus*). The slender feathers of its high crest are often conspicuous. Its sides are boldly barred.

The Long-tailed Partridge or Tree-Quail (*Dendrortyx macroura*), a species almost twice as heavy as the Bob-white, is distinctively Mexican, being found from Michoacán and Veracruz to Oaxaca. Legs, bill, and eyelids red; crown, face, and throat black; a light gray line above and back of eye, another back of and below eye; chest and upper back broadly streaked with rufous. The Highland Partridge or Tree-Quail (*D. leucophrys*), which is similarly long-tailed, is pale buff on fore part of crown, and

Long-tailed Partridge or *Gallina del Monte* (*Dendrortyx macroura*)
about 13 inches

Elegant Quail (*Lophortyx douglasi*)
about 10 inches

white on chin and throat. It ranges north-ward into Chiapas.

The Spotted or Thick-billed Wood-Quail (*Odontophorus guttatus*), which ranges from Panama to Oaxaca, Veracruz, Tabasco, and Campeche, is a little larger than a Bob-white, and is dark brown in general appearance. Its bill is very heavy, its breast and belly indistinctly spotted with white, and its throat black, streaked with white.

The Black-throated Quail (*Colinus nigrogularis*) of the Yucatán peninsula and Central America, is much like a Bob-white in general appearance, but in the male the throat and superciliary line are black and the feathers of the breast and belly are white bordered with black, producing a scaled effect.

The Elegant Quail (*Lophortyx douglasi*) is found from Sonora and Chihuahua to Jalisco and Nayarit. Male has slender pale buff crest; face white, finely spotted and streaked with black; upper part of body brown; under parts gray, neatly spotted with white on belly, sides, and flanks. Crest of female short and dark.

The Ocellated Quail (*Cyrtonyx ocellatus*), which ranges northward to Oaxaca and Chiapas, is superficially similar to the Harlequin Quail but lacks white spots on its under parts. The middle of the breast, the sides, and the flanks are extensively cinnamon-rufous or chestnut and the folded wing is boldly streaked with the same color (Blake).

Family Meleagrididae: Turkeys

The Wild Turkey (*Meleagris gallopavo*) ranges southward to Veracruz, Oaxaca, and Michoacán. The magnificent Ocellated Turkey (*Agriocharis ocellata*) is indigenous to Tabasco and the Yucatán peninsula. Brilliant "eye-spots" are a conspicuous fea-

201

ture of the plumage of a specimen in hand, but these probably do not show much in the field. The featherless head is blue, with yellow tubercles.

Family Gruidae: CRANES

The Sandhill Crane (*Grus canadensis*) winters southward to central Mexico.

Family Aramidae: LIMPKINS

The Limpkin (*Aramus guarauna*), which ranges from the southern United States to Argentina, and is not migratory, is so dependent upon certain large snails for food that it is very local in distribution. It has been reported from Oaxaca, Veracruz, Tabasco, and the Yucatán peninsula (FGM).

Family Rallidae: RAILS, GALLINULES, AND COOTS

All species of this family found in the United States have been reported from Mexico, but further information on their distribution is much needed. The King Rail (*Rallus elegans*) has been reported from Guanajuato and Veracruz (FGM). The Clapper Rail (*R. longirostris*) breeds in salt water marshes along both coasts and also in fresh water marshes in the State of México. The Virginia Rail (*R. limicola*) probably breeds more widely than records indicate. I have seen it at Lake Pátzcuaro, in Michoacán, and feel sure that it breeds there. The Black Rail (*Laterallus jamai-*

Gray-necked Wood Rail (*Aramides cajanea*)
15 inches

202

Sun Grebe or Finfoot (*Heliornis fulica*)
12 inches

censis) breeds in northwestern Baja California; the Yellow Rail (*Conturnicops noveboracensis*) at Lerma, not far southwest of Mexico City. The Sora (*Porzana carolina*) winters widely but does not breed. No one will have difficulty in identifying the Florida Gallinule (*Gallinula chloropus*), Purple Gallinule (*Porphyrula martinica*), or Coot (*Fulica americana*). The puzzling "new" rails, then, will be:

1. Gray-necked Wood-Rail (*Aramides cajanea*). 15 inches. Forehead and whole neck gray; rear part of crown brown; back and wings brownish-olive; breast and upper belly rufous-buff; belly and under tail coverts black; bill yellowish-green with red base; feet and eyes red. Swampy forest from Argentina to southern Tamaulipas,

Yucatán, and Oaxaca, principally along the coast.

2. Rufous-necked Wood-Rail (*A. axillaris*). 15 inches. Crown, neck, breast, and upper belly reddish-brown; chin and throat white; back and wings olive; middle of belly gray; under tail coverts black; bill grass-green with yellow base (Friedmann); feet red. Coastal lagoons from northern South America to Sinaloa and Yucatán.

3. Little Red Rail or Ruddy Crake (*Laterallus ruber*). 7 inches from bill-tip to tail-tip (skin). Except for gray of upper part of head, reddish-brown all over, richest on hind neck and upper back, palest on belly. Northern South America to Oaxaca, Yucatán peninsula, and southern Tamaulipas. I have never seen this species alive. Very little is known about it.

Family Heliornithidae: Sun Grebes or Finfeet

The Sun Grebe or Finfoot (*Heliornis fulica*) is about a foot long. Grayish-brown above, tinged with olive on back. Tail dark brown, tipped with white. Black and white pattern of head and neck shows in drawing. Chest gray; belly white; bill red above,

white below; feet yellowish-white, barred with black on toes. Ranges widely through South and Central America, having been found as far north as Boca del Río, Veracruz (Mengel and Warner), Chiapas, and Campeche.

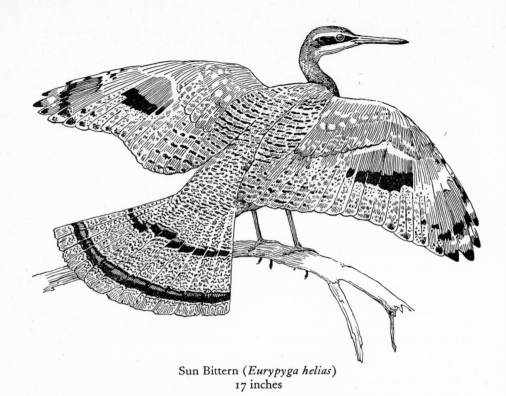

Sun Bittern (*Eurypyga helias*)
17 inches

Family Eurypygidae: SUN BITTERNS

The Sun Bittern (*Eurypyga helias*), like the Sun Grebe, ranges widely through Central and South America. It has been found in Chiapas and Tabasco (FGM). It is 17 inches long. The drawing gives a faint idea of the beauty of the bird's pattern, but the wonderful colors—the peculiar greenish-brown of the wings, the bright chestnut, black, and buff of the "eye-spots" on the primaries, and the cinamon of the chest—have to be seen at close range to be believed. Eyes red. Bird sometimes holds spread-wing position for some time as if conscious of the beauty thus displayed.

Family Jacanidae: JACANAS

The curious Jacana (*Jacana spinosa*), with its inordinately long toes, frontal shield, spurred wings, and black, maroon-chestnut, and pale green plumage, once seen will never be forgotten. Young birds are much less colorful, being gray above and white throughout the under parts. The species ranges from Argentina to the West Indies, extreme southern Texas, and Sinaloa, principally in coastal lowlands.

Family Haematopodidae: OYSTER-CATCHERS

Oyster-catchers inhabit the seacoast. Solid black birds breed along the Pacific side of the northern half of Baja California, but black and white birds occur on both coasts.

204

Whether all these belong to one diverse, wide-ranging species, *Haematopus ostralegus,* or whether the black birds (*bachmani*) belong to a separate species, is a question remaining to be settled.

Family Charadriidae: Plovers

The only "true" plover found in Mexico but not covered by guides to United States birds is the Collared Plover (*Charadrius collaris*), a small species (5½ inches) which looks something like the Semipalmated Plover (*C. semipalmatus*) but has a longer, wholly dark bill; no white ring around the neck; a narrow band of reddish-brown just back of the black crown-patch; and a reddish-brown wash on the sides of the neck. The spread wing shows little, if any, white. The species ranges widely through Central and South America, northward (principally on the seacoast) to Veracruz and Sinaloa.

Family Scolopacidae: Snipes, Sandpipers, and allies

One species of this family, the Willet (*Catoptrophorus semipalmatus*), breeds in Mexico—on the Tamaulipas coast, southward at least as far as the village of Tepejuahe (Robins). The numerous other species are transient or winter visitants. Almost all species found in the United States have been reported from Mexico.

Family Recurvirostridae: Avocets and Stilts

The Black-necked Stilt (*Himantopus mexicanus*) is a resident along the coast as well as at favorable places in the interior. The American Avocet (*Recurvirostra americana*), which is locally common in winter, breeds in San Luis Potosí (FGM).

Family Phalaropodidae: Phalaropes

All three Phalaropes have been recorded in Mexico or at sea offshore. The Wilson's Phalarope (*Steganopus tricolor*) is the most likely to be encountered in the interior.

Family Burhinidae: Thick-knees

The Double-striped Thick-knee (*Burhinus bistriatus*) has been reported from Chiapas, Oaxaca, Veracruz, and Tabasco (FGM). Ernest Edwards and Robert Lea, who encountered it in Chiapas, say that it is very noisy and hard to approach. It is about as big as a Night Heron and is grayish-brown except for the chin and throat, belly, and superciliary areas, which are white. Each superciliary line is bordered above by a broad dark streak.

Family Stercorariidae: Jaegers

To be looked for at sea. Very few Mexican records. Friedmann, Griscom, and Moore list the Pomarine (*Stercorarius pomarinus*) and Parasitic (*S. parasiticus*).

Family Laridae: Gulls and Terns

No species peculiar to Mexico. Virtually all species reported are discussed in guides to United States birds. The number of banded Herring Gulls (*Larus argentatus*) reported from Caribbean coasts is impressive.

Family Rynchopidae: Skimmers

The Black Skimmer (*Rynchops nigra*) breeds along the whole Pacific coast and on the Atlantic side southward to Yucatán.

Family Alcidae: Auks and allies

Alcids so far reported from Mexican waters are all small. The one most likely to be seen is the Xantus's Murrelet (*Endo-* *mychura hypoleuca*), a Pacific species which breeds on islands off Baja California.

Family Columbidae: Pigeons and Doves

The Red-billed Pigeon (*Columba flavirostris*), described on pages 102 and 104, ranges from Costa Rica to extreme southern Texas and southern Sonora. Other species found both in the United States and in Mexico are the Band-tailed Pigeon (*C. fasciata*), Mourning Dove (*Zenaidura macoura*), White-winged Dove (*Zenaida asiatica*), White-fronted Dove (*Leptotila verreauxi*), Inca Dove (*Scardafella inca*), and Ground Dove (*Columbigallina passerina*). The following more distinctively Mexican species are all rounded-tailed and rather short tailed with one exception, the Socorro Dove (*Zenaidura graysoni*), whose tail is long and pointed.

1. Rufous Pigeon (*Columba cayennensis*). Size of small domestic pigeon. Forehead, whole neck both in front and behind, upper back, chest, and lesser wing coverts rufous, with purplish reflections; rear part of crown gray, highly glossed with green and bronze; chin, throat, sides of head, and rump gray; lower back, tail, and most of the wings brownish-gray. Spread tail slightly lighter at tip on all but middle feathers. Argentina to Veracruz, Campeche, and Chiapas.

2. Scaled Pigeon (*C. speciosa*). Size of small domestic pigeon. Reddish-brown, with scaled effect on neck, chest, and upper back, the feathers dark on tips, with more or less concealed white and tan subterminal areas. Paraguay and Bolivia to Veracruz, Oaxaca, and Yucatán peninsula.

3. Short-billed Pigeon (*C. nigrirostris*). Notably smaller than domestic pigeon. Bill stubby and dark. No noticeable field-mark; dull purplish-gray on head, neck, and under parts; dark brownish-gray on upper part of body; wings and tail showing some brown when spread. Panama to Veracruz, in lowlands.

4. Gray-headed Dove (*Leptotila plum-* *beiceps*). Noticeably smaller than domestic pigeon. A dull-colored species, whitish on forehead, blue-gray on crown, slaty on occiput; fawn-colored below, palest on chin and passing to white on lower belly and under tail coverts; dark brown on upper part of body and tail. Outer tail feathers tipped with white. Colombia to Oaxaca and southern Tamaulipas in humid tropical rain forest (FGM).

5. Cassin's Dove (*Leptotila cassini*). Much like White-fronted Dove (*L. verreauxi*), which I have figured and discussed, but color of upper parts olive-brown throughout, except for the pale grey forehead. Bare space about eye *red,* not blue. Neck and chest pale purplish-gray. As in *verreauxi,* outer tail feathers tipped with white and under wings light brown, showing in flight. Northern Colombia to Tabasco and Chiapas.

6. Ruddy Quail-Dove (*Oreopeleia montana*). Shorter (but heavier-bodied) than Mourning Dove. Male rufous above, pinkish-cinnamon below, fading to buff on abdomen and under tail coverts; faint purple gloss on hind neck, crown, and back; a band of rufous below eye. Female grayish-olive in general tone. A ground-inhabiting forest bird with very wide range: Paraguay north to West Indies, Yucatán peninsula, southern Tamaulipas, and Guerrero.

7. White-faced Quail-Dove (*Oreopeleia albifacies*). Size of domestic pigeon. Whole front of head *pale* grayish-buff; blue-gray of crown fading into rufous of hind neck; sides of neck buff, vaguely streaked with dusky; upper part of body rufous, strongly glossed with purple on the back; breast brownish-gray; belly and under tail coverts buff. Nicaragua to Guerrero and Veracruz.

8. Blue Ground Dove (*Claravis pretiosa*). A little larger than Ground Dove (*Columbigallina passerina*). Male bluish-

gray all over, fading to white on forehead and deepening to slate on back; wings with sharply defined spots and bars of black. Female brown, with chestnut spots and bars on wings. Paraguay to Yucatán peninsula, southern Tamaulipas, and Oaxaca.

9. **Ruddy Ground Dove** (*C. talpacoti*). Size of Ground Dove. Male cinnamon-brown, paler on face and neck and tinged with purple below; female brown above, gray below, fading to white on throat and abdomen. Argentina to Sinaloa and Tamaulipas. Has been seen in southern Texas (Irby Davis).

10. **Plain-breasted Ground Dove** (*C. minuta*). Like Ground Dove, but under parts *plain* purplish-gray, fading to white on abdomen. Female grayish-brown except for throat, belly, and under tail coverts, which are grayish-white. Panama to Campeche, Veracruz, and Chiapas; also ranges widely in South America.

The Zenaida Dove (*Zenaida aurita*), which looks like a Mourning Dove with rounded (not pointed) tail and white-tipped secondaries, is found on islands off Yucatán. The beautiful Socorro Dove (*Zenaidura graysoni*) looks like a large Mourning Dove with rich ruddy under parts. The little-known Mondetoura Dove (*Claravis mondetoura*), which inhabits montane parts of northern South America and Central America, has been reported from four localities in Veracruz (FGM). The Caribbean Dove (*Leptotila jamaicensis*) inhabits the northern part of the Yucatán peninsula. An isolated race of the Quail-Dove (*Oreopeleia lawrencei*) inhabits southeastern Veracruz.

Family Psittacidae: PARROTS

Species with long, much-pointed tails

1. **Military Macaw** (*Ara militaris*). The only green macaw of Mexico. Inhabits the Andes (Colombia to Argentina) and parts of Mexico (northward to Nuevo León and central Tamaulipas in the east; a discrete population in extreme southern Sonora).

2. **Scarlet Macaw** (*A. macao*). The name describes the bird, but there is much yellow and blue, and some green, in the plumage. Bolivia to Oaxaca, Campeche, and southern Tamaulipas.

3. **Green Parakeet** (*Aratinga holochlora*). See page 161 for description. Nicaragua to Sonora, Chihuahua, Guanajuato, Nuevo León, and central Tamaulipas.

4. **Aztec Parakeet** (*A. astec*). See page 161 for description. Panama to Yucatán peninsula, southern Tamaulipas, and Oaxaca.

5. **Orange-fronted Parakeet** (*A. canicularis*). Green with *dull orange forehead*. Costa Rica to *western* Mexico (Durango and Sinaloa).

Species with shorter, pointed tails

1. **Thick-billed Parrot** (*Rhynchopsitta pachyrhyncha*). Green with red patch on forehead and lesser wing coverts; *under* primary coverts yellow. Usually found in pines in mountains. Northwestern Mexico, wandering occasionally into southern Arizona; reported from Veracruz.

2. **Maroon-fronted Parrot** (*R. terrisi*). Similar to above, but larger; no yellow on under wing coverts; forehead and patch on lesser wing coverts maroon or brown rather than red. Known only from mountains of Nuevo León, but similar bird inhabits high parts of southwestern Tamaulipas. The latter bird looked "black" on the forehead (Martin, Heed, and Robins).

Species with short tails

1. **Mexican or Blue-rumped Parrotlet** (*Forpus cyanopygius*). About size of English Sparrow. Adult male bright green except for bright blue of wings, lower back, and rump. Female and young male wholly green, without blue. Jalisco to Zacatecas and Sinaloa; Tres Marías Islands.

2. **Orange-chinned Parakeet** (*Brotogeris jugularis*). 6½ inches. Green with orange chin-spot. Colombia and Venezuela to Guerrero, Oaxaca, and Chiapas.

3. **Red-eared Parrot** (*Pionopsitta haematotis*). 9 inches. Head dark brownish-gray, darkest along hind edge of ear coverts. Auriculars partly red, not noticeably so. Neck and chest dull bronze. Rest of plumage

green, with brilliant red patch on side of body mostly concealed when wings are folded; more or less concealed dull red at base of tail; and much purplish-blue in the wings, especially the under side. Ecuador to Veracruz and Campeche.

4. White-crowned Parrot (*Pionus senilis*). 9 inches. Forehead, crown and throat white; rest of head dull blue; extreme lower throat and upper breast dull pink; chest and upper belly dull blue; wing quills blue and black; under tail coverts and base of tail red; rest of plumage green, bronzy on wing coverts. Panama to southern Tamaulipas, Yucatán peninsula, and Oaxaca.

5. Yellow-lored Parrot (*Amazona xantholora*). 10 inches. Male green, with white crown-spot, yellow loral spot, red patch about eyes, small black auricular spot, red primary coverts, and partly concealed red area at base of tail; most plumage anterior to tail coverts edged with black. Female similar, but crown-spot blue, almost no yellow in lores or red on face, and primary coverts green. Northern British Honduras to Yucatán peninsula.

6. White-fronted Parrot (*A. albifrons*). 11 inches. Sexes alike. Very similar to male of above, but little or no yellow in lores; white of top of head restricted to forehead; center of crown blue; red spot on wing includes primary coverts and alula. Plumage in general without black tipping. Costa Rica to southern Sonora, Durango, southeastern Veracruz, and Yucatán peninsula.

7. Red-crowned Parrot (*A. viridigenalis*). 11 inches. Forehead and crown bright red; feathers above and back of eye tipped with blue; large patch on secondaries red; all large wing feathers tipped with black; bright green otherwise. Northeastern Veracruz to San Luis Potisí, Nuevo León, and central Tamaulipas, occurring in oaks and pines on dry ridges as well as in lowland forests (Martin). Discussed on pages 144, 156, 170.

8. Red-lored Parrot (*A. autumnalis*).

Similar to Red-crowned Parrot, but red of head restricted to forehead and lores; rear part of crown blue; in Mexican subspecies, area in front of and below eye yellow. Large red patch in wings. Plumage of hind neck tipped with black, producing scaled effect. Southern Tamaulipas, Puebla, and Oaxaca to western Ecuador and northwestern Brazil; races found from Nicaragua south have no yellow on cheeks. Yellow-cheeked Parrot.

9. Lilac-crowned Parrot (*A. finschi*). 12 inches. Green with dull red forehead, dull lilac-blue crown and hind neck, and large red patch in wing; plumage of neck and under parts with distinct dark tipping. *Western* Mexico from Oaxaca to Durango and extreme northeastern Sonora.

10. Yellow-headed Parrot (*A. ochrocephala*). 14 inches. Whole head and neck bright yellow, some feathers of crown and hind neck tipped with red; bright green otherwise except for large patch of red in secondaries, concealed red areas on inner webs at base of outer tail feathers, yellow and red along front edge of wing, yellow tibial plumage, and bright yellow-green tail-tip. This description is of the subspecies *oratrix*, which occupies most of the Mexican part of the species' range; *tresmariae* (Tres Marías Islands) is similar but bigger-billed and greener (less yellowish) below; in *auro-palliata* (Oaxaca and Chiapas to Costa Rica), most of the head is green, the yellow being restricted to the nape and hind neck. The species as a whole ranges from Ecuador, Peru and Brazil to Colima, Nuevo León, Pueblo, central Tamaulipas, and Yucatán. Discussed on pages 106–107, 110–13, 156.

11. Mealy Parrot (*A. farinosa*). 16 inches. Dull grayish-green with light blue forehead and crown, red patch in wing, black-tipped primaries, and yellow-green tail-tip. Brazil and Ecuador to Veracruz and Oaxaca, in tropical rain forest. Races found from Panama south have no blue on the head.

Family Cuculidae: Cuckoos and Allies

Species found both in the United States and in Mexico are the Yellow-billed Cuckoo (*Coccyzus americanus*), which breeds southward to Sinaloa, Nuevo León, and

PLATE XIII
Blackish Crane-Hawk
(*Geranospiza nigra*)

southern Tamaulipas (possibly farther in the mountains); the Black-billed Cuckoo (*C. erythropthalmus*), a transient; the Black-eared or Mangrove Cuckoo (*C. minor*), which ranges northward to Sinaloa in the west and to central Tamaulipas in the east, breeding along the coast but also well away from it; the Road-runner (*Geococcyx californianus*), which ranges southward to Puebla, México, the Federal District, and Michoacán; and the Groove-billed Ani or *Garrapatero* (*Crotophaga sulcirostris*), which ranges widely in tropical lowlands, being found as far north as southern Texas in the east, and as southern Sonora in the west. In Jalisco it breeds to 5,000 feet and ranges to 6,300 feet (FGM).

The interesting Squirrel-Cuckoo (*Piaya cayana*), which inhabits tropical lowlands as far north as southern Tamaupilas, Durango, and southern Sonora, is little known. Its nesting habits, in particular, need to be studied. This species I have discussed and figured (p. 148).

The following species also are apt to be unfamiliar:

1. Striped Cuckoo (*Tapera naevia*). 11 inches (tail, 6 inches); bill much shorter than head; a fairly conspicuous crest. Upper parts buffy-brown (top of head, rufous), coarsely streaked with black except on rump and upper tail coverts; buff line over eye; throat, sides, and under tail coverts buff; belly white; outer tail feathers very narrowly tipped with buff. Callnote a melancholy, whistled *wheu,* slowly repeated (Sturgis). Argentina to Veracruz and Oaxaca.

2. Lesser Ground-Cuckoo (*Morococcyx erythropygus*). 10 inches. Dull brown above, glossed with green on wings and streaked with dusky on crown; under parts rufous-buff, palest on middle of throat and breast; bare area on face yellow about eye, blue back of eye (Ridgway); bare facial area bordered above first by black then by buffy line, below by black line; outer tail feathers black subterminally and on outer webs and tipped with buff. Western Costa Rica to southern Sinaloa, east as far as Puebla and eastern Oaxaca.

3. Pheasant-Cuckoo (*Dromococcyx phasianellus*). 15 inches (tail, 8 inches). Head small with noticeable crest; upper tail coverts remarkably long and somewhat plumelike. Upper parts brown, rusty on crown, grayish on upper tail coverts. Lesser wing coverts edged with white, producing a scaled effect. Secondaries, several primaries, upper tail coverts and rectrices tipped with grayish-white. Bold white line back of eye. Under parts dull white, streaked with dusky on the cheeks, throat and chest. Paraguay to Oaxaca, Veracruz, and Yucatán peninsula. Rare throughout its range.

4. Lesser Road-runner (*Geococcyx velox*). Much like the well-known Road-runner, but smaller; middle of foreneck and chest without dark streaking. Eyelids white, but bare area about lids light blue and back of eye orange (Zimmerman). Northern Nicaragua to Yucatán, México, Zacatecas, Durango, and Sonora.

5. Smooth-billed Ani (*Crotophaga ani*). Like Groove-billed Ani, but a little larger and bill smooth rather than furrowed. West Indies; islands off east coast of Mexico and Central America; and South America east of the Andes.

Family Tytonidae: Barn Owls

The Barn Owl (*Tyto alba*) ranges widely through Mexico.

Family Strigidae: Horned Owls, Screech Owls, and allies

Many species of owls are found both in the United States and in Mexico, among them the Great Horned (*Bubo virginianus*), Long-eared (*Asio otus*), Short-eared (*Asio flammeus*), Barred (*Strix varia*), Spotted (*S. occidentalis*), Screech (*Otus asio*), Spotted Screech (*O. trichopsis*), Scops (*O. scops flammeolus,* the form widely known as the Flammulated Screech Owl, to which I refer on page 90), Elf (*Micra-*

thene whitneyi), Burrowing (*Speotyto cunicularia*), Pygmy (*Glaucidium gnoma*), Ferruginous Pygmy (*G. brasilianum*), and Saw-whet (*Aegolius acadicus*). Among these the Great Horned probably ranges the most widely. The Burrowing ranges widely too, but it requires open prairielike areas, whereas the Great Horned, usually a woodland species, may live in treeless gulches miles from forest. The Short-ear is a winter visitant. The Long-ear is known to nest in northern Baja California. All the other species listed above breed widely in Mexico.

Some "full species" of owls listed from Mexico are probably geographical races of certain of the above. Since identifying these moot forms without collecting them is virtually impossible, detailed descriptions are rather pointless. The Vinaceous Owl (*Otus vinaceus*), Cooper's Owl (*O. cooperi*), and Guatemalan Screech Owl (*O. guatemalae*) may be races of *Otus asio* or of *O. trichopsis*. I seriously question whether the so-called Least Pygmy Owl (*Glaucidium minutissimum*) is specifically distinct from the Pygmy. The Guatemalan Barred Owl (*Strix fulvescens*) may be a race of the Barred Owl or of the Spotted Owl. *Aegolius ridgwayi* may be a race of the Saw-whet. What I have just said must stand as very brief descriptions of the several forms mentioned. My suspicion that a given "moot form" belongs to such-and-such a species means that the moot form looks much like said species. Thus: the Guatemalan Screech Owl is much like an ordinary Screech Owl except that its toes are featherless. Southern races of the Barred Owl are much less heavily feathered on their toes than the northern race—why not the same correlation between latitude and thickness-of-toe-feathering among Screech Owls?

Let not what I have just said be construed as indifference: all these "moot" owls need to be studied, *especially the living birds, in the field*. Knowledge of their behavior may give us far better clues to their relationships than comparison of skins has or can. Any owl with unfamiliar callnote ought to be studied with special care, and collected if possible, after careful observations have been recorded.

The following Mexican owls, all of them rather large, *and all but the first allegedly rare*, are not closely related to species found in the United States:

1. Wood Owl (*Ciccaba virgata*). 12 inches. No horns. Toes naked. No striking field-mark. Upper parts dark brown, mottled and barred with buff, especially on the scapulars; tail dusky, barred and tipped with light brownish-gray; buffy line above each eye; under parts buff, mottled on breast and broadly streaked on belly with dusky. Eyes dark brown. Call *boo, boo, boo, boo, boo*, etc., increasing in volume, then dying away. Northern Argentina to Sonora, Zacatecas, Nuevo León, and central Tamaulipas.

2. Black and White Owl (*C. nigrolineata*). 15 inches. No horns. Toes naked. Eyes probably dark brown, but reports differ. Upper parts brownish-black, barred with white on the neck, upper tail coverts, and tail; face black, with row of white spots above eyes; under parts white, heavily barred with black. Ecuador to Veracruz and Oaxaca.

3. Spectacled Owl (*Pulsatrix perspicillata*). 16–18 inches. No horns. Eyes deep yellow. Upper parts, sides of face, and broad chest-band very dark brown; broad line in front of and above eye, dull white; foreneck as far back as ear-coverts, white; belly and under tail coverts buff, sometimes marked with a few dusky bars; tail dark brown, barred indistinctly with buff. Northern Argentina to Oaxaca and Veracruz. A "large black owl" reported from southern Tamaulipas (Frank Harrison) is probably this species.

4. Crested Owl (*Lophostrix cristata*). 15–16 inches. Horns very prominent. Eyes yellow. Upper parts dark brown, almost black on head and back, with bold white line running above each eye through horn; scapulars sparsely barred, and lesser coverts spotted, with buff and white; under parts brown, finely vermiculated with buff; belly

paler than chest. Colombia to Veracruz and Oaxaca.

5. Striped Owl. (*Rhinoptynx clamator*). 13–15 inches long. Horns long. Toes feathered to claws. Eyes brown (Ridgway). Looks very much like a boldly marked Long-eared Owl. Brazil and Peru to Veracruz.

6. Stygian Owl (*Asio stygius*). 15–16 inches long. Horns long. Toes naked. Like a dark Long-eared Owl with comparatively plain upper parts and noticeable herringbone effect of dark markings on buff of belly. Northern Argentina to Sinaloa and Veracruz.

Family Nyctibiidae: Potoos

The Common Potoo (*Nyctibius griseus*) ranges from Paraguay to southern Tamaulipas, Campeche, and Sinaloa (also Jamaica and Hispaniola). It is like a huge gray Whippoorwill with yellow eyes, no "whiskers" to speak of, and the interesting habit of perching bolt upright on a vertical stub. While climbing a slope above the Río Sabinas in southern Tamaulipas I grasped at a slender stump for support only to have the whole top of it fly off—a potoo, no less! Length: 16 inches. Very little known, and much in need of study. Various descriptions of its callnotes do not agree very well. In Trinidad its local name, Poor-me-one, supposedly is imitative of the usual cry. A cry I heard in Tamaulipas was a rough, throaty *baw*.

Family Caprimulgidae: Nighthawks, Whippoorwills and allies

All species of this family listed for the United States are found in Mexico, the Nighthawk or Bullbat (*Chordeiles minor*), Trilling Nighthawk (*C. acutipennis*), Whippoorwill (*Caprimulgus vociferus*), and Poorwill (*Phalaenoptilus nuttalli*) as breeding birds, transients, or winter visitants (or all three); the Chuck-will's-widow (*Caprimulgus carolinensis*) as a transient and winter visitant; and the Pauraque (*Nyctidromus albicollis*) as a resident. The last (pp. 47, 70–71) ranges from Paraguay to southern Texas, the Yucatán peninsula, and Sinaloa.

The following distinctively Mexican species are to be looked for:

1. Salvin's Whippoorwill (*Caprimulgus salvini*). A dark species, about the size of the Whippoorwill, found from Nicaragua to eastern Mexico (Yucatán, southern Ta-maulipas, Nuevo León). Callnote: a rapidly delivered *chip-willow*.

2. Ridgway's Whippoorwill (*C. ridgwayi*). Buffy collar alleged to be diagnostic, but it certainly does not show in the field. Buff bars completely cross the dark primaries, but this is not a field-character either. I have seen the species many times in Michoacán, but never heard it. Honduras to Durango, Sinaloa, and Sonora.

The little Spot-tailed Whippoorwill (*Caprimulgus maculicaudus*), about 6 inches long, ranges widely in northern South America and there is a discrete population in Oaxaca (E. R. Blake). The virtually unknown Eared Poorwill (*Otophanes mcleodi*) has been reported from Chihuahua and Jalisco; the Yucatán Eared Poorwill (*O. yucatanica*) from Yucatán and Guatemala.

Family Apodidae: Swifts

Among the most spectacular of Mexico's swifts is the Cloud Swift or White-collared Swift (*Streptoprocne zonaris*), a bird with wingspread of twenty inches or more and brownish-black with white collar. Visitors to the beautiful waterfall at El Salto, San Luis Potosí sometimes marvel as these birds fly back of the fall in reaching their nesting or roosting places. Along the Río de la Alberca, near Tacámbaro, Michoacán, the Cloud Swifts plunged into a deep gorge at nightfall, shooting down past the brink of a waterfall with breath-taking boldness. Their roosting places were out of sight even in broad daylight because of the vertically zigzag walls the river had worn down through the rock. The Cloud Swift has a wide-range—Bolivia and Argentina north to Veracruz, San Luis Potosí, and the mountains of the Greater Antilles.

The well known Chimney Swift (*Chaetura pelagica*) migrates through eastern Mexico. The smaller Vaux's Swift (*C. vauxi*) breeds from southeastern Alaska to Venezuela. Northern birds migrate through Mexico. The Chestnut-collared Swift (*C. rutila*) ranges from Peru and Guiana to the mountains of Sinaloa, México, and Veracruz. These three species will have to be identified *with great care,* for they are all small and dark.

The Black Swift (*Cypseloides niger*) breeds from southern Alaska to the mountains of Costa Rica (also in the West In-dies) and migrates through Mexico. I have seen great flocks in San Luis Potosí, in which state it may breed.

The White-throated Swift (*Aëronautes saxatilis*) breeds widely in Mexico. I have seen it flying about the bell towers in Morelia, Michoacán. The beautiful Swallow-tailed Swift (*Panyptila cayennensis*), which has been reported from Veracruz (Moore), looks something like a White-throated Swift with very deeply forked tail. The known breeding range of this species is from Honduras to Ecuador and Brazil. The closely related San Geronimo Swift (*P. sancti-hieronymi*) of Guatemala is to be looked for in Chiapas.

The virtually unknown White-naped Swift (*Streptoprocne semicollaris*), which is as large as the Cloud Swift, is black with a white band across the hind neck. It has been reported from Sinaloa, Chihuahua, Morelos, Hidalgo, and Mexico (FGM).

Family Trochilidae: Hummingbirds

Of the fifty hummingbird species on the Mexican Check-List, eighteen have been recorded in the United States. Most of these are discussed in available guides. Many Mexican hummingbirds are, though small, easy to identify, for their shapes or patterns are highly distinctive. In several species adult males, adult females, and young are much alike. Another point in favor of the observer: hummingbirds are often so fearless that they feed at arm's length. At the edge of the spruce forest in the mountains between Pátzcuaro and Tacámbaro, Michoacán, I have sat in the heart of a tangle of giant salvia watching Rivoli's Hummingbirds (*Eugenes fulgens*), Blue-throated Hummingbirds (*Lampornis clemenciae*), Green Violet-ears (*Colibri thalassinus*) and—a blush of chagrin is in order —one or two "unknowns," feeding literally within four or five feet of my eyes among the scarlet flowers!

The following wholly "new" hummingbirds one should be prepared to identify:

1-2. Hermits. The Long-tailed Hermit (*Phaethornis superciliosus*) and Little Hermit (*P. longuemareus*) are dull-colored woodland species with noticeably curved bills and long, light-tipped middle tail feathers. The former (Bolivia and Brazil to Veracruz and Nayarit) is 6½ inches long, grayish-brown above, light buffy-gray below, with grayish-white superciliary line. The tail is 2½ inches long, of which the whole projecting tip (1 inch) is *white*. The latter (eastern Peru to Veracruz, Yucatán, and Oaxaca) is not quite 4 inches long, and the middle tail feathers are only a little longer than the rest. Gray-brown on head and neck, rufous-buff on the belly, with buff superciliary line, rufescent upper tail coverts, and light buff tail-tip.

3-5. Sabre-wings. Rather large hummingbirds with much-stiffened outer primaries and roaring flight. The easily identified Violet Sabre-wing (*Campylopterus hemileucurus*) is the largest (6 inches). Male: rich violet except for wings (dusky with green coverts) and tail (steel-blue with distal half of outer feathers white). Female and young: green above, gray below, with same tail-pattern as male. Panama to Guerrero and Veracruz. The Rufous Sabre-wing (*C. rufus*) is green above, light tan

Mexican Hummingbirds

1. Long-tailed Hermit (*Phaethornis superciliosus*), 6½ inches. 2. Dupont's Hummingbird, male (*Tilmatura duponti*), 3¼ inches. 3. Violet-crowned Hummingbird (*Amazilia violiceps*), 4 inches. 4. Violet Sabre-wing, male (*Campylopterus hemileucurus*), 6 inches.

below, with tan tail-edge and -corners (5 inches). El Salvador to mountains of Chiapas. The Wedge-tailed Sabre-wing (*C. curvipennis*) is green above, gray below, with blue gloss on tail and brilliant purplish-blue forehead and crown (5½ inches). It is sometimes called the Singing Hummingbird. Its spirited squealing, squeaking, and chippering is well worth *watching*: the bird turns and twists, putting much energy into its "song." Guatemala to Yucatán and southern Tamaulipas.

6. White-necked Jacobin (*Florisuga mellivora*). 4½ inches. Male: head rich blue, with white band across hind neck; upper part of body, including sides, rich green; belly, flanks, and under tail coverts pure white; two middle rectrices green, rest of tail white, narrowly tipped with black. Female: green above; pure white on belly and flanks; throat feathers with dusky cen-

ters and light tips, producing a scaled effect; tail *tipped* with white, very narrowly in middle to very broadly on outer pairs. Brazil and Peru to Oaxaca and Veracruz.

7. Green Violet-ear (*Colibri thalassinus*). 4¼ inches. Green with violet auriculars and blue-violet patch in middle of lower breast and belly; tail green-blue with dark subterminal band and clear pale blue tip. Female duller. Peru and Bolivia to mountains of San Luis Potosí and Jalisco.

8. Prevost's Mango (*Anthracothorax prevosti*). 5 inches. Described on page 180. El Salvador to Yucatán peninsula and central Tamaulipas.

9. Abeillé's Hummingbird (*Abeillia abeillei*). 3 inches. Bill straight and short for a hummingbird. Male: green with glittering green gorget and blue-black tail. Female: green above, gray below, middle tail feathers green, the rest blue-black with

213

gray tips. Nicaragua to Oaxaca and Veracruz.

10. Fork-tailed Emerald (*Chlorostilbon caniveti*). 3¼ to 4 inches, some races being much longer-tailed than others. Bill straight and rather short for hummingbird; tail forked, noticeably so in male. Tuft of downy, pure white feathers on leg. Male: green, more sparkling on crown and under parts; throat somewhat bluish in certain lights; tail blue-black, tipped with brownish-gray. Female: green above, gray below, with dark gray auriculars and white line back of eye; four middle tail feathers blue-green, the rest gray basally, steel-blue subterminally, and white-tipped. Colombia and Venezuela to Sinaloa, Durango, southern Tamaulipas, and Yucatán. In the race found from Sinaloa to Guerrero (*auriceps*) the crown of the male is brilliant golden yellow and the tail long and very deeply forked. The race found on islands off the Yucatán coast (*forficatus*) is larger and the outer tail feathers broader and less tapering. In the vicinity of Tamazunchale, San Luis Potosí, individuals of the comparatively short-tailed nominate race are to be seen on telephone wires along the highway.

11. Dusky Hummingbird (*Cynanthus sordidus*). 3½ inches. One of the dullest of Mexico's hummers. Bronze-green above, dullest on forehead, crown, and upper tail coverts; a light gray spot back of eye; under parts deep gray except for white tufts on legs. Tail in male gray basally, bronzy-green through terminal half; in female middle four feathers bronzy-green, the rest black subterminally, tipped with pale brownish-gray. Oaxaca and Guerrero to Hidalgo, Puebla, and Jalisco.

12–19. Amazilias. Species of the genus *Amazilia* are middle-sized and not very bright-colored. Bill nearly straight and in many species *red*. Tail not conspicuously forked or patterned. One species, the Yucatán Hummingbird (*A. yucatanensis*) ranges from British Honduras northward to Yucatán and southern Texas. The northernmost race, the Buff-bellied Yucatán Hummingbird (*A. y. chalconota*), I have described on page 108. The very similar

Rufous-tailed Hummingbird (*A. tzacatl*), which differs in being darker and in having gray belly and chestnut lores, ranges from Colombia to southern Tamaulipas (casually to southern Texas). The Berylline Hummingbird (*A. beryllina*) is rich sparking green except for the wings (purplish-black; secondaries chestnut basally), under tail coverts (rufous), and tail (dark purplish-brown with coppery, bronze, and purple reflections). El Salvador and Honduras to southern Sonora, southern Chihuahua, and Veracruz. The Cinnamomeous Hummingbird (*A. rutilis*) is dull green above, plain tan below, with green-tipped rufous tail. Costa Rica to Yucatán, Durango, and Sinaloa. The Red-billed Azurecrown (*A. cyanocephala*) is brilliant blue on the crown, pure white on the throat and middle of the breast and belly, green otherwise. Nicaragua to Yucatán peninsula, Oaxaca, and southern Tamaulipas. The Blue-tailed Hummingbird (*A. cyanura*) is deep green above, sparkling grass-green below, with metallic blue-violet tail. Guatemala to Chiapas. The Violet-crowned Hummingbird (*A. violiceps*) is violet or violet-blue on the crown, dull bronze-green on the rest of the upper parts (glossed with purple on the tail), and pure white underneath. Chiapas to Sonora and Chihuahua (has been taken in Arizona). The White-bellied Emerald (*A. candida*), one of the plainest of the genus, is green above and plain white below (except for a few shining green spots on the sides of the throat and chest). Costa Rica to Yucatán peninsula, Oaxaca, and San Luis Potosí.

20. Striped-tailed Hummingbird (*Eupherusa eximia*). 4 inches. Male: deep green above, glittering grass-green below, secondaries rufous with dusky tips; under tail coverts white; tail black except for white of basal two-thirds of two outermost pairs of feathers. Female: similar, but gray below, secondaries without dusky tips, and less white on tail. Panama to Guerrero and Veracruz.

21–22. Blue-throated Hummingbird and allies. The Amethyst-throated Hummingbird (*Lampornis amethystinus*) has a shining purple gorget, dull green upper parts, gray breast and belly, and a grayish-white spot back of the eye. 4¾ inches. Female similar, but *brown*-throated. Honduras to Nayarit and southern Tamaulipas. The Green-throated Mountain Gem (*L. viridi-pallens*) is about the same size, green above, grayish-white below, each throat feather of the male with a shining *pale* green tip. Female similar but white-throated and tail corners gray. Honduras to mountains of Chiapas.

23. Garnet-throated Hummingbird (*Lam-prolaima rhami*). 4¾ inches. Male green above, with rufous wings (primaries tipped with dusky) and purplish-black tail; gorget gleaming purplish-rose color, bordered at either side by velvety black; chest shining blue; sides and belly black; under tail coverts blue-black edged with white. Female similar but under parts plain gray.

El Salvador and Honduras to Guerrero, México, and Veracruz.

24–25. Star-throats. Two species, both with rather long, heavy bills, occur in Mexico. The Long-billed Star-throat (*Helio-master longirostris*). 4½ inches. Male has glittering blue-green crown and rich rose gorget, the latter bordered at either side by a streak of light gray; upper parts otherwise green; under parts gray, palest in middle, green on sides. Tail blue-black, the outer pairs tipped with white. Female similar, but throat dusky and crown green. Bolivia to Oaxaca, Guerrero, and Veracruz. The Plain-capped Star-throat (*H. constanti*). Similar, but no shining crown-patch in male. In both sexes throat feathers orange-red to rose-red, edged with pale gray. Costa Rica to Durango and southern Sonora.

26–27. Shear-tails. Two species inhabit Mexico. In both, the males have deeply

Mexican Hummingbirds (males)
1. White-necked Jacobin (*Florisuga mellivora*), 4½ inches. 2. Fork-tailed Emerald (*Chlorostilbon caniveti*), 3½ inches. 3. Bumblebee Hummingbird (*Atthis heloisa*), 2½ inches. 4. Long-billed Star-throat (*Heliomaster longirostris*), 4½ inches.

forked tails. Male Slender Shear-tail (*Doricha enicura*) is black on chin with violet gorget and long outermost tail feathers are black. Under parts of female cinnamon-buff. Eastern Salvador and Honduras to mountains of Chiapas. Male Mexican Shear-tail (*D. eliza*) has reddish-purple gorget, and outermost rectrices are broadly edged with tan along inner webs. Female dull buffy-white below. Veracruz, Tabasco, and Yucatán peninsula (drier parts).

28. Dupont's Hummingbird (*Tilmatura duponti*). Male (3¼ inches) green above and on belly; gorget feathers black basally, tipped with violet-blue; chest buffy-white; tail long and deeply forked, the middle two feathers green, the outer ones blue-black tipped and banded with white, the outermost with bold band of rufous (proximally) and white halfway to the tip. Female short-tailed and under parts cinnamon-buff throughout. Nicaragua to Veracruz and Jalisco.

29. Beautiful Hummingbird (*Calothorax pulcher*). Much like the Lucifer Hummingbird (*C. lucifer*), which ranges into the United States, but in male tail longer and outer rectrices broader, with rounded (not pointed) tips. Chiapas to Puebla and Guerrero.

30–31. Bumblebee Hummingbird (*Atthis heloisa*). 2½ inches. Male: beautiful rose-violet gorget; green above and white on belly; tail blue-black with rufous base and white corners. Female: more black in tail; throat spotted with metallic bronze; sides rufous. Honduras to Tamaulipas, Nuevo León, southern Sinaloa, and southern Chihuahua. These tiny hummingbirds may be of two species; those of northern races (outermost primary narrowed at the tip) have been widely known as Heloise's Hummingbird; those from Chiapas, Guatemala, and Honduras (outermost primary not narrowed at tip) have been called Elliot's Hummingbird.

Family Trogonidae: Trogons

Red on belly and under tail coverts

1. Coppery-tailed Trogon (*Trogon elegans*). 12 inches. Described on pages 115–16 and 122; adult male shown in Plate IX. Costa Rica to Río Grande Valley and mountains of southern Arizona.

2. Mexican Trogon (*T. mexicanus*). Like Coppery-tail, but in tail of male middle feathers glossy green and three outer pairs boldly tipped with white squares. Female without white on sides of head or white chest-band; brown of breast fades into pink of lower belly and under tail coverts. Guatemala to mountains of Chihuahua and central Tamaulipas.

3. Barred-tailed Trogon (*T. collaris*). Like Coppery-tail, but male shining green above (including middle tail feathers) and outer rectrices black, *narrowly barred with white;* female without white on sides of head, and outer tail feathers largely white with narrow but distinct subterminal black band. Northern South America to Veracruz, San Luis Potosí, Yucatán peninsula, and Oaxaca.

4. Massena Trogon (*T. massena*). 13½ inches. Tail *wholly dark.* Male green on head, neck, back, rump, and middle tail feathers, with red belly and under tail coverts; female plain gray except for red of lower belly and under tail coverts. Colombia to Veracruz, Campeche, and Oaxaca.

5. Eared Trogon (*Euptilotis neoxenus*). A large species with rather slender bill and feathers on sides of nape long and slender, forming "ears." Male: shining green above and on chest, passing to blue-green on rump and deep shining blue on middle tail feathers; three outer pairs of rectrices boldly tipped with white; belly and under tail coverts bright red; flanks black. Female: similar, but head slate (brownish on cheeks, chin and throat) fading to light gray on chest; red of under parts less intense than in male. Michoacán to Zacatecas and Chihuahua.

6. Quetzal (*Pharomachrus moccino*). Adult male: gorgeous golden green to green-blue head and upper parts, long, curled wing coverts, excessively long, wavy upper tail coverts, and brilliant red belly

unmistakable. Female and young: no elongate upper tail coverts; gray on belly. Costa Rica to high mountains of Chiapas.

Yellow or orange on belly and under tail coverts

7. Citreoline Trogon (*Trogon citreolus*). 12 inches. Male: dark gray on head, chest, and wings; green on back; blue on rump and upper tail coverts; and green-blue on middle tail feathers. Outer three pairs of rectrices boldly tipped with white squares. Lower chest white, fading into orange-yellow of belly and under tail coverts. Female: similar but duller; white tipping of outer tail feathers more extensive and less squared-off in effect. Costa Rica to Sinaloa,

southern Tamaulipas, and Yucatán peninsula. Eastern Mexican race widely known as Black-headed Trogon.

8. Violaceous Trogon (*T. violaceus*). 9½ inches. Male: black on head and neck, passing into rich purple-blue on lower throat and chest; back, rump, upper tail coverts, and middle tail feathers greenish-blue, the latter tipped with velvet black. Outer pairs of rectrices white-tipped and barred with white subterminally. Belly and under tail coverts yellow-orange. Female: gray on head, chest, and upper part of body, including tail; wing feathers with narrow white bars. Northern South America to southern Tamaulipas, eastern San Luis Potosí, and Yucatán peninsula.

Family Alcedinidae: KINGFISHERS

The Belted Kingfisher (*Megaceryle alcyon*) is not known to breed in Mexico, but it is widely distributed there as a transient and winter visitant.

The much larger Ringed Kingfisher (*M. torquata*), which I have discussed (p. 110), ranges from Tierra del Fuego to the West Indies, southern Sinaloa, Nuevo León, and central Tamaulipas.

The Amazon Kingfisher (*Chloroceryle amazona*) is about the size of the Belted but dark glossy green above and white below, the male with broad rufous chestband, the female with dark green chestband. The species ranges widely through South America and northward to southern Tamaulipas and Sinaloa.

The Green Kingfisher (*C. americana*) which I have discussed (pp. 62, 65–66, 71) and figured, ranges from Paraguay and southern Brazil to southern Texas and southern Arizona.

The Pygmy Kingfisher (*C. aenea*), which is only 5½ inches long, is dark glossy green above (with white spotting in the scapulars and larger wing and tail feathers); orange-buff on the throat; bright rufous on the sides and flanks; and white on the belly and under tail coverts. In the male the chest is also bright rufous; but in the female there is a greenish-black chest-band. Ranges from northern South America to Yucatán peninsula, Veracruz, and Oaxaca.

Family Momotidae: MOTMOTS

Larger species (14–17 inches) with racket-tipped tail

1. Blue-crowned Motmot (*Momotus momota*). Crown wholly blue and under parts green in northernmost race, *coeruliceps* (discussed on pp. 135, 181), but in some races crown black surrounded by blue, and under parts more or less extensively rufous. Auriculars and tear-shaped spot in chest black. South and Central America northward to Yucatán peninsula, Oaxaca, Nuevo León, and central Tamaulipas.

2. Russet-crowned Motmot (*M. mexicanus*). Under parts light greenish-blue, with black spot in middle of chest; top of head and hind neck orange-russet, with black and blue auricular patch, pale blue back and rump, and blue wings and tail. Guatemala to extreme southern Sonora, Durango, Zacatecas, and Puebla.

3. Keel-billed Motmot (*Electron carinatum*). Bill decurved, flattened, and broad. Top of head and hind neck green; superciliary region bright blue; lores, area

about eyes, auriculars and chest-spot black; back, scapulars, and rump olive-green; under parts light olive-green washed with cinnamon. Costa Rica to Veracruz.

4. Turquoise-browed Motmot (*Eumomota superciliosa*). 14 inches (tail 8 inches). Most notable feature of plumage: the slightly irridescent pale turquoise blue patch or "brow" above each eye. Middle of chin and throat black, bordered at either side by pale blue line. Lores and elongate ear coverts black, bordered below by narrow pale blue line. Most of wings and tail rich turquoise blue, but tip and under side of tail black. Belly, sides, under tail coverts, and middle of back rufous. Rest of plumage brownish-green. Central America to Yucatán peninsula, Veracruz, and Oaxaca.

Smaller species having no rackets on tail

5. Blue-throated Motmot (*Aspatha gularis*). 11 inches. Green with bright blue throat; spot of blue on belly; blue tail-tip; black auriculars; small spot of black on lower throat; and orange-buff area about eyes. Tail strikingly graduated, the outermost feathers being much less than a third as long as the middle pair. Central America to Chiapas.

6. Tody Motmot (*Hylomanes momotula*). 7 inches. In general green, with rufous crown (brighter behind than in front), bright blue superciliary spot, black auriculars, buffy-white lores and throat, and grayish-white belly and under tail coverts. Central America to Veracruz.

Family Galbulidae: JACAMARS

One species found in Mexico—the Rufous-tailed Jacamar (*Galbula ruficauda*). 10 inches. Shining green on upper parts (including middle tail feathers), and rufous on belly, under tail coverts, and outer tail feathers. Throat white in male, buff in female. Bill about two inches long and sharp, slender, and straight. Look for the species in dense woods. Northern South America to Veracruz and Chiapas.

Family Bucconidae: PUFF-BIRDS

The Puff-birds are rather large-headed, soft-plumaged birds with a reputation for sitting stupidly on dead branches while waiting for insects to fly past. They perch upright and look something like kingfishers. They are not bright-colored, but some species are boldly black and white. The sexes are alike. Two species inhabit Mexico.

1. Large-billed Puff-bird (*Notharchus hyperrhynchus*). 9½ inches. Top of head, lores, back, rump, wings, tail, broad chestband, and bars on the flanks glossy bluish-black; the upper tail coverts, rump, and wing plumage narrowly edged with white; forehead, noticeable collar, belly, and under tail coverts white, tinged with buff. Eyes dark red. Bill black. Often perches in very top of high dead tree at edge of forest (van Rossem). Oaxaca and Chiapas to northern South America.

2. Soft-wing (*Malacoptila panamensis*). 7¾ inches. Grayish-brown above, brightening to chestnut or rufous on rump and upper tail coverts. Crown, hind neck, back, and wing coverts spotted, and forehead, ear coverts, and sides of the neck streaked, with buff. Plumage of chin and malar region long and rather shaggy, brown, streaked with white. Middle of throat and chest plain buff; rest of under parts buffy-white, streaked with dusky on chest and sides. Eye red. Bill about as long as head, rather sharply pointed, and curved downward at tip. Usually seen on bare branches not far from ground in the forest. Tabasco and Chiapas to northern South America.

Family Ramphastidae: TOUCANS

The Emerald Toucanet (*Aulacorhynchus prasinus*) is Mexico's only green toucan. It is 15 inches long, with black and yellow bill (see Plate XVI), white throat, and chestnut under tail coverts and tail-tip. Central America to Veracruz, eastern San Luis Potosí, and Guerrero. I have seen it among large trees along the highway just south of Tamazunchale, San Luis Potosí.

The somewhat larger (16 inches) Collared Aracari (*Pteroglossus torquatus*) ranges from northern South America to the Yucatán peninsula, Veracruz, and Oaxaca. Bill boldly black and white. In general dark on whole head and upper parts, mixed yellow and red on under parts, with black chest-spot and *black band across the belly*. Rump and upper tail coverts red. Chestnut "collar" across upper back is not conspicuous.

The largest Mexican toucan is the Keel-billed or "Banana-billed" (*Ramphastos sul-*

Collared Aracari Toucan (*Pteroglossus torquatus*)
16 inches

furatus). It has a huge bill (greenish-yellow with red tip) and is black with bright yellow throat, white upper tail coverts, and red under tail coverts. It ranges from northern South America to Veracruz, eastern San Luis Potosí, and Oaxaca. I have seen it along the Río Axtla, just north of Tamazunchale.

Family Picidae: Woodpeckers

Many woodpeckers are found both in the United States and Mexico, notably the Red-shafted Flicker (*Colaptes cafer*), which breeds and winters widely in the mountains (among winter birds are individuals of races breeding north of Mexico); the Hairy Woodpecker (*Dendrocopos villosus*), which is montane, non-migratory, and black *and brown* rather than black and white from Veracruz, Puebla, and Michoacán southward; the Ladder-backed Woodpecker (*D. scalaris*), which I have discussed and figured; the Nuttall's Woodpecker (*D. nuttalli*), which inhabits northwestern Baja California; the Arizona Woodpecker (*D. arizonae*), which breeds southward to Michoacán; the Acorn Woodpecker (*Balanosphyra formicivora*), which breeds in montane parts of Mexico; the Golden-fronted Woodpecker (*Centurus aurifrons*), which breeds widely, being represented by several geographical races; the Gila Woodpecker (*C. uropygialis*) which breeds southward to Jalisco and probably Michoacán; the Lewis's Woodpecker (*Asyndesmus lewis*), which winters in northwestern Mexico; the Yellow-bellied Sapsucker (*Sphyrapicus varius*) which winters throughout the republic; and the Williamson's Sapsucker (*S. thyroideus*), which winters south to Jalisco and Durango. The not-very-well-known Gilded Flicker (*Colaptes chrysoïdes*) breeds in Baja California, Sonora, and Sinaloa.

Of the above-named species the most puzzling is apt to be the Golden-fronted, for there are many different "golden-fronts" in Mexico. The form that most bird students know from experience in Texas is pale gray below. The distinctively Mexican races and allied species are darker, some conspicuously so. In some races of *aurifrons,* notably *grateloupensis* (southern Tamaulipas to central Veracruz) and *polygrammus* (Chiapas and Oaxaca) no band of gray separates the red crown-patch from the orange of the nape. In Yucatán there is a difficult-to-understand overlapping of *two* "golden-fronts," both red-bellied rather than yellow-bellied, one small (7 inches), the other large (10 inches). To me the small one (*rubricomus*) appears to represent *aurifrons,* while the large one (*dubius*), with its wholly red pileum and exceedingly fine white back-barring, seems to be a distinct species. Milton Trautman informs me that the two birds inhabit the same general areas, the smaller feeding in the lower, more open woods; the larger in the big forest. The so-called Golden-cheeked Woodpecker (*Centurus chrysogenys*), which ranges from Sinaloa to Oaxaca, has the general appearance of a Golden-front; but the whole face, above and below, and the rear part of the crown are golden yellow, and a narrow black ring encircles the eye.

The Gila Woodpecker and its allies are puzzling too. Peters lists eight races, all Mexican or partly so. To me the most southward-ranging of these, *hypopolius* (Gray-breasted Woodpecker), seems to be a separate species if for no other reason than that it has a partly concealed patch of red under the eye. This bird ranges from Puebla and Morelos to Guerrero and Oaxaca.

Now for the distinctively Mexican woodpeckers—those having no very close relatives in the United States. Three of these I have discussed and figured—the Flint-billed (*Phloeoceastes guatemalensis*), Lineated (*Dryocopus lineatus*), and Bronzed (*Piculus aeruginosus*). The Flint-billed ranges from Central America to central Tamaulipas, the Yucatán peninsula, and Sinaloa; the Lineated from northern Argentina to central Tamaulipas, Nuevo León, and southern Sinaloa; the Bronzed from Puebla and northern Veracruz to central Nuevo León and southern Tamaulipas. The distribution of the last is puzzling. In Nuevo León it does not inhabit the lowlands apparently; but along the Sabinas, in southern Tamaulipas, it is fairly common at river level as well as in the foothills to the west. It may be a geographical race of the Ruddy-green Woodpecker (*P. rubiginosus*), a very similar species which differs in having the markings of the under parts clear-cut bars rather than spots. Range: northern South America to Yucatán peninsula, southern Veracruz, and Oaxaca. The Gray-crowned Woodpecker (*P. auricularis*) is also similar to the Bronzed, but the top of the head is gray, wholly without red in either sex. It ranges from Guerrero to southern Sonora. If the three forms above discussed are to be considered one species, they probably should be called the Ruddy-green Woodpecker, not only because the name *rubiginosus* antedates the other two, but also because the name "ruddy-green" suits the group quite well.

The following species need special discussion:

1. Strickland's Woodpecker (*Dendrocopos stricklandi*). Size and general appearance of Downy Woodpecker, but dark parts of plumage dark *brown,* not black; under parts heavily streaked with brown; and middle of back barred with white. Mountains of Veracruz and Puebla to the Federal District, México, and Michoacán. I have seen this species near Río Frío, at an elevation of over 13,000 feet, along the highway between Mexico City and Puebla.

2. Smoky Woodpecker (*Veniliornis fumigatus*). Size of Downy. Dark brown, washed with golden yellow on back, scapulars, sides, and wings. A vague buff streak below eye. Pileum red in male. Bolivia to southern Tamaulipas, Puebla, and Oaxaca. Fairly common in the beautiful forests about the Rancho del Cielo, near Gomez Farias, Tamaulipas. It is so dark, and quiet so much of the time, that it can easily be missed.

3. Chestnut-colored Woodpecker (*Celeus castaneus*). 10 inches. Conspicuously crested. Warm chestnut-brown all over, lighter and unmarked on head, inconspicuously spotted and barred with black elsewhere except on the tail and larger wing feathers. Large red area below eye in male. Costa Rica to Yucatán peninsula, Veracruz, and Oaxaca.

4. Black-cheeked Woodpecker (*Tripsurus pucherani*). 7½ inches. Forehead yellow. Top of head red except for black spot directly above eye and white area back of eye. Sides of head black. Under parts, except for red of belly, olive-brown barred with black. Rump and upper tail coverts white. Rest of body black, the back barred, and the wings and tail sparsely spotted, with white. Northern South America to Veracruz, Puebla, and Oaxaca.

5. Imperial Ivory-bill (*Campephilus imperialis*). One of the largest woodpeckers of the world. About as long as a Raven, and black with large white patch in each wing. Male's crest is scarlet and somewhat recurved. Female's whole head is black, but her crest is long and very strongly recurved. Inhabits the mountains from Michoacán to Durango, Chihuahua, and Sonora. Very rare.

Family Dendrocolaptidae: Woodcreepers

All woodcreepers of Mexico, males, females, adults and young alike, are rufous (unbarred) on the larger wing and tail feathers and rump. The first species one is apt to see in travelling southward along the main highway from Laredo to Mexico City is the Ivory-billed Woodcreeper (*Xiphorhynchus flavigaster*), described and figured on pp. 149–50. It ranges from Costa Rica to southern Tamaulipas, the Yucatán peninsula, and Sinaloa. Its alarm cry is a lively *feed-le* or *feed-ler*. Its song, a series of loud notes, produces a rising and falling effect—a matter of volume as well as of pitch—at times sounding much like that of Canyon Wren.

2. The smaller (8½ inches) Spotted-crowned Woodcreeper (*Lepidocolaptes affinis*) ranges north to Victoria, Tamaulipas, but I have never seen it in low

country thereabouts. Along the Río Sabinas, near Gomez Farias, Tamaulipas, I have seen it at river level in winter and spring, but I believe it nests at higher elevations. Its throat is plain buff. Otherwise it is woods brown, spotted on the crown and streaked throughout the breast and belly with buff, the streaks being tear-shaped and narrowly edged with black. Song: *sue swee-tswee-tswee,* very different from the rise and fall song of *Xiphorhynchus* (Martin). Bolivia

to central Tamaulipas, México, and Guerrero.

3. The Streaked-headed Woodcreeper (*L. souleyeti*) is very much like the above except that the top of the head is *streaked* rather than spotted. There may well be differences in behavior, but I do not know of them. Northern South America to Veracruz and Guerrero.

4. The beautiful White-striped Woodcreeper (*L. leucogaster*) is buffy-white on

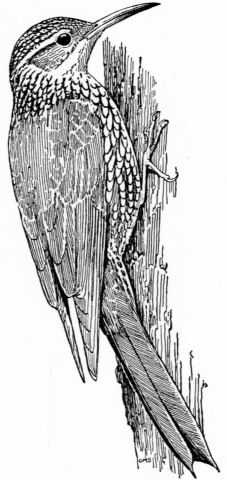

White-striped Woodcreeper (*Lepidocolaptes leucogaster*)
9 inches

the face and under parts, finely streaked with black on the breast, sides, and belly. Length: 9 inches. Oaxaca to San Luis Potosí, Veracruz, Zacatecas, Durango, and Sonora. A well defined species, strictly endemic to Mexico.

5. Spotted Woodcreeper (*Xiphorhynchus erythropygius*). 8 inches. Olive-brown (rufescent on wings, rump, and tail), *spotted* throughout head, neck, back, and under parts with grayish-buff. Colombia and Ecuador to Veracruz and Guerrero (Peters).

6. Ruddy Woodcreeper (*Dendrocincla homochroa*). 7½ inches. Bill straight and rather short. Rich reddish-brown all over, without markings. Venezuela to Yucatán peninsula and Oaxaca.

7. Tawny-winged Woodcreeper (*D. anabatina*). 7½ inches. Dark olive-brown except for tawny rectrices and remiges, buff chin, and small buff spots on throat and chest. Tawny of wings shows plainly in flight (Eisenmann). Bill straight and rather short. Panama to Yucatán peninsula, Veracruz, and Oaxaca.

8. Barred Woodcreeper (*Dendrocolaptes*

certhia). 10 inches. Rather long, heavy bill. Wings and tail rufous; otherwise barred all over with black and brown, the bars of about equal width. The only *barred* woodcreeper of Mexico. Brazil and Bolivia to Campeche and Veracruz.

9. Strong-billed Woodcreeper (*Xiphocolaptes promeropirhynchus*). 12 inches. Largest Mexican woodcreeper. Wings and tail rufous; plumage otherwise olive-brown, darkest on crown, and fading to buff on throat and chin. Head, neck, and breast rather finely streaked with buff. Bolivia to Veracruz and Guerrero.

10. Wedge-bill (*Glyphorynchus spirurus*). 5½ inches. Bill short, straight, and very sharp, somewhat upturned. Olive-brown save for wings and tail, which are rufous, and throat and upper breast which are marked with triangular spots of buff. Bolivia and Brazil to Veracruz.

11. Olivaceous Woodcreeper (*Sittasomus griseicapillus*). 5¾ inches. Olive-gray on head, under parts, and upper back, fading into rufous on lower back, wings, and tail. Paraguay and Bolivia to southern Tamaulipas, Yucatán peninsula, and Jalisco.

Family Furnariidae: Ovenbirds

The Mexican species of this family are much in need of study. Common names used here are provisional. I have never seen a "leaf-scraper," so don't know whether the bird scrapes leaves or not, but Hellmayr and others have used the name. The relationships of the Furnariidae to the Dendrocolaptidae are poorly understood at best. One species of those discussed below, the so-called Scaly-throated Tree-hunter, has a somewhat stiffened tail, and may be a woodcreeper.

1. Rufous-breasted Spinetail (*Synallaxis erythrothorax*). 6 inches. Rufous on chest, sides, rump, and tail; dark brownish-gray on head and back; ashy-gray on middle of belly, with indefinite patch of grayish-white streaks in mid-throat. Central America to Yucatán peninsula, Veracruz, and Oaxaca.

2. Little or Plain Xenops (*Xenops minutus*). 4½ inches. Tail short. Olive-brown

with rufous wings and tail, light gray throat, buff superciliary line, and short, silvery white malar stripe. Bill short and slightly upturned. Bolivia and Brazil to Yucatán peninsula, Veracruz, and Oaxaca.

3. Scaly-throated Tree-hunter (*Anabacerthia striaticollis*). 6 inches. Bill short, rather heavy, and slightly upturned. Tail rather long and spine-tipped. Brown, toward grayish on crown and hind neck, buffy on throat, and rufescent on wings and tail, with fairly conspicuous buff superciliary line. Throat vaguely scaled with dusky. Bolivia and Peru to Veracruz and Guerrero. Feeds about tips of branches in manner of chickadee or warbler rather than creeping about trunk like woodcreeper (Edwards).

4. Ruddy-throated Automolus (*Automolus rubiginosus*). 8½ inches. Reddish-brown above and on chest, rich reddish-

Rufous-breasted Spinetail (*Synallaxis erythrothorax*)
6 inches

buff on throat, olive-brown on belly. Bill rather long and straight. Northern South America to Veracruz and Guerrero.

5. Buff-throated Automolus (*Automolus ochrolaemus*). 8 inches. Olive-brown with rufous tail, buff superciliary, and clear orange-buff throat. Northern South America to Veracruz and Oaxaca.

6. Tawny-throated Leaf-scraper (*Sclerurus mexicanus*). 7½ inches. Rich dark olive-brown with rufous throat, breast, and upper tail coverts. Northern South America to Veracruz, México, and Chiapas.

7. Scaly-throated Leaf-scraper (*S. guatemalensis*). 7 inches. Dark olive-brown in general. Feathers of throat grayish-white with dark edges; those of breast rufous medially. Northern South America to Veracruz and Tabasco.

Family Formicariidae: Antbirds

The northernmost species of this family, the Barred Antshrike (*Thamnophilus doliatus*), is fairly common in brushy tangles along the Río Sabinas in southern Tamaulipas. Its pretty song—a series of rapidly descending liquid notes, almost trilled—is to be heard along the main highway in dry lowlands from about kilometer mark 600 southward. The male (see figure) is unmistakable, but the female is plain rufous above and tan below, unbarred. 7 inches. Southern Tamaulipas and Yucatán to Bolivia and Brazil.

2. Dusky Antbird (*Cercomacra tyran-*

nina). 5½ inches. Male dark gray; female olive-gray above, rufous-buff below. In both sexes a largely concealed patch of pure white in the back. Northern South America to Veracruz and Chiapas.

3. Dotted-winged Antwren (*Microrhopias quixensis*). 4¼ inches. Male glossy black with white spots on wing coverts and tips of tail feathers; female gray above, rich rufous below, with white markings similar to those of male. Both with partly concealed spot of pure white in back. Brazil and Peru to Veracruz and Oaxaca.

4. Russet Antshrike (*Thamnistes ana-*

batinus). 5½ inches. Sexes alike. Tawny-olive above, brightening to rufous on wings and tail; a faint yellowish-gray superciliary line; spot in middle of back orange-rufous, bordered behind by inconspicuous, interrupted black bar. Under parts yellowish-gray, deepening to tawny-olive on chest and sides. Tabasco to northern South America.

5. Great Antshrike (*Taraba major*). 8 inches. Male black above, white below, with white spots on tips of lesser wing coverts; female rufous above, white below. Argentina to Veracruz and Tabasco.

The above-named species feed in shrubbery and low trees for the most part. The following are almost wholly terrestrial.

6. Black-faced Antthrush (*Formicarius analis*). 7½ inches. Tail short. Dark brown above, dark ashy-gray below. Lores, malar region, chin, and throat black (except for light spot in lores), bordered behind by band of dark rufous; under tail coverts rufescent; belly whitish. Northern South America to Yucatán peninsula, Veracruz, and Oaxaca.

7. Scaled Antpitta (*Grallaria guatimalensis*). 8 inches. Tail stubby; body about size of Bob-white's. Upper parts olive-brown, toward gray on crown, toward rufous on wings and tail. Crown and back feathers edged with dusky, producing scaled effect. Under parts orange-buff in some races, pale

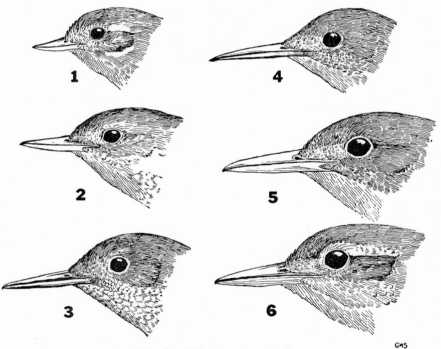

GMS

Heads of Mexican Ovenbirds

1. Plain Xenops (*Xenops minutus*), 4½ inches. 2. Scaly-throated Tree-hunter (*Anabercerthia striaticollis*), 6 inches. 3. Scaly-throated Leaf-scraper (*Sclerurus guatemalensis*), 7 inches. 4. Tawny-throated Leaf-scraper (*Sclerurus mexicanus*), 7½ inches. 5. Ruddy-throated Automolus (*Automolus rubiginosus*), 8½ inches. 6. Buff-throated Automolus (*Automolus ochrolaemus*), 8 inches.

Barred Antshrike, male (*Thamnophilus doliatus*)
7 inches

yellowish-buff in others, lightest (sometimes buffy-white) on lores and throat. A more or less complete band of black spots across chest. Northern South America to Jalisco, Morelos, and Veracruz.

Family Cotingidae: Cotingas

One of Mexico's most beautiful birds is the Lovely Cotinga (*Cotinga amabilis*), which ranges from Costa Rica to Veracruz and Oaxaca. 7¼ inches. Male bright blue with much black in the wings and tail, dark purple throat, and dark purple chest-patch. Female gray, lighter below than above, spotted with dusky on breast and sides.

The most northward-ranging species of the family, the Rose-throated Becard (*Platypsaris aglaiae*), I have discussed (pp. 13–15, 24, 96, 99, 123) and figured. It breeds in small numbers just north of the border in Arizona and Texas. A bird of lowland forests, it often feeds in shrubbery near the ground but prefers high trees near water for nesting. It ranges eastward to Yucatán and southward to Costa Rica. In all Mexican races the throat of the adult male is red.

Another cotinga which I have discussed (p. 159) and figured is the Masked Tityra

226

(*Tityra semifasciata*). 9 inches. Bolivia and Peru to southern Tamaulipas, Yucatán, and Sinaloa.

The Black-crowned Tityra (*Tityra inquisitor*) resembles the above quite closely but is smaller (7½ inches) and has no naked red area about the eye. Male black throughout forehead and crown; female black on crown, white on forehead, rufous on auriculars. Argentina and Paraguay to Yucatán, Veracruz, and Oaxaca. Both this species and the above inhabit Yucatán, but whether they live side by side in the same woodlands I cannot say.

The Black-capped Becard (*Pachyramphus major*), sometimes called the Mexican Becard, is found from Central America to Yucatán, southern Tamaulipas, Nuevo León, and Sinaloa. 6 inches. Male, blue-black above, ashy-gray below, with gray rump and hind neck, white stripe down each side of back, white wing-edgings and tail-tipping. Female, tan above, dull greenish-yellow below, with black crown; wings and tail mostly brownish-black; outer tail feathers black basally, broadly tipped with tan (tail-pattern noticeable as bird flies, for tan of tip becomes orange in bright light).

Little known species are: *Lipaugus unirufus* (northern South America to Veracruz), *Rhytipterna holerythra* (northern South America to Oaxaca) and *Attila spadiceus* (Bolivia and Brazil to Yucatán, Veracruz, Puebla, and Sinaloa). In all these the sexes are alike. The first two are plain rufous all over (*L. unirufus* being 10 inches long, *R. holerythra* a little under 8); the last, sometimes called the Polymorphic Attila (8 inches), varies from olive to rufous above and from white to yellow below, but always has a yellow rump and gray streaking on the chest. Hellmayr has called *L. unirufus* the Rufous Piha and *R. holerythra* the Rufous Mourner. For me these names are meaningless, for I know nothing about the birds.

Family Pipridae: Manakins

Four Manakins range northward into Mexico. They are easy to tell apart, females of the Yellow-thighed and Long-tailed species being alike in color, but the latter has *very long* middle tail feathers.

1. Yellow-thighed Manakin (*Pipra mentalis*). 4¼ inches. Very short-tailed. Male black except for scarlet of top of head and light yellow of thighs. Female olive, a little lighter on throat and belly than on chest. Young male like female but with some red feathers on head. Ecuador and Colombia to Veracruz and Yucatán.

2. Long-tailed Manakin (*Chiroxiphia linearis*). 7½ inches. (Slender middle feathers extend beyond rest of tail 3 inches in male, 1½ inches in female). Male black with deep red crown-patch and light blue back. Female olive—resembles female *Pipra mentalis*, but is long-tailed. Immature male like female but with red crown-patch. Costa Rica to Oaxaca and Chiapas.

3. White-collared Manakin (*Manacus candei*). 4¾ inches. Male: crown black; rest of head, chest, upper back, and lesser wing coverts snow white; tail, most of wings, and band across middle of back black; rump and upper tail coverts yellowish-green; belly and under tail coverts bright yellow. Female olive above and on chest, gray on throat, yellow on belly and under tail coverts. Northern Costa Rica to Veracruz, Tabasco, Quintana Roo, and Chiapas.

4. Thrushlike Manakin (*Schiffornis turdinus*). 6 inches. Dull olive-brown, lightest on chin and belly and slightly rufescent on wings and tail. Whole tail rather long and general proportions thrushlike. Bolivia and Brazil to Veracruz.

Family Tyrannidae: New World Flycatchers

All species of this family listed from the United States migrate through Mexico, breed there, or winter there (or all three). Identifying migrants and winter visitants may be difficult not alone because they resemble certain distinctively Mexican forms, but also because they are comparatively silent or undemonstrative. The readiness with which one recognizes a familiar call-note, such as the clear *pee-a-wee* of the Eastern Wood Pewee (*Contopus v. virens*), the bold *Quick! Three beers!* of the Olive-sided Flycatcher (*Nuttallornis borealis*), or the far-carrying *creep* of the Crested Flycatcher (*Myiarchus crinitus*) amid the welter of unknown bird sounds is, however, reassuring.

The Lawrence's Dusky-capped Flycatcher (*M. tuberculifer lawrencei*), described on page 109, is, it will be recalled, a race of a species which ranges northward into southern Arizona. The Sulphur-bellied Flycatcher (*Myiodynastes luteiventris*), José María or Greater Pewee (*Contopus pertinax*), Buff-breasted Flycatcher (*Empidonax fulvifrons*), Olive-backed Kingbird (*Tyrannus melancholicus*), Beardless Flycatcher (*Camptostoma imberbe*), and Brown-crested Flycatcher (*Myiarchus tyrannulus*) are in the same category, except that the last three breed in southern Texas as well.

Certain United States species and their Mexican allies need special discussion: the Ash-throated Flycatcher (*Myiarchus c. cinerascens*) breeds as far south as Sinaloa, Durango, and Tamaulipas, and winters throughout the republic. Another race (*pertinax*) is resident in Baja California. But what of the little known *nuttingi* (Sinaloa and Chihuahua southward) and *brachyurus* (Chiapas southward): are they races of *cinerascens*, or separate species? I cannot say, for I have not studied the *living* birds. As skins, they certainly resemble *cinerascens* in shape and color.

Myiarchus tyrannulus, mentioned above, may be conspecific with the well-known *M. crinitus*. Certainly the two birds resemble one another not only morphologically but in bearing, nesting habits, and call-notes. As for the small (6¾ inches) *M. yucatanensis*, a bird I have never seen alive, it probably is a distinct species; at least it

must be distinct from *tyrannulus*, for that bird also inhabits Yucatán.

The wood pewees are puzzling. The sweet-voiced eastern United States bird, *virens*, migrates through Mexico. The comparatively harsh-voiced *richardsoni* (Western Wood Pewee), which is believed by some ornithologists to be a race of *virens*, winters in, breeds in, and migrates through Mexico. But what about *cinereus* (South America to Yucatán, Veracruz, and Chiapas): is it actually a distinct species? Certainly it looks very much like *virens*, and would doubtless be identified as such save, possibly, for its voice.

Mere mention of the genus *Empidonax* is enough to rouse shouts of protest or sighs of resignation. All the "United States species" will have to be identified *with very great care,* for they may be virtually silent. The Western Flycatcher (*E. difficilis*) breeds in the Mexican mountains and occurs widely as a winter visitor and transient. The southern *salvini* (Chiapas southward) and *dwighti* (Chiapas southward) are believed by Moore to represent two species, respectively *difficilis* and *flavescens*, but the latter is, outwardly at least, only an intensely bright edition of *difficilis*.

The Pine Flycatcher (*E. affinis*) breeds high on piney slopes from Chihuahua, Durango, Nuevo León (probably), and Tamaulipas south to Veracruz, México, and Michoacán. I have collected breeding specimens in the last three states. It is rather narrow-billed; the tone of the underparts is warm; and the outer web of the outer tail feather is almost white, but none of these is a very good field-mark. Usually the bird stays rather well above ground. It is common in the pines just below snow line on Popocatepetl.

The White-throated Flycatcher (*E. albigularis*) is brown in general tone above and grayish-white on the throat. The gray chest and pale yellow belly are washed with buff. Southern Tamaulipas (Miller and Poppy), Durango, Chihuahua, and Sinaloa to Central America. *E. timidus* of Durango is probably a race of *albigularis*.

Distinctive Middle American flycatchers

228

one is sure to see when visiting Mexico are:

1. Boat-billed Flycatcher (*Megarynchus pitangua*). See pp. 145–46. Lowlands from southern Tamaulipas, Yucatán, and Jalisco to Paraguay and Argentina. Resembles superficially the Derby Flycatcher or Kiskadee (*Pitangus sulphuratus*) which inhabits lowlands from southern Texas and Sinaloa to Argentina (pp. 13, 43–44, 59, 65, 145).

2. Social Flycatcher (*Myiozetetes similis*). See pp. 146–47. Sinaloa and southern Tamaulipas to Argentina; lowlands.

3. Fork-tailed Flycatcher (*Muscivora tyrannus*). Unmistakable with its very long, forked tail, white under parts, black pileum (with concealed yellow patch), gray back, and dark wings and tail. Veracruz to Argentina; lowlands. Reported from southern Texas (Irby Davis). The other flycatcher with long, forked tail is the Scissor-tailed Flycatcher (*M. forficata*), a species which migrates through Mexico, winters from southern Mexico to Panama, and breeds principally in Texas and Oklahoma. The Scissor-tail has no black on its head in any plumage and its sides are washed with salmon pink.

4. Thick-billed Kingbird (*Tyrannus crassirostris*). Size of other kingbirds; brownish-gray above (concealed yellow crown-patch), throat white, chest pale gray, belly pale yellow. Bill very heavy. Sinaloa to Oaxaca and Puebla. A noticeable species in the Autlán district of Jalisco (Zimmerman and Harry).

5. Streaked Flycatcher (*Myiodynastes maculatus*). So much like the Sulphurbellied Flycatcher that I continue to wonder whether it may be merely a color-phase or plumage-stage of that bird, but general tone of under parts less yellow. Callnotes and nesting habits may be drastically different from those of *luteiventris,* but much of what A. O. Gross has written of *maculatus* in Panama might be said of *luteiventris* as I have observed that bird in Tamaulipas. Both *maculatus* and *luteiventris* summer along the Río Sabinas in southern Tamaulipas, and *maculatus* presumably breeds there; but life histories of the two species need to be worked out. *Maculatus* ranges from Yucatán, southern Tamaulipas, and Oaxaca southward into South America.

6. Pirate Flycatcher (*Legatus leucophaius*). 5½ inches. Dark olive-brown above (partly concealed yellow crownpatch); throat and middle of belly grayish-white; chest and sides heavily streaked with gray; sides, flanks, and under tail coverts washed with pale yellow. Noisy and querulous. Steals nests of other birds. San Luis Potosí, Veracruz, Quintana Roo, and Oaxaca to Argentina. I have seen this bird near the Río Axtla bridge just north of Tamazunchale, San Luis Potosí.

7. Northern Royal Flycatcher (*Onychorhynchus mexicanus*). 7¼ inches. Unmistakable if fanlike crest of long, coppery-orange feathers (each tipped with steel-blue) is visible. Olive-brown above, yellowish-buff below. Tail fading to buff at base. A large-billed species ranging from Yucatán and Veracruz to Colombia.

8. Tufted Flycatcher (*Mitrephanes phaeocercus*). 5 inches. Inconspicuous triangular crest. Dark olive-brown above, dull dark rufous on chest fading to rich buff on belly. Often lifts and flutters wings briskly on alighting. Southern Tamaulipas, Chihuahua, and Sonora to Peru and Bolivia. To be seen along the main highway in woods just south of Jacala, Hidalgo.

From this point on we must deal with small species which I have seen but little, if at all, afield. Close examination of specimens shows many to be instantly recognizable from bill shape (see p. 230), and experience I have had with a few species leads me to suspect that each may be readily identifiable from callnotes or behavior. Proceeding not phylogenetically, but from the more to the less boldly characterized, we have:

9. White-tipped Tody-Flycatcher (*Todirostrum cinereum*). 4 inches. Bill, like that of tody (*Todus*), long and flat. Under parts light yellow. Whole top of head slaty-black; back gray with olive tinge; wings slaty, the secondaries and greater coverts edged with light yellow; tail black, the outer feathers tipped with white. Yucatán, Veracruz, and Chiapas to South America.

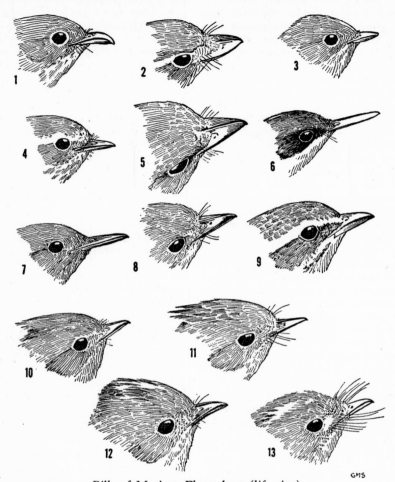

Bills of Mexican Flycatchers (life size)

1. Bent-bill (*Oncostoma cinereigulare*), 3¾ inches. 2. Stub-tailed Spade-bill (*Platyrinchus cancrominus*), 3¾ inches. 3. Beardless Flycatcher (*Camptostoma imberbe*), 4½ inches. 4. Tyrannulet (*Tyranniscus villissimus*), 4¾ inches. 5. Short-billed Flat-bill (*Rhynchocyclus brevirostris*), 6 inches. 6. White-tipped Tody-Flycatcher (*Todirostrum cinereum*), 4 inches. 7. Ochre-bellied Flycatcher (*Pipromorpha oleaginea*), 5½ inches. 8. Sulphury Flat-bill (*Tolmomyias sulphurescens*), 5½ inches. 9. Pirate Flycatcher (*Legatus leucophaius*), 5½ inches. 10. Tufted Flycatcher (*Mitrephanes phaeocercus*), 5 inches. 11. Belted Flycatcher (*Xenotriccus callizonus*), 5½ inches. 12. Yellow-bellied Elaenia (*Elaenia flavogaster*), 6½ inches. 13. Sulphur-rumped Flycatcher (*Myiobius sulphureipygius*), 4¾ inches.

10. Slate-headed Tody-Flycatcher (*T. sylvia*). 4 inches. Crown ashy-gray; upper part of body olive-green, the wing feathers with yellow edgings; throat and breast gray, vaguely streaked; belly white; sides, flanks, and under tail coverts pale yellow. Veracruz and Oaxaca to Brazil.

11. Belted Flycatcher (*Xenotriccus callizonus*). 5½ inches. Rather long, pointed crest. Olive-brown above, with buff wing-bars and secondary edgings; pale yellow below, with *clear-cut orange-brown band* across chest. The only Mexican flycatcher with such a chest-band. Chiapas (Brodkorb and Staebler) to Guatemala. A very little known species much in need of study.

12. Short-billed Flat-bill (*Rhynchocyclus brevirostris*). 6 inches. Bill very broad. Dull olive-green except for pale yellow belly. Chest vaguely streaked. Yucatán, Veracruz, and Oaxaca to South America.

13. Stub-tailed Spadebill (*Platyrinchus cancrominus*). 3¾ inches. Instantly recognizable from short, very wide bill and short tail, for no other Mexican flycatcher has both of these characters. Olive-brown above and on sides; white on throat, superciliary line, and vague spot on auriculars; belly and under tail coverts pale buffy-yellow. Yucatán, Veracruz, and Chiapas to Costa Rica.

14. Sulphury Flat-bill (*Tolmomyias sulphurescens*). 5½ inches. Not nearly so wide-billed as the two species just listed. Top of head and hind neck ashy-gray, fading to bright olive-green of back, wings, and tail; throat and chest light ashy-gray; belly, sides, and under tail coverts pale yellow. Yucatán, Veracruz, and Oaxaca to South America.

15. Yellow-bellied Elaenia (*Elaenia flavogaster*). 6½ inches. Olive-gray above with two indistinct grayish-white wing-bars and patch of yellowish-white concealed in crest plumage; throat grayish-white; chest olive-gray, paler than back; belly light buffy-yellow. Yucatán, Veracruz, México, and Chiapas to Argentina.

16. Greenish Elaenia (*Elaenia viridicata*). 5 inches. Olive-green above except for gray of top of head and partly concealed yellow crown-patch; throat grayish-white, fading to ashy-gray of chest; belly light yellow. Southern Tamaulipas (Lea), Yucatán, and Jalisco to Argentina.

17. Bent-bill (*Oncostoma cinereigulare*). 3¾ inches. Bill club-shaped, thick, and curiously bent. Top of head dark ashy-gray; rest of upper parts olive-green, with yellowish wing-feather edgings; throat and chest light ashy-gray, vaguely streaked with darker gray; belly, sides, and under tail coverts pale yellow. Veracruz, Yucatán, and Oaxaca to Colombia.

18. Tyrannulet (*Tyranniscus villissimus*). 4¾ inches. Dark ashy-gray on top of head except for grayish-white spot above eye and partly concealed white at base of forehead plumage; upper part of body olive-green; throat and chest pale ashy-gray, vaguely streaked with darker gray; belly and sides pale yellow, vaguely streaked with gray. Chiapas to northern South America.

19. Ochre-bellied Flycatcher (*Pipromorpha oleaginea*). 5½ inches. Olive above; throat olive-gray fading to olive of chest; belly, sides, and under tail coverts ruddy-ochre. Veracruz and Chiapas to South America.

20. Sulphur-rumped Flycatcher (*Myiobius sulphureipygius*). 4¾ inches. Crown, hind neck, and back brownish-olive, the crown with a bright yellow patch; wings dark brown, without bars; rump pale yellow; tail black; throat buffy-white; chest and sides dull orange-buff; belly and under tail coverts pale yellow. Veracruz and Yucatán to Ecuador.

Family Alaudidae: Larks

Mexico has only one true lark—the wide-ranging Horned Lark (*Eremophila alpestris*). The species inhabits dry plains throughout the republic. Burleigh, Semple and I saw hundreds of breeding pairs along the Puebla-to-Jacala highway in the vicinity of Lake Alchichica in the early spring of 1939.

Family Hirundinidae: Swallows

All United States swallows are found in Mexico—plus the following:

1. Gray-breasted Martin (*Progne chalybea*). 6½ inches. Resembles female Purple Martin (*P. subis*) but top and sides of head, hind neck, and back all brownish-black, glossed with blue, without hint of gray collar on hind neck. Tamaulipas, Coahuila, Yucatán, and Oaxaca to Argentina. Recorded in southern Texas in midsummer. The northernmost colony I have seen was nesting about the Axtla bridge, twenty miles north of Tamazunchale, San Luis Potosí.

2. Mangrove Swallow (*Iridoprocne albilinea*). 5 inches from bill-tip to tips of folded wings. Like a small Tree Swallow (*I. bicolor*) with white rump, white spot above lores, and (in fresh plumage) noticeable white edges on tertials and inner secondaries. Two breeding specimens in my collection are wholly without white in the wings, so the light edgings must wear off

rapidly. Tamaulipas and Sonora to Panama (probably farther south). Primarily coastal, but occurs along rivers in eastern Mexico far from the sea (Irby Davis).

The Violet-green Swallow (*Tachycineta thalassina*) nests at high elevations in many parts of Mexico. In this species the sides of the rump are white.

3. Black-capped Swallow (*Notiochelidon pileata*). 5 inches. Whole top of head blue-black; back brown, fading to black on wings and tail; middle of under parts white, but chin flecked with brown, and sides, flanks and under tail coverts solid brown. Highlands of Chiapas (Brodkorb and Staebler) and Guatemala.

Any swallow which looks like a Cliff Swallow (*Petrochelidon pyrrhonota*), but whose pinkish-buff throat is wholly without black or dusky, is apt to be a Cave Swallow (*P. fulva*).

Family Corvidae: Crows and Jays

Large, black, crowlike birds in mountainous districts are likely to be Ravens (*Corvus corax*), but "big crows" in desert country southward as far as Guanajuato are more likely to be White-necked Ravens (*C. cryptoleucus*). Small crows are sure to be Mexican Crows (14 inches), a lowland species I have seen in numbers along the main highway from Linares, Nuevo León, to Valles, San Luis Potosí. It is found also in the west—from Sonora to Colima (see pp. 102–103).

The well-known Steller's Jay (*Cyanocitta stelleri*) and Scrub Jay (*Aphelocoma coerulescens*) range southward far beyond the border, the former in the Sierra Madre to Central America, the latter throughout most of the plateau. The Mexican Jay (*A. ultramarina*) (see pp. 53–54, 75, 92–94, 96, 98), also occurs throughout most of the plateau northward to southern Arizona and southwestern Texas. The Clark's Nutcracker (*Nucifraga columbiana*) breeds southward into montane northern Baja

California and has been reported from Nuevo León (Starker Leopold).

The Green Jay (*Xanthoura yncas*), discussed on pages 15–17, 23, 38, etc., is found in the lowlands from southern Texas to South America (except for part of Central America). It inhabits the Yucatán peninsula, but in western Mexico is found north only to Jalisco.

The following jays do not regularly range northward to the United States border:

1. Brown Jay (*Psilorhinus morio*). See pages 46–47 for description. Tamaulipas and Nuevo León to Tabasco. Known in Tamaulipas as the *Papán,* in southern Veracruz as the *Pepe* (Wetmore). Whether Brown Jays with white-tipped outer tail feathers (see below) belong to this, or to a separate, species remains to be settled.

2. White-tipped Brown Jay (*P. mexicanus*). Almost exactly like the Brown Jay (see above) except that its outer tail feathers are tipped with white. Wetmore's statement (1943 *Proc. U. S. Natl. Mus.*, 93: 298)

that "...*P. m. mexicanus* is found throughout the area inhabited by the two accepted subspecies of *Psilorhinus morio*," is sorely in need of confirmation. In Tamaulipas, Nuevo León, and southeastern San Luis Potosí I have seen literally hundreds of "true" Brown Jays, but not a single "white-tipped" bird. Hellmayr, very properly to my way of thinking, questions the occurrence of *mexicanus* in Tamaulipas. I suspect that the White-tipped Brown Jay is a color-phase of the Brown. At Tres Zapotes, Veracruz, Wetmore (*op. cit.,* p. 297) found the two forms "in about equal number, . . . feeding and traveling in company." The northern part of *morio's* range is, nevertheless, without white-tipped birds.

3. San Blas Jay (*Cissolopha san-blasiana*). 12 inches. A handsome species which might well be known as the Black and Blue Jay. It has an inconspicuous frontal crest. Rich blue on back, rump, wings, and tail; solid black otherwise. Western: found regularly from Guerrero to Nayarit and irregularly farther north; a flock reported even from southern Arizona (Phillips).

Whether the Beechey's Jay (*beecheyi*) of Sonora and Sinaloa, the Yucatán Jay (*yucatanica*) of the Yucatán peninsula, Tabasco, British Honduras, and eastern Guatemala, and the above-discussed Black and Blue Jay are races of the same species is a question. The Beechey's Jay (14 inches) has little or no frontal crest and the blue of its upper parts is richly purplish. The Yucatán Jay (13 inches) has a slight frontal crest and the blue of its upper parts is cerulean. To me it appears that the three birds are well defined races of one species. Young Yucatán Jays are white throughout the head and under parts and their outer tail feathers are tipped with white. I do not know what the young of the other two forms are like.

4. A well-named species is the Unicolored Jay (*Aphelocoma unicolor*), which is deep blue all over (wing and tail feathers dull black underneath). 12 inches. Veracruz, Puebla, and México to El Salvador and Honduras.

5. The handsome Magpie-Jay (*Calocitta formosa*) is Mexico's only strikingly long-tailed corvid. Adult males in full feather are two feet long (tail 15 inches), with showy crest of soft feathers. In general, blue above, white below, with boldly white-tipped outer tail feathers, and black (sometimes white-tipped) crest. Amount of black on head varies, some birds being white on face and throat with narrow black chest-band, others black throughout most of face and throat. This variation is partly geographical. The species ranges from southern Sonora, western Chihuahua, and Puebla to Costa Rica.

6. Black-throated Jay (*Cyanolyca pumilo*). 10 inches. Dark glossy blue with black forehead, face, and throat, black separated from blue by narrow white line passing across fore part of crown back over each eye. Chiapas to El Salvador.

7. White-throated Jay (*Cyanolyca mirabilis*). 9 inches. Whole head and neck black except for large white throat-patch and bold white line passing directly across fore part of crown, backward above each eye, and down back of auriculars; dull blue otherwise. Guerrero.

8. Azure-hooded Jay (*Cyanolyca pulchra*). 13 inches. Front and lower part of head black; rear of crown pale blue, the blue and black separated by white line curving back behind auriculars; body dull blue. Veracruz and Oaxaca to northern South America.

9. Dwarf Jay (*C. nana*). 9 inches. Purplish blue on pileum, "pale grayish-purplish-blue" on throat (Ridgway), boldly black throughout rest of head; plain grayish-blue otherwise. Mountains of Veracruz, México and Oaxaca.

10. The spectacular Tufted Jay (*Cyanocorax dickeyi*), described by Robert T. Moore in 1935, is a large (about 14 inches), spectacularly crested, purplish-blue, black and snow-white bird with a unique and very noticeable feature: the white distal half of the tail. Southeastern Sinaloa.

Family Paridae: TITMICE

No species of this family is confined to Mexico. The Mexican Chickadee (*Parus sclateri*) ranges northward into the mountains of southeastern Arizona and southwestern Texas, the Bridled Titmouse (*P. wollweberi*) into the mountains of south-ern New Mexico and Arizona, and the Black-eared Bush-tit (*Psaltriparus melanotis*) into the mountains of southwestern Texas. Some ornithologists consider all bush-tits one species, calling *melanotis* a race of *P. minimus*.

Family Sittidae: NUTHATCHES

The White-breasted Nuthatch (*Sitta carolinensis*) and Pygmy Nuthatch (*S. pygmaea*) range southward in the mountains respectively at least to Oaxaca and Michoacán. I found a Pygmy Nuthatch's nest in a dead pine at about 10,000 feet elevation not far from the Pátzcuaro-to-Ta-cámbaro highway, in Michoacán, in the spring of 1949. The Pygmy Nuthatch and Brown-headed Nuthatch (*S. pusilla*) of the southeastern United States probably belong to the same species and might well be united under the common name of Pine Nuthatch.

Family Certhiidae: CREEPERS

The well-known Brown Creeper (*Certhia familiaris*), the only certhiid found in the New World, breeds southward in Middle America as far as Nicaragua. Two or more races breeding exclusively in the United States (or United States and Canada) probably winter to some extent in Mexico.

Family Chamaeidae: WREN-TITS

The Wren-tit (*Chamaea fasciata*) ranges from Oregon to lat. 30° N. in Baja California along the coast (Hellmayr).

Family Cinclidae: DIPPERS

The famous American Dipper (*Cinclus mexicanus*) was first described by Swainson, whose type was taken at Temascalte-pec, in the state of México. The species breeds from Alaska to Panama along cold mountain streams.

Family Troglodytidae: WRENS

Most wrens of the United States are found in Mexico—the Long-billed Marsh Wren (*Telmatodytes palustris*) in winter and during migration; the Short-billed Marsh Wren (*Cistothorus platensis*) very locally in marshes, the Bewick's Wren (*Thryomanes bewicki*) in semiarid districts, the Rock Wren (*Salpinctes obsoletus*) and Cactus Wren (*Campylorhynchus brunneicapillus*) in deserts, and the Canyon Wren (*Catherpes mexicanus*) about cliffs and canyons, the year around, throughout the greater part of the republic. The Carolina Wren (*Thryothorus ludovicianus*) breeds southward to southern Tamaulipas, Nuevo León, and San Luis Potosí (Lowery and Newman). To our surprise Burleigh and I encountered it from 1,700 to 7,000 feet elevation in the vicinity of Monterrey, Nuevo León (see p. 84). The House Wren (*Troglodytes aëdon*) occurs principally as a winter visitant and transient, but the race *parkmanni* breeds southward into northern Baja California. The Brown-throated Wren (*T. brunneicollis*), which looks very much like a House Wren with brown throat and chest, ranges widely in montane parts of Mexico, breeding northward to southern

Arizona (Herbert Brandt). This species I have discussed on page 84.

The following Mexican wrens do not range northward to the United States border:

1. White-bellied Wren (*Nannorchilus leucogaster*). 3¾ inches. Unbarred. Brownish-gray above, grayish-white below, with noticeable white superciliary line. Tinkling, somewhat rhythmical song. Thickets in lowlands from Yucatán peninsula, southern Tamaulipas, and Colima to Oaxaca and Chiapas (possibly farther south). Fairly common near the highway at the Mesa de Llera, Tamaulipas.

Allies of House Wren

2. *Troglodytes musculus*. This species breeds from coastal southern Tamaulipas, the Yucatán peninsula, Oaxaca, and the West Indies southward to Argentina and Chile. Various observers have reported its nesting about clearings, even in man-made birdhouses. It is very much like the House Wren in color, size, and proportions. The Clarion Island Wren (*tanneri*) certainly looks like a House Wren too. The mountain-loving *brunneicollis* probably is a distinct species; but at this writing *aëdon, tanneri*, and *musculus* appear to me to comprise one great "conspecies." Under the circumstances it seems inadvisable to coin a common name for *musculus* until we know that it is actually a distinct species. It may briefly be described as a rufescent House Wren.

Allies of Carolina Wren

3. White-browed Wren (*Thryothorus albinucha*). 5 inches. Dark brown above, grayish-white below, with distinct white superciliary line. Rectrices gray, barred with black, the two outer pairs with white barring on the outer webs. Yucatán, eastern Quintana Roo, and parts of Guatemala and Nicaragua. Griscom believes that this bird is a subspecies of the Carolina Wren.

4. Spotted-breasted Wren (*Thyrothorus maculipectus*). 5 inches. Described and figured on pp. 125–26. Southern Tamaulipas, Yucatán peninsula, and eastern Oaxaca to Central America.

5. Happy Wren (*T. felix*). 5½ inches. Light olive-brown above, rufescent on crown, and barred with dusky on tail; buffy-white below, deepening to buff on sides and flanks; sides of head boldly streaked with black and white. Southern Sonora and Durango to Oaxaca; Tres Marías Islands. A bird of riverside thickets; song of rhythmically repeated phrases (Storer).

6. Sinaloa Wren (*T. sinaloa*). 5 inches. Grayish-brown above, rufescent on rump and tail, grayish-white below, deepening to reddish-brown on the flanks. A noticeable white superciliary line. *Under tail coverts barred with black*. Sinaloa to Guerrero. A bird of open woodlands with very fine song (Storer).

7. Plain Wren (*T. modestus*). 5¼ inches. Crown and hind neck gray, fading to light reddish-brown on wings, rump, and tail. Buffy-white below, deepening to rufous-buff on sides, flanks, and under tail coverts, the last *without bars of any sort*. Chiapas to Panama.

8. Rufous and White Wren (*T. rufalbus*). 6 inches. Bright rufous above, white below, deepening to gray on sides; bold white superciliary line; wings, tail, and under tail coverts barred with black. Chiapas to northern South America.

9. Banded Wren (*T. pleurostictus*) 5½ inches. Light olive-brown above, barred with black on wings and tail. Sides of neck streaked with black and white. Under parts white, boldly barred with black on sides, flanks, and under tail coverts. Morelos and Guerrero to Costa Rica.

Wood Wrens

The wood wrens (*genus Henicorhina*) are very short-tailed. They inhabit heavily forested areas, keeping close to the ground as a rule. Their songs are rich and noticeable.

10. Gray-breasted Wood Wren (*H. leucophrys*). 4 inches. Dark brown above, toward gray on crown, and rufescent on lower back, rump, and tail; superciliary line, throat, and streaks on side of head white; breast and belly gray; sides, flanks,

and under tail coverts olive-brown. Veracruz, Puebla, and Michoacán to South America.

11. White-breasted Wood Wren (*H. leucosticta*). 4 inches. Very much like the above, but throat and breast white, deepening to gray on sides and to olive-brown on flanks, belly, and under tail coverts. Quintana Roo, Campeche, Veracruz, Puebla, and Oaxaca to South America.

Allies of Cactus Wren

Campylorhynchus brunneicapillus, the Cactus Wren familiar to all ornithologists who have visited the southwestern United States, is a "true" cactus wren, for it spends much of its time in cactus. Some of the so-called "cactus wrens" of Mexico may not see a cactus during the course of their lives, however, for they live among oaks, pines and spruces at high elevation. One of the great surprises of my experience in Michoacán in 1949 was coming upon a noisy band of Gray Wrens (*C. megalopterus*) among oaks at about 8,000 feet, just south of Pátzcuaro. The birds fed among the sprawling epiphytes which grew on the mossy boughs.

C. brunneicapillus breeds from the southwestern United States southward through desert areas of virtually the whole of Mexico. Whether it lives side by side with some of the forms discussed below I am not sure, but many ornithologists regard the following as separate species:

12. Rufous-naped Wren (*C. rufinucha*). 7 inches. Northwestern race (*rufinucha*: Veracruz and adjacent parts of Oaxaca) very similar to *brunneicapillus,* but forehead and crown solid brownish-black, white superciliary line very distinct, nape and hind neck rufous, and under parts buffywhite, thinly spotted with dusky. Southern race (*nigricaudatus*: Chiapas to El Salvador) immaculate below and rufous of upper parts includes rump and wings. *Humilis* (Colima, Michoacán, Guerrero, and southern Oaxaca) may be a race of *rufinucha* or a separate species; in any event it is smaller (6½ inches); it has less black on the crown than either *rufinucha* or *nigri-*

caudatus; and it is less extensively rufescent above than the latter. Under parts immaculate; upper tail coverts and rectrices boldly barred with dusky and grayish-buff.

13. Spotted Wren (*C. jocosus*). 6 inches. Like a very small *brunneicapillus* with graybrown crown, bold black and white streaking on hind neck and upper back, and white under parts, heavily marked, except on the throat, with round black spots. Puebla, Morelos, Guerrero, and Oaxaca. *Gularis* (Sonora to Querétaro and Michoacán, eastward to western Tamaulipas) may be a subspecies of *jocosus,* but van Rossem considered the two forms distinct species because of marked differences between the juvenal plumages (*Bull. Brit. Ornith. Club,* 1938: 11). *Gularis* is 6¼ inches long. Adults are like adult *jocosus* but the crown is rufescent; the flanks, lower belly, and under tail coverts are washed with rufous; and the black spotting of the under parts is restricted largely to the chest. A nestling specimen in my collection taken by Ernest Edwards near Quiroga, Michoacán, on May 28, 1948, has a brownish-black crown.

14. Banded-backed Wren (*C. zonatus*). 8 inches. Dark grayish-brown above, streaked on hind neck and banded on wings and tail with buffy-gray; throat and chest white, boldly spotted with black; belly, flanks, and under tail coverts plain rufousbuff. Veracruz, Puebla, and Oaxaca to northern South America.

16. Gray Wren (*C. megalopterus*). 7¾ inches. Dusky above, much streaked and barred with pale buffy-gray; buffy-gray below, thickly spotted on throat and chest, and barred on flanks and under tail coverts, with dark grayish-brown. Callnotes noisy and clacketty, given as birds chase each other about in twos (possibly pairs), one pecking at the other in flight. Veracruz, México, Morelos, and Michoacán to Oaxaca.

17. Chiapas Wren (*C. chiapensis*). 8¼ inches. Whole top of head and hind neck brownish-black; a black line through eye; superciliary line and under parts buffywhite, deepening to rich buff on flanks and under tail coverts. Back, wings, and middle tail feathers rufous. Tail otherwise black-

ish-brown except for subterminal bar of white. Chiapas and Guatemala.

18. Sumichrast's Wren (*Hylorchilus sumichrasti*). 5¾ inches. Long-billed and stub-tailed; rich dark brown above; throat light buffy-gray; chest rufous-buff; belly and under tail coverts dark umber—belly faintly barred with black and minutely flecked with white. Veracruz.

Family Mimidae: THRASHERS, MOCKINGBIRDS AND ALLIES

Most species found in the United States breed southward into Mexico, the Curve-billed Thrasher (*Toxostoma curvirostre*) to Oaxaca (see pp. 22, 37); the Crissal Thrasher (*T. dorsale*) to northern Baja California, Chihuahua, Sonora, and probably Coahuila (see p. 184); the Leconte's Thrasher (*T. lecontei*) in northwestern Sonora and along a coastal strip of Baja California; the California Thrasher (*T. redivivum*) in Baja California southward to lat. 30° N. (Hellmayr); and the Bendire's Thrasher (*T. bendirei*) to northern Sonora (winters to northern Sinaloa). The Brown Thrasher (*T. rufum*) has not been recorded in Mexico; but the Long-billed Thrasher (*T. longirostre*), which looks very much like the Brown (see pp. 36–37, etc.) breeds from southern Texas to Veracruz, Querétaro, Puebla, and Mexico. The Sage Thrasher (*Oreoscoptes montanus*) winters in Chihuahua and Tamaulipas.

The Mockingbird (*Mimus polyglottos*) breeds southward to Jalisco, Oaxaca and Veracruz, and winter populations may be swelled to some extent by visitors from the north. The Catbird (*Dumetella carolinensis*) winters widely, probably chiefly in the east.

An exclusively Mexican thrasher is the Ocellated (*Toxostoma ocellatum*), 11 inches long. Brownish-gray above, buffy-white below, the under parts marked with large, round, dark spots. Puebla, México, and Oaxaca. The Cozumel Thrasher (*T. guttatum*), a small (9½ inches), black-billed edition of the Long-billed Thrasher, is found only on Cozumel Island. The Ash-colored Thrasher (*T. cinereum*) is confined to Baja California. 9 inches. Gray above; buffy-white below; breast, belly, and sides marked with dusky *triangular* spots.

The Blue Mockingbird (*Melanotis caerulescens*), discussed on pages 149 and 151, is grayish-blue. Plumage of head and breast dusky basally, having somewhat streaked appearance. Eyes dark brown. 10 inches. Song loud, broken, composed of both harsh and sweet notes and phrases. Veracruz, Puebla, Morelos, and Mexico in the east; Chihuahua and Sonora to Oaxaca in the west; Tres Marías Islands.

Blue and White Mockingbird (*M. hypoleucus*). Similar to above, but sides of head solid black and under parts (except for blue-gray of sides, flanks, and under tail coverts) pure white. Chiapas, Guatemala, and northern Honduras. Though widely considered a subspecies of *caerulescens*, its color pattern is very different, and occurrence of occasional partly white individuals among Tres Marías Islands birds is not a very strong argument for considering the two forms conspecific.

The remarkable Black Catbird (*Melanoptila glabrirostris*) of Cozumel Island and coastal Yucatán, Quintana Roo (?), British Honduras, and northern Honduras, is about 9 inches long and solid glossy black.

On Socorro Island occurs an endemic genus and species—the Socorro Thrasher (*Mimodes graysoni*).

Family Turdidae: THRUSHES

All thrushes found in the United States have been reported from Mexico, a possible exception being the Gray-cheeked (*Hylocichla minima*), which almost certainly migrates through Mexico. Richard Robins believes he has seen this species in Tamaulipas. Among "our" species breeding in Mexico are the Robin (*Turdus migratorius*), Townsend's Solitaire (*Myadestes townsendi*), Hermit Thrush (*Hylocichla guttata*), Eastern Bluebird (*Sialia sialis*), Mexican Bluebird (*S. mexicana*) and Mountain Bluebird (*S. currucoides*). All these but *Sialia sialis* breed exclusively in the mountains, the Robin southward to Veracruz and Oaxaca; the Townsend's Solitaire to Durango (Paul S. Martin); the Hermit Thrush to Baja California; the Eastern Bluebird to El Salvador and Nicaragua; the Mexican Bluebird to Veracruz, Puebla, México, and Michoacán; and the Mountain Bluebird to Chihuahua. In southern Texas and northern Tamaulipas the Eastern Bluebird breeds in the lowlands.

The following Mexican species of *Turdus* are instantly recognizable as robins from behavior alone. They are all about robin-size too.

1. Rufous-collared Robin (*T. rufitorques*). Male black, with rufous collar, widest on chest. Female dark gray, with faint hint of rufous collar on breast. Bill yellow. Chiapas to Guatemala and El Salvador.

2. Rufous-backed Robin (*T. rufo-palliatus*). Sexes alike. Top of head and hind neck ashy-gray; back and wing coverts pale reddish-brown; primaries, secondaries, rump, and tail gray; throat white, streaked with dusky; chest light brown; sides and flanks rufous; belly white. Sonora and Durango to Puebla and Oaxaca; Tres Marías Islands.

3. White-throated Robin (*T. assimilis*). Sexes alike. Grayish-olive above; breast, upper belly, sides, and flanks light grayish-brown; throat, lower belly, and under tail coverts white; chin and upper throat streaked with dusky leaving lower throat pure white. Southern Tamaulipas, Sinaloa, and Durango to Panama.

4. Gray's Robin (*T. grayi*). Sexes alike (see p. 135). Central Tamaulipas, Nuevo León, Yucatán, and Guerrero to northern Colombia.

5. Black-billed Robin (*T. ignobilis*). Sexes alike. Plain olive-brown, darker above than below, and slightly rufescent on sides and flanks. Chiapas to northern South America.

6. Black Robin (*T. infuscatus*). Adult male grayish-black, with faint gloss; bill and feet yellow. Immature male dark olive-gray, brightest on wings and chest; greater wing coverts tipped with buff; throat and belly lighter than back. Adult female olive-brown above, tawny on chest, light brownish-gray on belly; throat grayish-buff, streaked with dusky. Veracruz and Oaxaca to Guatemala and El Salvador in the mountains.

Solitaires

7. Brown-backed Solitaire (*Myadestes obscurus*) (see pp. 77–79). In the mountains from Nuevo León, central Tamaulipas, Sonora, and Chihuahua to El Salvador. *Jilguero*.

8. Slate-colored Solitaire (*M. unicolor*). 7½ inches. Slate-gray all over except for obscure white tipping on outer tail feathers, and two white spots near eye—one on upper lid, the other on lower. Veracruz and San Luis Potosí to Nicaragua. *Clarín*.

Nightingale-Thrushes

These interesting birds resemble Hermit Thrushes in that they so often flit rapidly off through the undergrowth, alight at considerable distance, and peer at the observer with their large dark eyes.

9. Black-headed Nightingale-Thrush (*Catharus mexicanus*). 6½ inches. Top of head slaty-black; sides of head gray; back, wings, and tail grayish-olive; under parts white except for light olive-gray of chest-band, sides, and flanks. Bill and eyelids bright orange-yellow; feet dull yellow. Female less bright than male. Tamaulipas and Veracruz to Panama.

10. Russet Nightingale-Thrush (*C. occidentalis*). 6½ inches. Russet above, brightest on top of head; gray below, palest on throat, belly, and under tail coverts, obscurely streaked with dusky and washed with buff on chest. Bill and feet dull-colored. Chihuahua, Durango, Tamaulipas, México and Jalisco to Panama.

11. Orange-billed Nightingale-Thrush (*C. aurantiirostris*). 6 inches. Russet above, slightly rufescent on wings, rump, and upper tail coverts; throat, belly, and under tail coverts white; chest-band, sides, and

238

flanks light clear gray. Bill and eyelids orange; feet dull orange. Tamaulipas, Chihuahua, and Jalisco to northern South America.

Aztec Thrush

12. The Aztec Thrush (*Ridgwayia pinicola*) is one of Mexico's most remarkable thrushes. 8½ inches. Male dark brownish-gray on whole head, neck, chest, and upper parts, and white on belly and under tail coverts. Wings and tail broadly tipped with white; patch of white at base of primaries; greater coverts pale buff at base; outer web of outer tail feather white. Female the same in pattern, but head and back brown, rather noticeably streaked with buff. Southern Chihuahua and northwestern Durango to Veracruz and Oaxaca, high in the mountains.

Aztec Thrush (*Ridgwayia pinicola*)
8½ inches

Family Sylviidae: GNATCATCHERS AND GNATWRENS

The well-known Blue-gray Gnatcatcher (*Polioptila cærulea*) breeds widely in Mexico, the populations of some areas being swelled in winter by visitants from the United States. The form *nelsoni,* which breeds in Chiapas and Oaxaca, may be a subspecies of *cærulea*. Male *nelsoni* in breeding dress appears to be black-crowned; actually, the top of the head is glossy greenish-slate, bordered in front and at sides by a line of black.

The Plumbeous Gnatcatcher (*P. melanura*), a familiar bird of the southwestern United States, breeds in arid brushlands south to southern Tamaulipas, Nuevo León, Durango, and northern Baja California (see p. 28).

The Black-capped Gnatcatcher (*P. nigri-*

239

ceps), which ranges from Sonora to Nayarit (and probably Jalisco), is glossy blue-black on the upper part of the head and blue-gray on the back, darkening to slate on the wings and to black on the upper tail coverts and middle rectrices. Much of the outer part of the tail is white. Under parts white, washed with very pale bluish-gray on chest and sides. Female: pileum gray, slightly darker than back.

Nigriceps, just described, may be a race of *P. plumbea,* a wide-ranging species in which the upper part of the head of the male in breeding season is glossy blue-black. Some races are white-lored at certain seasons. The Yucatán race (*albiventris*) is very white below. The species (not including *nigriceps*) ranges from Guerrero, Chiapas, and Yucatán to Brazil.

Gnatwren

The Long-billed Gnatwren (*Ramphocaenus rufiventris*) was formerly thought to belong to the family Formicariidae, but its behavior resembles that of the gnat-catchers. Wetmore says that it jerks "the narrow tail up and down . . . at times cocking it over the back like a wren." 5 inches. Top of head russet, brightening to rufous on auriculars and sides of neck. Rest of upper parts dark brownish-gray, the outer tail feathers tipped with white. Chin and throat white, the latter vaguely streaked with dusky. Belly buff, brightening to pale rufous on sides and flanks. Veracruz, Yucatán, Oaxaca, and Chiapas to Colombia and Ecuador.

Long-billed Gnatwren (*Ramphocaenus rufiventris*)
5 inches

Family Regulidae: Kinglets

The Golden-crowned Kinglet (*Regulus regulus*) breeds in spruce forests in the mountains from Hidalgo, Veracruz, Mexico, and Michoacán to Guatemala. The Ruby-crowned Kinglet (*R. calendula*) winters widely. A well-defined race, *obscurus,* is endemic to Guadalupe Island, off Baja California.

PLATE XV
Great Curassow or *Faisán Real*
(*Crax rubra*)

Family Motacillidae: Pipits

Two pipits winter in Mexico, the Water Pipit (*Anthus spinoletta*) and Sprague's Pipit (*A. spraguei*). These are described in guides to United States birds.

Family Bombycillidae: Waxwings

The Cedar Waxwing (*Bombycilla cedrorum*) wanders widely through Mexico in winter. I have seen it as far south as Lake Pátzcuaro, in Michoacán.

Family Ptilogonatidae: Silky Flycatchers

The Phainopepla (*Phainopepla nitens*), mentioned on page 183, has been reported from the plateau southward as far as México, Puebla, and Veracruz.

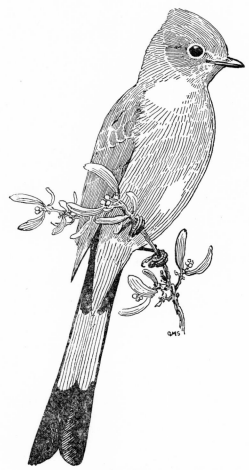

Gray Silky-Flycatcher (*Ptilogonys cinereus*)
8 inches

The Gray Silky Flycatcher (*Ptilogonys cinereus*), a crested bird 8 inches long, appears to be blue-gray, with black wings and tail. Actually, the eye-ring, forehead, and throat are light ashy-gray, the auriculars and a band across the hind neck gray-brown, the sides and flanks olive, the middle of the belly white, and the under tail coverts bright yellow. All the tail feathers but the middle pair are crossed by a broad white band which is clearly visible below. Feeds on mistletoe berries. Callnote a clearly enunciated *took-a-look*. Durango, Zacatecas, Veracruz, and southern Tamaulipas (Robins) to Guatemala at rather high elevations. In the vicinity of Pátzcuaro, Michoacán, it is fairly common among oaks and pines at about 8,000 feet.

Family Laniidae: SHRIKES

The Loggerhead Shrike (*Lanius ludovicianus*) inhabits Mexico southward as far as Oaxaca. It is a bird of the open, of course, and is especially common in semiarid districts. Some races are resident, but the winter population of any given area is apt to be composed partly of birds from farther north. Many birds of the midwestern United States are believed to winter well southward in Mexico.

Family Cyclarhidae: PEPPER-SHRIKES

The Rufous-browed Pepper-Shrike (*Cyclarhis gujanensis*) is a chunky, stub-billed, heavy-footed bird with olive-green back, wings, and tail, and light yellow under parts. 6 inches. Head gray except for dull orange-rufous of forehead and superciliary area. Climbs as it feeds, bill-shape and manner suggesting a little parrot. Surprisingly clear, melodious song. Southern Tamaulipas and Yucatán to South America.

Family Vireolaniidae: SHRIKE-VIREOS

Two species inhabit Mexico. Easy to identify because wholly unlike other birds. The larger is the Chestnut-sided Shrike-Vireo (*Vireolanius melitophrys*). 7 inches. Whole crown and hind neck clear gray; back, wings, and tail rich olive-green; under parts white except for rich brown of chest-band and sides. Broad black line through eye and narrower black line separating white of malar region from that of throat. Superciliary area bright yellow. Eye "pale olive-yellowish" (Edwards). Female duller than male. Veracruz, México, Morelos, and Michoacán to Guatemala.

Green Shrike-Vireo (*Smaragdolanius pulchellus*). 5 inches. Tail proportionally shorter than in above species. Rich glossy green with clear blue crown, bright yellow throat, and dull yellow belly. Races south of Mexico have less blue on head. Veracruz to Colombia.

Family Vireonidae: VIREOS

All United States vireos are Mexican to some extent. Some migrate to or through Mexico and also are represented by breeding races. *Vireo o. olivaceus,* the well-known Red-eyed Vireo, migrates through Mexico to northern South America, passing *through* the breeding ground of *V. o. flavoviridis,* the Yellow-green Red-eyed Vireo. *Flavoviridis* sings like a Red-eye and looks like one, but is larger and brighter, the sides, flanks, and under tail coverts being yellow. Has been reported from extreme southern Texas and may breed there. Breeds regularly in lowlands from central Tamaulipas, central Nuevo León, and Sinaloa to Panama.

Another species which breeds in Mexico and also occurs as a transient and winter visitant, is the Warbling Vireo (*V. gilvus*). Breeds in highlands. Even the little known races *amauronotus* (Veracruz), *eleanorae* (southern Tamaulipas, Hidalgo), and *brewsteri* (Chihuahua) are recognizable as Warbling Vireos from their singing. I have never heard the race *strenuus* (Chiapas).

The White-eyed Vireo (*V. griseus*) breeds widely in Atlantic and Pacific coastal lowlands, but its range is not continuous. The race inhabiting Yucatán peninsula (*semiflavus*) is strongly yellow throughout the under parts. Some ornithologists believe that *semiflavus, ochraceus,* and *paluster* of the Pacific lowlands, together with *pallens* of Central America, form a distinct species. Breeding White-eyed Vireos of Tamaulipas, Nuevo León, and San Luis Potosí belong to the small race *micrus;* throughout this same area the larger races *griseus* and *noveboracensis,* from the United States, winter to some extent.

The Hutton's Vireo (*V. huttoni*), Solitary Vireo (*V. solitarius*), Bell's Vireo (*V. belli*), and Black-whiskered Vireo (*V. antiloquus*) all breed in Mexico—Hutton's in the mountains southward to Oaxaca and Michoacán; the Solitary in the mountains to Veracruz in the east and probably to Central America in the west; the Bell's to Durango and Guanajuato; and the Black-whiskered along the coast of Yucatán. The Solitary and Bell's migrate into, or through, Mexico also.

The Black-capped Vireo (*V. atricapillus*) and Gray Vireo (*V. vicinior*) winter in Mexico. The former has been reported from Tamaulipas, México, and Sinaloa; the latter from Sonora and Durango.

The Philadelphia Vireo (*V. philadelphicus*) is a transient, likely to be encountered in woodland anywhere.

The following Mexican vireos are quite different from species found in the United States:

1. Golden Vireo (*Vireo hypochryseus*). 5¼ inches. Olive above, bright yellow below, with fairly noticeable yellow superciliary line. Chihuahua and southern Sonora to Jalisco and Oaxaca; Tres Marías Islands.

2. Slaty Vireo (*Neochloe brevipennis*). 5 inches. Unlike any other vireo in color, but song recognizable as a vireo's (Frank M. Chapman). Slaty-gray with white chin and belly and clear yellowish-olive crown, wings, and tail. Eyes white. Veracruz and Guerrero. One of Mexico's least-known birds.

3. Gray-headed Greenlet (*Hylophilus decurtatus*). 4¼ inches. Crown and hind neck clear gray; rest of upper parts bright olive; throat and chest pale gray; belly white; sides, flanks, and under tail coverts yellowish-olive. Much like adult male Tennessee Warbler (*Vermivora peregrina*) but bill heavier. Song: *re seck re seck re seck* (Wetmore). Veracruz and Oaxaca to northern South America.

4. Tawny-crowned Greenlet (*Hylophilus ochraceiceps*). 4¾ inches. Upper parts warm brown, brightening to yellowish-tawny on crown; throat and foreneck olive-gray, fading to buff on chest, sides, and flanks; belly and under tail coverts pale yellowish-gray. Veracruz, Campeche, and Oaxaca to Brazil.

5. Baird's Vireo (*Vireo bairdi*). 4¾ inches. Dull brown above, brightening to cinnamon on auriculars and sides of neck. Lores and interrupted eye-ring white. Two pale yellow wing-bars. Under parts white except for cinnamon sides and olive flanks. Cozumel Island, off coast of Yucatán.

Family Coerebidae: Honey Creepers

These three species are found in Mexico:

1. Cinnamon-bellied Diglossa (*Diglossa baritula*). 4¼ inches. Bill slightly upturned; strongly hooked at tip. Male dark bluish-gray above and on chin and upper throat; rest of under parts cinnamon. Female much duller: olive-gray above and on chin and throat; cinnamon-buff on chest, belly

and under tail coverts. Veracruz, Puebla, México, Guanajuato, and Colima to Guatemala, in the highlands.

2. Blue Honey Creeper (*Cyanerpes cyaneus*). 4½ inches. Bill long, slender, pointed, and decurved. Adult male: rich, glossy purplish-blue except for turquoise-blue crown, black line through eye, and black

back, wings, and tail; under wing coverts yellow; legs and feet bright pinkish-red. Adult female: bright olive-green above, pale yellow below, streaked with pale olive-gray on throat, chest, and sides; feet dull red. Immature male like adult female except for blotches of incoming black and blue plumage. Veracruz, Yucatán, and Oaxaca to Brazil, Peru, and Bolivia (east of Andes); Cuba and Tobago.

3. Bananaquit (*Coereba flaveola*). 4½ inches. Sexes alike. Crown sooty-gray, bordered at either side by bold white superciliary line; rest of head, including whole chin and throat, light gray; rest of upper parts grayish-olive, except for yellowish-olive of rump and white patch at base of primaries; breast and sides lemon-yellow; flanks olive; belly and under tail coverts white. All tail feathers but middle pair tipped with white on inner webs. Veracruz, Oaxaca, Cozumel and Holbox Islands (off Yucatán), and West Indies to Paraguay, Argentina, and Peru.

Family Parulidae: Warblers

So many of the well-known warblers of the United States winter in, or migrate through, Mexico that the observer must be on the alert for almost any species in fall, winter, and spring. I have never, however, seen a Black-throated Blue (*Dendroica caerulescens*), Cape May (*D. tigrina*), Cerulean (*D. cerulea*), Black-poll (*D. striata*), or Palm Warbler (*D. palmarum*) in Mexico. Most of these species are known to migrate east of Mexico, either across the Gulf or through the West Indies.

Among "United States warblers" which inhabit Mexico are the little known Colima (*Vermivora crissalis*), which breeds in the mountains from southwestern Texas south to western Tamaulipas, Coahuila (probably), Michoacán, and Colima; the Pitiayumi (*Parula pitiayumi*), which breeds in the lowlands northward to the lower Río Grande valley, southern Sonora, and southern Chihuahua; the Yellow (*Dendroica petechia*), which breeds among willows and cottonwoods in the central plateau and in mangroves along both coasts; the Yellow-breasted Chat (*Icteria virens*), which breeds as far south as southern Tamaulipas, Guanajuato, and Jalisco; and the following, all of which breed northward in the mountains to the extreme southwestern United States: Olive Warbler (*Peucedramus olivaceus*), Grace's Warbler (*Dendroica graciae*), Red-faced Warbler (*Cardellina rubrifrons*), and Painted Redstart (*Setophaga picta*).

Mangrove-inhabiting Yellow Warblers do not intergrade with interior races. Males of coastal races are more or less chestnut on head. Race inhabiting Atlantic coast (southern Tamaulipas and Yucatán to Costa Rica) is *bryanti;* that inhabiting Pacific coast (Sonora to Nayarit; Baja California) is *castaneiceps.*

The Thick-billed Yellow-throat (*Chamaethlypis poliocephala*), often called the Río Grande Yellow-throat (so listed from the United States), breeds widely in Mexican lowlands, sometimes in a marshy situation, sometimes on a brushy slope, northward to the Yucatán peninsula, the lower Río Grande valley, and Sinaloa (see p. 39).

The Mexican yellow-throats of the genus *Geothlypis* are an extremely interesting lot. In general they resemble each other, through the breeding side by side at Lake Pátzcuaro of such forms as *speciosa* and *melanops* (Edwards) clearly indicates that there are two or more full species. *Geothlypis* is, of course, very local in breeding distribution. Vast areas of Mexico are without marshes or sedgy stream margins, hence without breeding *Geothlypis*. Where marshlands are extensive two or more species are to be looked for.

Breeding races of the familiar *G. trichas* (the "witchitty, witchitty bird") are *insperata* (lower Río Grande valley) *chryseola* (Sonora and Chihuahua), *modesta* (southern Sonora, Sinaloa, Nayarit, Jalisco, and Colima), and *melanops* (Veracruz, Oaxaca, México, and Michoacán). Other races move southward into Mexico in winter.

Yellow-throats more or less closely related to *G. trichas* are the Belding's (*G. beldingi*) of Baja California, a much larger species (5½ inches) with yellow band directly back of the black facial mask; the Alta Mira (*G. flavovelata*) of coastal southern Tamaulipas and northern Veracruz, possibly an Atlantic subspecies of *beldingi,* and certainly very similar in color pattern, but much smaller (4¾ inches); the Chapala (*G. chapalensis*) of Jalisco, similar to both the above in color, and intermediate in size; the Hooded (*G. nelsoni*) of Hidalgo, Tamaulipas (Heed and Robins), Veracruz, and Puebla, distinguished by the broadness of the black facial mask and the vagueness of the grayish-olive band just back of it; and the Black-polled (*G. speciosa*) of Veracruz and Michoacán, black throughout the whole top of the head, fading to olive on the occiput. Further study may show that *beldingi, flavovelata,* and *chapalensis* are really one species: they are certainly alike in having a yellow band back of the facial mask. The only *nelsoni* I have seen were in grass along small streams at considerable elevation in Veracruz. Black-polled Yellowthroats which I observed at Lake Pátzcuaro were much like *trichas* in behavior.

The following species of the Parulidae do not range northward to the United States:

1. Hartlaub's Warbler (*Vermivora superciliosa*) (see pp. 55–57). In the mountains from Chihuahua, Nuevo León, Sonora (probably), and Tamaulipas to Nicaragua.

2. Red-breasted Chat (*Granatellus venustus*). 5¾ inches. Tail as long as head and body. Male blue-gray above except for black of forehead, superciliary region, facial mask and middle tail feathers, and white of broad line back of eye, two indistinct wingbars, and extensive tipping of outer tail feathers. Under parts white except for more or less complete narrow black chest-band and bright pinkish-red mid-breast, mid-belly, and under tail coverts. Female similar in pattern, but forehead and lores woodsbrown blending into gray of crown and back; line back of eye buff; malar region, chin and throat dull white; chest and belly

buff; upper chest tinged with pink. Sinaloa to Oaxaca; Tres Marías Islands.

3. Gray-throated Chat (*G. sallaei*). 5 inches. Tail slightly *shorter* than head and body. Male rich bluish-gray on head and upper parts, including sides; middle of throat whitish-gray; black spot above short white postocular streak. Chest, middle of belly, and under tail coverts bright pinkish-red. Tail bluish-slate, outer two pairs of feathers very narrowly tipped with white. Female gray above except for buff forehead and superciliary line; buff below, palest on throat and middle of belly; outer tail feathers more extensively tipped with white than in male. Veracruz, Yucatán, and Oaxaca to eastern Guatemala.

4. Slate-throated Redstart (*Myioborus miniatus*). 5½ inches. Sexes alike. Upper parts, including sides and flanks, bluish-gray except for black forehead, orange-brown crown-patch, and black middle tail feathers; chin and throat slaty; middle of breast and belly scarlet in some races, orange or yellow in others; under tail coverts dark gray basally, boldly tipped with white; outer tail feathers with extensive white tipping. Southern Sinaloa, Chihuahua, Veracruz, and Puebla to Bolivia and Peru. Mexican races (*hellmayri* of Chiapas and *miniatus* of area to north) are both red-bellied, the shade being toward orange in *hellmayri. Aurantiacus* of Costa Rica and *acceptus* of Panama are orange- and yellow-bellied, respectively.

5. Fan-tailed Warbler (*Euthlypis lachrymosa*). 6 inches. Sexes alike. See pp. 171–72. Sonora, Chihuahua, and southern Tamaulipas to northern Nicaragua, in lowlands and lesser foothills.

6. Red Warbler (*Ergaticus ruber*). 5 inches. Sexes alike. Adults red all over, except for ear coverts, which are light silvery-gray. Young birds cinnamon-brown or russet, with gray ear coverts. Sinaloa and Durango to Veracruz and Oaxaca, high in mountains.

7. Pink-headed Warbler (*E. versicolor*). 5 inches. Sexes alike. Whole head and neck dull pink with silvery gloss; body red, brighter below than above; wing with ill-

defined pinkish bar. Southern Chiapas and Guatemala.

8. Yellow-crowned Warbler (*Basileuterus culicivorus*). 5¼ inches. See page 136. Jalisco, Nuevo León, and central Tamaulipas to Paraguay and northern Argentina. Song: *chew chewee chew wechet* (Martin). The northeastern Mexican race, *brasheri,* has long been known as Brasher's Warbler.

9. Bell's Warbler (*B. belli*). 5¼ inches. Middle of crown chestnut, bordered by lines of black which meet at forehead; lores and ear coverts chestnut, bordered above by bright yellow superciliary line; back, rump, wings, and tail olive; under parts bright yellow, deepening to olive on sides and flanks. Southern Tamaulipas and Jalisco to Guatemala, in the mountains.

10. Rufous-capped Warbler (*B. rufifrons*), 4¾ inches. Sexes alike. See pp. 45–46. Sonora, Chihuahua, central Nuevo León, and southern Tamaulipas to Guatemala, breeding principally in the mountains but descending to lowlands in winter.

Family Ploceidae: Weaver-finches

The English Sparrow (*Passer domesticus*) has established itself widely in cities and agricultural districts. I believe we did not see it in the city of Morelia, however, and in Pátzcuaro the familiar dooryard birds were House Finches and Canyon Wrens.

Family Icteridae: Grackles, Orioles, Cowbirds, and allies

This family is well represented in Mexico, virtually all "United States species" being found there. Essentially Middle American species which range regularly northward to the southwestern United States include the Red-eyed Cowbird (*Tangavius aeneus*), Black-headed Oriole (*Icterus graduacauda*), and Hooded Oriole (*I. cucullatus*). The Great-tailed Grackle (*Cassidix mexicanus*) is so common south of the border that one comes to think of it as Mexican, though of course it ranges widely through the southeastern United States also. The Brewer's Blackbird (*Euphagus cyanocephalus*) is common in Mexico in winter, but the Rusty Blackbird (*E. carolinus*) has never, so far as I know, been recorded there. The well-known Baltimore (*Icterus galbula*), Bullock's (*I. bullocki*), Orchard (*I. spurius*) and Scott's Orioles (*I. parisorum*) are common as transients. The first three of these winter in southern Mexico; the last winters widely in western Mexico and may breed there.

A good way to proceed in learning the distinctive Mexican icterids is to begin with the following black or mostly-black ones:

1. Sumichrast's Blackbird (*Dives dives*). 10 inches. Black with rather dull gloss; eyes dark brown; tail rounded and not troughed; bill as long as head. Flies across road, plunging quickly into thicket; lifts tail nervously as it feeds or perches; often seen at water's edge; song loud and clear, a repeated *plop-year, plee-toy,* or *coo-plee,* with liquid quality at first, and often sung from crown of high tree. Southern Tamaulipas, Yucatán peninsula, and Puebla to Nicaragua.

2. Yellow-billed Cacique (*Amblycercus holosericeus*). 9 inches. Dull black with white eyes and pale greenish-yellow bill. Usually feeds near ground in dense brush along streams or roads. Often goes about in pairs. Vigorous in hacking at bark with sharp bill. Song astonishingly loud and rich. Callnote a dull grunt. Southern Tamaulipas, Yucatán, and Puebla to Peru and Bolivia.

3. Slender-billed Grackle (*Cassidix palustris*). Male 13 inches, female 11 inches. Similar to Great-tailed Grackle but decidedly smaller and male less glossy throughout and more reddish-violet on head, neck, and breast. Female noticeably black on rump and tail in contrast to rusty-brown of back. Marshes about Mexico City.

4. Giant Cowbird or Rice Grackle (*Psomocolax oryzivorus*). Male 13½ inches, fe-

male 11½ inches. Tail square or slightly rounded, untroughed. Bill short and thick. In male tips of feathers glossed with purplish-blue, the neck plumage forming a ruff or mantle. Female duller and without ruff. Veracruz and Tabasco to Paraguay and Bolivia.

5. Mexican Cacique (*Cassiculus melanicterus*). Male 11½ inches, female 10 inches. Noticeable wavy crest. Bill yellowish-white. Male: black, with rump, tail coverts above and below, bold patch in wing coverts, and outer tail feathers bright yellow. Female: dark olive-slate above, sooty-gray below, with yellow spotting on forehead, some olive in yellow of rump, and yellow tail feathers edged with olive. Sinaloa (irregularly, southern Sonora) to Chiapas. Colonial.

Oropendolas

6. Montezuma Oropendola (*Gymnostinops montezuma*). Male 22 inches, female 17 inches. Bill somewhat longer than head, sharply pointed, black at base and orange on distal half; bare skin of face pinkish in life. A thin crest. Eyes brown. Whole head, neck, and upper chest black; body and wings maroon-chestnut; tail bright yellow except for two dark brown middle feathers. Flight slow and labored, like that of crow. Song delivered with exaggerated bowing forward, spreading of wings, and elevating of tail. Colonial. Southern Tamaulipas, Quintana Roo, and Oaxaca to Panama.

7. Wagler's Oropendola (*Zarhynchus wagleri*). Male 13½ inches, female 11 inches. Thin crest. Bill greenish-white, thickened at base, both above and below, forming slight casque. Rich brown except for glossy black of back, belly, wings and two middle tail feathers, and bright yellow of rest of tail. Callnotes loud and arresting. One note a crashing sound "suggestive of the cutting of dry brush with a machete" (Sturgis). Veracruz and Chiapas to northern South America.

Orioles

8. Black-throated Oriole (*Icterus gularis*). 10 inches. See page 109. Female a little duller than male and young birds still duller. Central Tamaulipas, Yucatán peninsula, and Guerrero to Guatemala and Honduras.

9. Spotted-breasted Oriole (*I. pectoralis*). 9 inches. Sexes similar. Rich orange except for black of lores, chin, throat, back, wings, and tail; sides of chest boldly spotted with black; small patch of white at base of primaries; secondaries edged with white. Oaxaca and Chiapas to Costa Rica.

10. Wagler's Oriole (*I. wagleri*). 9 inches. Adult male: black with yellow belly, sides, flanks, and rump (black under tail coverts); a band of chestnut bordering black of chest in Sonora and Chihuahua race. Female: yellow below except for black of face and throat-patch; crown and rump olive; back, wings, and tail dark grayish-olive, the back vaguely streaked. Immature male like female, but yellow of under parts brighter, face and throat with irregular black spotting. Sonora, Chihuahua, and Nuevo León to Nicaragua.

11. Yellow-tailed Oriole (*I. mesomelas*). 9 inches. Sexes alike. Bright yellow (orange on head) except for black of lores, throat-patch, back, wings, and much of tail. Patch on wing (lesser, middle, and some greater coverts) bright yellow. Middle four tail feathers black, the rest black at base, broadly tipped with yellow. Veracruz, Yucatán, and Oaxaca to northern South America.

12. Yellow-backed Oriole (*I. chrysater*). 9 inches. Male: dull orange-yellow except for black of forehead, face, chin, throat, wings, and tail. Some lesser wing coverts yellow. Female similar, but duller; wings and tail dark olive-brown (without markings); black throat-patch bordered with brownish-orange. Yucatán, Veracruz, and Chiapas to northern South America (range presumably continuous throughout Central America).

13. Orange Oriole (*I. auratus*). 8 inches. Male: bright orange-yellow (richest on head and chest), except for black of face, throat, wings, and tail. Lesser wing coverts boldly tipped, and remiges edged, with white. Female: wings dark brownish-gray; tail and back olive; black throat-patch

veiled with yellow; wings with two narrow white bars. Yucatán.

14. Black-cowled Oriole (*I. prosthemelas*). 8 inches. Male glossy black except for yellow of lesser wing coverts, rump, belly, sides, flanks, and under tail coverts; black of breast bordered by indistinct band of chestnut. Female duller: whole of hind neck and back olive; rump and upper tail coverts yellow. Veracruz and Yucatán to Panama. *Northropi, melanopsis, dominicensis* and *portoricensis* of the West Indies and *prosthemelas* may all be races of one species.

15. Flame-headed Oriole (*I. pustulatus*). 8 inches. Male: orange-scarlet on face, sides of head, and breast, fading to pale orange on belly; lores and throat black; back dull yellow, boldly streaked with black; rump and upper tail coverts orange; wings black, with two narrow white bars and white edgings; tail black with white tips on outer three pairs of feathers. Female duller. Chihuahua, Sonora, Puebla, México, and Veracruz to Costa Rica; Tres Marías Islands. *I. sclateri* (Costa Rica to Oaxaca) is yellow-rather than orange-headed and the black streaks on the back are very broad. Probably a subspecies of *pustulatus*.

16. Abeillé's Oriole (*I. abeillei*). 7½ inches. Adult male: black above except for yellow line between nostril and top of eye, and large white patch in wing; rich orange-yellow below except for black of chin, throat, sides, and flanks. Middle two rectrices black, the rest yellow with black tips. Female: olive-gray above with two white wing-bars; yellow on forehead and face; throat with hint of black patch in middle, but malar region, chin, throat, and chest dull yellow otherwise; rest of under parts

gray, fading to white in middle of belly. Immature male like female but with black throat-patch and more or less black on head and sides of chest. High parts of San Luis Potosí, Guanajuato, Puebla, México, Morelos, Veracruz, and Jalisco (Hellmayr). I have seen it also in Michoacán, in spruce forest at about 10,000 feet elevation along the Pátzcuaro-Tacámbaro highway. Said to intergrade with Bullock's Oriole in northern Durango.

17. Fuertes's Oriole (*I. fuertesi*). 6¼ inches. Adult male: black on head, neck, upper chest, back, and tail. Wing blackish-brown except for pale brown lesser coverts and white of bar and edgings. Breast, belly, sides, flanks, rump, and upper and under tail coverts pale brown. Female: olive-gray above, with two white wing-bars; pale yellow below, deepening to olive on sides and flanks. Immature male like female but with black throat-patch. Coastal lowlands of southeastern Tamaulipas and Veracruz. Wetmore has reported specimens taken at Tlacotalpam and El Conejo, Veracruz. Northern limits of range to be worked out. May intergrade with *spurius* in coastal northeastern Tamaulipas.

Meadowlarks

Both the Eastern Meadowlark (*Sturnella magna*) and Western Meadowlark (*S. neglecta*) inhabit Mexican grasslands, the former widely as a breeding bird, the latter as a breeding bird in the northern part of the central plateau and as a winter visitor as far south as Jalisco and Guanajuato. Eastern Meadowlarks breeding from Sinaloa and Durango to Michoacán and Guanajuato are buffy-orange on the chest. They belong to the well-defined race *auropectoralis,* described by Saunders.

Family Thraupidae: TANAGERS

The best known tanager of the United States, the Scarlet (*Piranga olivacea*), is an extremely rare bird in Mexico. In migrating to and from its winter home in South America it passes chiefly through the West Indies and along the east coast of Central America (Cooke). The Summer Tanager

(*P. rubra*) breeds in northeastern Mexico (south as far as northern Durango, according to Hellmayr), and winters extensively; the Hepatic Tanager (*P. flava*) breeds widely (mountains of southwestern Texas, southern New Mexico, and southern Arizona to Argentina); and the Western Tanager (*P. ludovicians*) breeds in the mountains of northern Sonora (van Rossem) and winters throughout the republic.

The following species do not reach the United States border:

1. Flame-colored Tanager (*P. bidentata*). See page 157. Sinaloa, central Nuevo León, and central Tamaulipas to Panama; Tres Marías Islands.

2. White-winged Tanager (*P. leucoptera*). See page 178. Southern Tamaulipas, Puebla, and Mexico to northwestern Bolivia.

3. Red-headed Tanager (*P. erythrocephala*). 6 inches. Male: whole head and neck vermilion except for blackish lores, the lower part pinkish with silvery sheen; back, wings, and tail yellowish-olive; under parts bright yellow, deepening to olive on sides and fading to pale yellow on belly and under tail coverts. Female: olive-green above, dull yellow below. Sonora and Chihuahua to Oaxaca.

4. Rose-throated Tanager (*P. roseo-gularis*). 6¾ inches. Male: ashy-gray (lighter below than above), with dull red crown, wings, and tail, and rosy chin, throat, and upper breast. Female: gray with yellowish-olive crown, wings, and tail and dull yellow chin and throat. Yucatán peninsula (including Cozumel and Mujeres Islands) and eastern Guatemala.

5. Yellow-winged or Abbot Tanager (*Thraupis abbas*). 7 inches. Sexes alike. Head small; bill short, thick, and finchlike. Head and upper breast grayish-blue, fading to grayish-olive on belly and to grayish-slate on back. Lesser wing coverts gray-blue; greater coverts olive; remiges brownish-black, with bold yellow spot at base of primaries. Tail brownish-black. Usually stays high in trees along rivers. Song a not very musical series of short phrases, almost chips. Southern Tamaulipas, San Luis Potosí, and Veracruz to northern Nicaragua.

6. Blue-gray Tanager (*T. episcopus*). 6½ inches. Light bluish-gray with clear blue wings and tail, the blue brightest on lesser wing coverts. Veracruz, Tabasco, and Quintana Roo to Brazil and Peru.

7. Velvet Tanager or Scarlet-rumped Tanager (*Ramphocelus passerini*). 6½ inches. Bill short, thick, and finchlike, swollen at base of lower mandible. Male: rich velvety black except for brilliant orange-scarlet of rump and upper tail coverts. Female: head and neck plain gray, brightening to dull orange on chest and orange-olive on back; lower back, rump, and upper tail coverts dull orange; wings and tail gray-brown, the feathers edged with olive-orange; belly and under tail coverts olive-gray. Tabasco to Panama.

8. Crimson-collared Tanager (*Phlogothraupis sanguinolenta*). 7½ inches. Sexes alike. Bill short and finchlike, somewhat decurved, and very light-colored—a conspicuous field-character (Wetmore). Plumage glossy blue-black except for deep red of crown, whole neck, chest, and upper and under tail coverts. Veracruz, Quintana Roo, and Oaxaca to Costa Rica and Panama.

9. Black-throated Shrike-Tanager (*Lanio aurantius*). 8 inches. Bill heavy, strongly hooked, and with conspicuous tooth on cutting edge of upper mandible. Male: black on head, neck, wings, and tail; bright yellow otherwise, the upper breast tinged with brown where it borders the black. Female: head gray, the crown tinged with olive; back brownish-olive; rump orange-olive; wings and tail olive-brown; breast yellowish-olive, brightening to yellow on belly; under tail coverts dull orange-buff. Veracruz, Quintana Roo, and Oaxaca to Honduras. *L. melanopygius* and its allies (Costa Rica and Panama) comprise a closely related, but separate, species.

10. Gray-headed Tanager (*Eucometis penicillata*). 6¾ inches. Bill short but not very heavy. Sexes alike. Head, above and below, ashy-gray; upper part of body olive, brightest on rump; below rich yellow with olive flanks. Southern Veracruz (Wetmore) and Yucatán peninsula to Bolivia and Paraguay.

Ant-Tanagers

The interesting Ant-Tanagers of the genus *Habia* range northward to Nayarit and southern Tamaulipas. Little bands of these comparatively terrestrial birds move about through thicker parts of the forest, chattering noisily. Their alarm notes are harsh, suggesting those of thrashers or jays, but their songs are loud, rich and rhythmical. Two species exist virtually side by side in eastern Mexico, and they are hard to tell apart in the field. I do not know how to distinguish them on the basis of songs or callnotes, and what I have said above may possibly apply to only one species, not to both. Along the Río Sabinas, in southern Tamaulipas, the favorite habitat of one species (*gutturalis*) is the thicketted floodplain, while the other (*rubica*) seems to prefer the slopes above the river. Each species may nest semi-colonially. Here are descriptions:

11. Red Ant-Tanager (*Habia rubica*). 7 inches. Male: dull reddish-brown above except for bright red crown-patch, bordered at either side with black; dull pale red below, brightest on throat and chest, and gray on flanks. Female: olive-brown above, olive-buff below, with dull orange crown-spot. Southern Tamaulipas, Yucatán peninsula, and Nayarit to Argentina and Paraguay.

12. Red-throated Ant-Tanager (*H. gutturalis*). 8 inches. Male: dull pinkish-brown above except for partly concealed bright red crown-patch, which is not bordered with black; dull rosy-red below, brightest on throat and chest and fading to pinkish-gray on sides and flanks. Female rich woods brown above and on chest, sides, and flanks; buffy-yellow on throat; pale yellowish-brown on belly and under tail coverts; no crown patch, though feathers of middle of crown are somewhat brighter at base than are those of superciliary region. Southern Tamaulipas, Yucatán peninsula, and Oaxaca to Colombia.

Stub-billed Tanagers

The stub-billed tanagers of Mexico belong to the genera *Chlorophonia* and *Tanagra*. They are chunky, proportionately large-headed birds. Those of the genus *Tanagra* are usually called euphonias. Euphonias are stub-tailed as well as stub-billed and are very fond of mistletoe berries.

13. Blue-crowned Chlorophonia (*Chlorophonia occipitalis*). 5½ inches. Male: bright glistening green above except for pale blue crown-spot and narrow pale blue collar across hind neck; chin, throat, and sides glistening green; rest of under parts bright yellow, yellow of breast separated from green of throat by narrow black and brown line. Female: similar but green of throat fades gradually into yellow of belly and under tail coverts. Veracruz and Chiapas to Costa Rica and Panama.

14. Bonaparte's Euphonia (*Tanagra lauta*). See pp. 151–52. Southern Tamaulipas, Yucatán, and Oaxaca to Costa Rica and Panama.

15. Lesson's Euphonia (*T. affinis*). 3¾ inches. See pp. 151–52. Southern Tamaulipas, Yucatán, and Oaxaca to Costa Rica.

16. Godman's Euphonia (*T. godmani*). 3¾ inches. Much like the above; but in male yellow of forehead is pale, and under tail coverts are white, not yellow; in female back of head gray, in contrast to olive of back. Sonora to Nayarit and Colima.

17. Blue-hooded Euphonia (*T. elegantissima*). 4½ inches. Male: forehead orange-brown, followed first by narrow black line then by light blue of whole crown and hind neck; back, wings, and tail rich glossy purple; chin and throat purplish-black; rest of under parts deep orange-tawny. Female: olive-green above except for blue of crown and orange-brown of forehead; yellowish-olive below except for brownish-yellow of throat. Southwestern Sonora (van Rossem), Guanajuato, and southern Tamaulipas (Robins and Heed) to Costa Rica. Common in montane forest just north of Jacala, Hidalgo.

18. Gould's Euphonia (*Tanagra gouldi*). 3¾ inches. Male: forehead bright yellow; rest of upper parts olive with bluish gloss; sides of head, chin, throat, and chest olive, without gloss; sides and flanks olive, the feathers tipped with bright yellow; mid-breast, mid-belly, and under tail coverts deep tawny. Female: similar, but forehead rusty, and tawny of under parts restricted to under tail coverts. Quintana Roo, Veracruz, and Oaxaca to Panama.

Genus *Tangara*

The large tropical genus *Tangara,* which

is represented by so many forms in South America, is represented by this one species in Mexico:

19. Golden-masked Tanager (*Tangara nigro-cincta*). 5¼ inches. Sexes alike. Plumage at base of bill, both above and below, black, fading to purple then to pale blue on fore-crown, auriculars, malar region, and chin; rear part of crown, hind neck, and sides of neck shining golden-buff (changing to oil-green and coppery-orange in certain lights), this buff area connecting with reddish-brown of throat; chest and back black; wings and tail black, the feathers edged with shining green and blue; lesser wing coverts purplish-blue; rump shining blue; flanks purplish-blue, greenish in certain lights; belly and under tail coverts white. Tabasco and Chiapas southward into South America.

Bush-Tanagers

Most tanagers of this group are dull, and their short, stubby bills give them the general appearance of finches. The only Mexican species is:

20. Common Bush-Tanager (*Chlorospingus ophthalmicus*). 5½ inches. Sexes alike. Head grayish-brown above, light gray below, with white spot just back of eye; back, wings, and tail olive; chest, sides, and flanks yellowish-olive; belly light gray; under tail coverts yellowish-olive. San Luis Potosí, Veracruz, and Guerrero to Costa Rica.

Thrush-Tanager

Among Mexico's most remarkable birds is the Thrush-Tanager. Its bill is long and thrushlike. It ranges well northward in the tropical zone of *western* Mexico, but not in the east:

20. Thrush-Tanager (*Rhodinocichla rosea*). 7¾ inches. Male: uniform slaty-gray except for clear rose-red of superciliary line, chin, throat, mid-breast, mid-belly, and under tail coverts. Female: the same in pattern, but the pink replaced by clear rich tawny, fading to white on belly. Sinaloa to northern South America.

Family Fringillidae: Finches

Many species of this large family are common to the United States and Mexico. The non-migratory Cardinal (*Richmondena cardinalis*) ranges widely in the lowlands. Of the several races three are endemic to islands—respectively the Tres Marías, Tiburón, and Cozumel. The Pyrrhuloxia (*Pyrrhuloxia sinuata*) breeds from the border south to Puebla, Zacatecas, Guanajuato, and Nayarit. An isolated race is endemic to the Cape district of Baja California. The Rose-breasted Grosbeak (*Pheucticus ludovicianus*) winters from southern Mexico to northern South America and is a common transient in eastern Mexico. The Black-headed Grosbeak (*P. melanocephalus*) breeds in the mountains south as far as Oaxaca and Veracruz and is also a winter visitant and transient. The Blue Grosbeak (*Guiraca caerulea*) breeds in lowlands south to Oaxaca and Chiapas, and is also a transient and winter visitant. The Evening Grosbeak (*Hesperiphona vespertina*) breeds in the mountains southward to Veracruz, Puebla, and Oaxaca. Less familiar, more distinctively Mexican grosbeaks are the following:

1. Crimson-collared Grosbeak (*Rhodothraupis celaeno*). 8¾ inches. See pages 137–39. Brushy woods of central and southern Tamaulipas, southern Nuevo León, San Luis Potosí, Puebla, and northern Veracruz. Usually sings from a hidden position rather than from the top of a bush or tree. Fairly common in sweet gum forests at 3,400 feet elevation along Antiguo Morelos to San Luis Potosí highway (Irby Davis).

2. Yellow Grosbeak (*Pheucticus chrysopeplus*). 8½ inches. Male: yellow on head, neck, rump, and under parts (except for white under tail coverts); back black with yellow spots down the middle; wings and tail black with white markings. Female: olive above, streaked with dusky; face, middle of crown, and superciliary region suffused with yellow; wings and tail olive-gray, the former with white markings;

under parts yellow, duller than in male. Northwestern South America to Sonora, Durango, and Puebla, chiefly in highlands. In the race *aurantiacus* (Chiapas and Guatemala) the bright parts are rich golden-orange.

3. Black-faced Grosbeak (*Caryothraustes poliogaster*). 7¼ inches. Facial patch black; plumage bordering this patch yellow, deepening to yellowish-olive on crown, sides of neck, and chest; scapulars, rump, and upper tail coverts slaty-gray; rest of upper parts olive; under wing coverts light yellow; sides and flanks gray; belly and under tail coverts pale yellowish-gray. Bill black with bluish-gray base. Panama to Oaxaca, Tabasco, and Veracruz; "a forest bird that ranges high in the trees" (Wetmore).

4. Blue-black Grosbeak (*Cyanocompsa cyanoides*). 7 inches. Bill very heavy. Male dull blue-black, with hint of dull indigo on forehead, superciliary region, and lesser wing coverts. Female and immature male rich dark brown, toward black on wings and tail and toward rusty on chest and belly. Northern South America to Chiapas, Tabasco, and Veracruz. A bird of forest undergrowth; callnote a "metallic *clink*, sometimes two-syllabled" (Sturgis).

5. Abeillé's Grosbeak (*Hesperiphona abeillei*). See page 178. Chihuahua to southern Tamaulipas, Veracruz, Puebla, Oaxaca, and Guatemala, breeding supposedly only in the mountains but wintering to some extent in the lowlands.

Saltators

These interesting large finches are sure to puzzle the newcomer. No short description will serve for all three Mexican species. The sexes are alike.

6. Black-headed Saltator (*Saltator atriceps*). 10 inches. Head, neck, and chest black, except for large white spot on throat; back, rump, wings, and tail yellowish-olive, bright in full sunlight; belly, sides, and flanks gray; under tail coverts rufous. Black on lower throat and chest varies, some birds being almost wholly white there. The race *suffusus* (southern Veracruz) has dark brown throat-patch. A noisy, noticeable species in spring. Callnotes rough and loud, among them *chuh, chuck-er,* and *choo-eek*. Occasionally sings a flight-song. Frequent tangles of vines and bamboo, usually along streams. Yucatán peninsula, southern Tamaulipas, and Oaxaca to Panama.

7. Gray Saltator (*S. coerulescens*). 9 inches. Head, neck, and upper part of body slaty-gray except for distinct white superciliary line and buffy-white streak down middle of chin and throat; chest, sides, and flanks dark olive-gray, brightening to rufous-buff on belly and under tail coverts. Argentina and Paraguay to Yucatán peninsula, southern Tamaulipas, Durango, and Sinaloa, in lowland thickets. More retiring and usually harder to see than Black-headed Saltator. Song in Tamaulipas a clear *chuck, chuck-er-preeee!* strongly suggestive of an interrupted Cardinal's song.

8. Buff-throated Saltator (*S. maximus*). 8 inches. Much like Black-headed Saltator in color, but decidedly smaller and more of a forest bird (Wetmore). Black restricted to chin, sides of throat, and upper chest. Upper part of head dark gray (olive on crown), with narrow white superciliary line. Middle of chin white; middle of throat brownish-buff. Back, rump, wings, and tail yellowish-olive; belly and sides dark gray; flanks olive; belly buffy-white; under tail coverts rufous. Bolivia and Brazil to Quintana Roo, Campeche, Tabasco, Veracruz, and Oaxaca.

Buntings

Most United States birds commonly called buntings occur in Mexico—the Painted (*Passerina ciris*) chiefly as a transient and winter visitant (though Warner and Mengel have reported it from Veracruz in July); the Lazuli (*P. amoena*) and Indigo (*P. cyanea*) as winter visitants and transients; the Varied (*P. versicolor*) as a resident from the border to Guatemala in drier lowlands; the Lark Bunting (*Calamospiza melanocorys*) as a transient and winter visitant; the Dickcissel (*Spiza americana*) as a transient, sometimes abundant. Buntings which do not range northward to the United States are:

9. Blue Bunting (*Cyanocompsa parel-*

lina). 5¼ inches. See page 135. Nicaragua to Yucatán peninsula, central Tamaulipas, Nuevo León, Puebla, and Sinaloa in brushy lowlands.

10. Leclancher's Bunting (*Passerina leclancheri*). 5 inches. Male: top of head golden-olive; area about eye bright yellow; rest of upper parts, including sides of head, clear cerulean blue, tinged on back with olive; under parts yellow, deepening to orange on lower throat and chest. Female: crown, hind neck, and back grayish-olive, brightening to blue on ear coverts, rump, and wing and tail edgings; under parts and area about eye pale yellow, brightest on chest. Colima to Oaxaca (and possibly Puebla) in dry lowlands.

11. Rosita's Bunting (*P. rositae*). 5¼ inches. Male: upper parts cerulean blue, purplish on head; eye-ring white; chin grayish-white; throat cerulean; chest and upper belly scarlet, veiled with blue; flanks, lower abdomen, and under tail coverts salmon-pink. Female: upper parts grayish-brown, darkest on crown; back tinged with olive-green; lesser wing coverts, rump, upper tail coverts, and edges of wing and tail feathers grayish-blue; under parts deep pinkish-buff. Oaxaca and Chiapas.

12. Yellow-faced Grassquit (*Tiaris olivacea*). 4 inches. Male: head and chest black except for yellow of superciliary line, upper throat, and spot under eye; rest of body olive, grayish on belly, buffy-yellow on under tail coverts. Female: grayish-olive, with hint of yellow on throat and of black on chest. West Indies; northern South America to southern Tamaulipas, Yucatán, and Oaxaca, chiefly in lowlands.

House Finch and allies

The House Finch (*Carpodacus mexicanus*) ranges southward through the Mexican plateau to Veracruz, Puebla, Oaxaca, Michoacán, and the Cape district of Baja California. The race *clementis* is endemic to certain Baja California islands. The Purple Finch (*C. purpureus*) breeds southward into Baja California. The Cassin's Purple Finch (*C. cassini*) breeds southward to the San Pedro Mártir range

in Baja California and winters southward on the plateau to Veracruz.

Seedeaters and allies

Only one species of seedeater inhabits Mexico—*Sporophila torqueola,* the Collared Seedeater. The northernmost race, *sharpei* of the lower Río Grande valley and Tamaulipas (see pp. 35–36), is characterized by the incompleteness of the adult male's black chest-band. In *torqueola* (Sinaloa to Puebla and Oaxaca) the chest-band is complete and the rump and most of the under parts are clear bright cinnamon. In *morelleti* (eastern Mexico south of Tamaulipas), a larger race than either *sharpei* or *torqueola,* the underparts and rump are buffy-white; the chest-band is very broad; and the throat is more or less black.

13. Thick-billed Seed-Finch (*Oryzoborus funereus*). 4½ inches. Very heavy-billed; male dull black except for white underwing and small white patch at base of primaries. Female olive-brown above and on chest; light tawny-cinnamon on throat, belly, and rump. Young males resembles female. Likes marshy places. Northern South America to Veracruz, Tabasco, and Oaxaca.

14. Blue-black Grassquit (*Volatinia jacarina*). 4 inches. Adult male in midsummer glossy blue-black, with concealed small white patch in front of base of wing. Female olive-brown above, buffy below, streaked with olive-brown on chest. Young male resembles female. The fact that *all* midsummer males in a large series of specimens before me are solid black, and that no winter or spring male is without brown, strongly suggests that the adult male's winter plumage is brown-tipped and that the black breeding plumage results at least partly from wear. Goes about in flocks. Males have a habit of flying straight up several inches from a perch and straight down again, in a sort of flip-flop. Sinaloa and southern Tamaulipas to Paraguay and northern Argentina.

Siskins and Goldfinches

The Pine Siskin (*Spinus pinus*) breeds in the mountains, south to Chiapas and

253

western Guatemala (van Rossem). The Common Goldfinch (*S. tristis*) occurs principally as a winter visitor (south to Veracruz, Nuevo León, and Coahuila), but breeds in northwestern Baja California. The Arkansas or Dark-backed Goldfinch (*S. psaltria*) breeds in lowlands virtually throughout the republic, though I find no records for Tabasco and southern Veracruz. The Lawrence's Goldfinch (*S. lawrencei*) breeds southward into northern Baja California. There is one distinctively Middle American species:

15. Black-headed Siskin (*S. notatus*). 4¾ inches. Sexes alike. Whole head and neck black; back yellowish-olive; wings and tail black with yellow markings; rump and upper tail coverts yellow; breast, sides, and flanks yellowish-olive, brightening to clear yellow on belly and under tail coverts. Sonora, Chihuahua, San Luis Potosí (and probably southern Tamaulipas and Nuevo León) to northern Nicaragua, chiefly in the mountains.

Crossbills

The Red Crossbill (*Loxia curvirostra*) breeds widely in the mountains. I have seen it repeatedly along the highway between Mexico City and Puebla.

Yellow Finch

16. Yellow Finch (*Sicalis luteola*). 4½ inches. Sexes similar (female duller). Forehead, sides of head and neck, and rump olive-yellow; crown and hind neck yellowish-olive; back and scapulars grayish-brown, streaked with black; wing-bars brown; entire under parts, including malar region and supraloral spot, canary yellow. Veracruz, Chiapas, and Guatemala; also in South America. Rare and little known. F. W. Loetscher, Jr. has encountered it in the vicinity of Jalapa, Veracruz.

Slaty Finch

17. Slaty Finch (*Spodiornis rusticus*). 4¾ inches. Adults slate-color all over; young plain dark brown above, buff below, heavily streaked with dusky on chest and sides. Known from Chiapas (Brodkorb and Staebler) and Veracruz. Species ranges also from Costa Rica southward to northern Bolivia. Very little known.

Rufous-capped Atlapetes and allies

The genus *Atlapetes* is represented by numerous forms in South and Middle America, and several species inhabit Mexico. They are ground-inhabiting and dull-colored for the most part, and easily identifiable providing they are clearly seen. In all species the sexes are alike.

18. Rufous-capped Atlapetes (*A. pileatus*). 5¾ inches. See pp. 56–57. The plateau, from Chihuahua, Nuevo León, and Tamaulipas to Veracruz, México, Oaxaca, and Michoacán.

19. White-naped Atlapetes (*A. albinucha*). 7 inches. Top of head and hind neck black, with white stripe down middle of crown; rest of upper parts blackish-slate except for two faint gray wing-bars; under parts yellow, deepening to olive-gray on sides and flanks; under tail coverts light olive-gray on sides and flanks; under tail coverts light olive-gray. Veracruz, Oaxaca, Chiapas, and probably San Luis Potosí; northern Colombia.

20. Yellow-throated Atlapetes (*A. gutturalis*). 7½ inches. Like the above except that only the chin and throat are yellow; rest of under parts gray, palest in middle of belly and darkest on sides, flanks, and under tail coverts. Chiapas to northern Colombia in subtropical zone.

21. Chestnut-capped Atlapetes (*A. brunnei-nucha*). 8¼ inches. Forehead and sides of head black except for white supraloral spot and chestnut of crown and hind neck, the chestnut bordered along sides with golden-brown; rest of upper parts olive; chin, throat, and middle of belly white; a narrow black chest-band; sides, flanks, and under tail coverts gray, tinged with olive. San Luis Potosí, Veracruz, and Oaxaca to southern Peru.

22. San Martín Atlapetes (*A. apertus*). About 8 inches. Very similar to the above, but with no black chest-band and no yellow along sides of chestnut crown-patch. Highlands of southern Veracruz (Wetmore).

254

23. Green-striped Atlapetes (*A. virenticeps*). 8 inches. Upper part of head black except for midline on crown and superciliary lines, all of which are white from forehead to above eye, olive-green from there to occiput; rest of upper parts olive; chin and throat white; broad chest-band gray; sides, flanks, and under tail coverts olive-gray; middle of belly white. Jalisco, Michoacán, Morelos, Puebla, México, and Guanajuato. Hellmayr regards this bird as a subspecies of *torquatus,* but the fact that *torquatus* is not found between Michoacán and Costa Rica is a rather strong argument for regarding *virenticeps* as a full species. Note, however, that *A. albinucha* (above) has a strikingly interrupted range.

Orange-billed Sparrow

24. Orange-billed Sparrow (*Arremon aurantiirostris*). 6½ inches. Upper part of head black with gray midline on crown and white superciliaries, all extending from forehead to occiput; rest of upper parts dark olive-gray, except for bright yellow spot at bend of wing. A broad black chest-band. Throat and middle of belly white; sides, flanks, and under tail coverts dark olive-gray. Bill orange. Tabasco and Oaxaca to northern South America.

Olive Sparrow and allies

The Olive Sparrow (*Arremonops rufivirgatus*) ranges northward to southern Texas and southern Sinaloa. Along the Río Grande I have seen it as far upstream as Laredo, where it breeds locally. A non-migratory species, it ranges south to Costa Rica, occurring throughout the Yucatán peninsula. See pp. 21, 49, etc.

25. Green-backed Sparrow (*Arremonops conirostris*). 6 inches. Similar to the above, but whole top and sides of head gray, with line through eye and at either side of crown blackish-brown; upper parts decidedly *greenish*-olive; chest and sides gray; under tail coverts olive-buff. Yucatán peninsula, Tabasco, and Chiapas to northern South America.

Towhees

The Green-tailed Towhee (*Chlorura chlorura*) winters southward at last as far as Michoacán (Edwards) and Guanajuato. The Spotted Towhee (*P. maculatus*), which ranges so widely in montane parts of the United States, breeds southward to southern Durango, Nayarit, México, the eastern border of Michoacán, Oaxaca, Chiapas, and western Guatemala. Sibley regards all Spotted Towhees as races of the Red-eyed Towhee (*P. erythrophthalmus*). The strongly greenish *macronyx,* which inhabits thickets in the Mexico City region, has been considered a distinct species by many ornithologists. The well known Brown Towhee (*Pipilo fuscus*) breeds widely on the plateau, southward to Michoacán, México, Puebla, Veracruz, and Baja California. The Abert's Towhee (*P. aberti*) breeds southward to northwestern Sonora. The one wholly distinctive Mexican towhee is:

26. Collared Towhee (*Pipilo ocai*). 8 inches. An exceedingly variable species, but all forms alike in possessing rufous patch on rear part of crown; olive-green back, rump, wings, and tail; gray sides; olive-brown flanks; white belly; and rufous-buff under tail coverts. In some races the whole chin and throat are white and there is a bold white superciliary line and broad black chest-band. In the Michoacán race, *nigrescens,* which I know well from field experience, some birds are solid black on the whole chin, throat, and upper chest, others more or less extensively white on the throat. The principal callnote of birds which lived near our camp along the Pátzcuaro-Tacámbaro highway was a loud *jree* or *dree,* quite suggestive of the *chewink* or *joree* of *P. erythrophthalmus.*

Ground Sparrows

The Ground Sparrows (genus *Melozone*) are like Brown Towhees (*Pipilo fuscus*) in proportions and bearing. Neither of the two species has ever been recorded north of the United States border. The sexes are alike.

27. Rusty-crowned Ground Sparrow (*Melozone kieneri*). 7 inches. Upper parts olive-gray except for orange-rufous patch

on rear of crown and below ear coverts; white supraloral spot; and incomplete white eye-ring. Lores and area surrounding eye-ring almost black. Under parts white except for dusky blotch in middle of chest, grayish-brown sides and flanks, and buff under tail coverts. Sonora and Chihuahua to Puebla, Chiapas, Guatemala, and El Salvador.

28. White-eared Ground Sparrow (*M. leucotis*). 7½ inches. Lores creamy-white; crown slate-gray bordered by black stripes which meet at forehead; yellow line back of eye broadens back of ear coverts, occupying side of neck; rest of head, including chin and throat, black; ear coverts with large spot of silvery-white; back, rump, wings, and tail dark olive-brown; middle of breast and belly white; a black blotch on chest; sides gray; flanks olive; under tail coverts rufous-buff. Chiapas to Costa Rica.

Striped Sparrow

This chunky finch I first saw perched on a bush in open pine woods near Las Vigas, Veracruz. I more recently encountered it at about 8,000 feet above Pátzcuaro, Michoacán:

29. Striped Sparrow (*Oritrurus superciliosus*). 6¾ inches. Brown above, much streaked with black; gray below, unstreaked, fading to brown on sides and flanks; whole area between buff superciliary line and buff throat, black, except for fine pale streaks on ear coverts. Northern Sonora, northern Chihuahua, Durango, and San Luis Potosí to Michoacán, Puebla, and Veracruz. Usually feeds on ground, but may, when flushed, fly high into a pine and stay there quietly for some time.

Rufous-crowned Sparrow and allies

The genus *Aimophila* is widely represented in Mexico, the Rufous-crowned Sparrow (*A. ruficeps*) being the best known species (see pp. 75–76). This bird breeds from well north of the border to the southern limits of the plateau. The Botteri's Sparrow (*A. botterii*) also ranges widely. In the vicinity of Brownsville, Texas, it is a low country bird. At the Mesa de Llera,

not far south of Victoria, Tamaulipas, it inhabits thicket-studded grasslands. In some parts of the Central Plateau it is found at considerable elevation in grass in pine forest. The Cassin's Sparrow (*A. cassini*) breeds southward to northern Sonora and southern Texas, migrating southward into Mexico. The Rufous-winged Sparrow (*A. carpalis*) breeds in some numbers in Sonora and northern Sinaloa as well as in Arizona. All of these species are covered in guides to United States birds. The following are distinctively Middle American species:

30. Five-striped Sparrow (*A. quinquestriata*). 5½ inches. Grayish-brown above, with narrow white superciliary line. Chest and sides dark gray. Throat black with broad white line down middle and narrow white line at each side. Belly and under tail coverts grayish-white. Black blotch on chest. Sonora and Chihuahua to Jalisco.

31. Bridled Sparrow (*A. mystacalis*). 5¾ inches. Crown, hind neck, and back grayish-brown, streaked with black; white of supraloral streak connects with white eye-ring; blackish area between eye and bold white malar streak; throat black. Scapulars, rump, sides, flanks, and under tail coverts pale rufous. Two narrow buffy-white wing-bars. Chest ashy-gray, fading to white on belly. Highlands of Oaxaca, Puebla, and Veracruz.

32. Black-chested Sparrow (*A. humeralis*). 6¼ inches. Top of head dark grayish-brown, becoming lighter on hind neck and passing gradually into rufous of back and scapulars; middle of back feathers faintly streaked with dusky and edged with buff; rump warm brown; wings and tail dark brown with grayish-brown edgings; no wing-bars; sides of head blackish, connecting with broad black chest-band; white of throat and malar area separated by narrow black line. Sides brownish-gray, brightening to rufous on flanks and under tail coverts; belly white. Highlands from Puebla and Morelos to Colima and Jalisco. This species, which I have seen along the Río de la Alberca, in Michoacán, has the interesting habit of singing in duet.

33. Russet-tailed Sparrow (*A. rufi-*

PLATE XVI
Emerald Toucanet
(*Aulacorhynchus prasinus*)

cauda). 6–7 inches. Crown blackish-brown, with buff-white line down middle and bold white superciliary; coverts and lores blackish-brown; back, rump, wings, and tail warm russet; back and scapulars streaked with dusky; lesser wing coverts rufescent; rump and upper tail coverts without streaks. Throat and belly white; chest ashy-gray, indefinitely streaked with white; sides, flanks, and under tail coverts light rufous. Durango, Jalisco, and Puebla to Costa Rica.

34. Rusty Sparrow (*A. rufescens*). 7–7½ inches. Crown chestnut with buff mid-line in front, changing through rufous to brown on occiput; sides of head brown, buffy in supraloral area and malar region; throat buffy, bordered at either side by narrow black line; back, rump, wings, and tail dark reddish brown; middle of back faintly streaked with dusky; chest, sides, flanks, and under tail coverts brownish-buff; belly white. Sonora, Chihuahua, and southern Tamaulipas (Heed) to Costa Rica.

35. Cinnamon-tailed Sparrow (*A. sumichrasti*). 5½ inches. Upper parts reddish-brown, brightest on tail and lesser wing coverts; crown, hind neck, and back streaked with black; midline of crown grayish-buff; superciliary line buffy-white; malar streak buff, bordered above and below by short dusky stripe; throat pale buff, fading to gray on chest and white on belly; sides, flanks, and under tail coverts rufous-buff. Oaxaca. The Oaxaca Sparrow (*A. notosticta*), which I have never seen alive, is said to be "remarkable for its black bill and dark brown crown-stripes" (Hellmayr).

Mexican finches not yet mentioned in the appendix are covered by guides to United States birds, but I should point out that the following breed in Mexico: Grass-

hopper Sparrow (*Ammodramus savannarum*), Savannah Sparrow (*Passerculus sandwichensis*), Black-throated Sparrow (*Amphispiza bilineata*), Sage Sparrow (*A. belli*), Chipping Sparrow (*Spizella passerina*), Black-chinned Sparrow (*S. atrogularis*), Lark Sparrow (*Chondestes grammacus*), Red-backed Junco (*Junco phaeonotus*), Oregon Junco (*J. oreganus*), and Song Sparrow (*Melospiza melodia*). The Worthen's Sparrow (*Spizella wortheni*), which probably is a race of the Field Sparrow (*Spizella pusilla*), breeds in New Mexico, Tamaulipas, and probably Coahuila and Nuevo León. The Red-backed Junco breeds well southward in the mountains, being common among the pines on Popocatepetl. The Song Sparrow will be instantly recognizable from its appearance as well as from its *chup* of alarm, whether it is in a flower bed in Mexico City or in wildest part of Michoacán.

The Fox Sparrow (*Passerella iliaca*) and Golden-crowned Sparrow (*Zonotrichia coronata*) are in a special category in that the Mexican part of their winter range is chiefly Baja California.

The following, in addition to most of the breeding species listed above, winter in Mexico: Vesper Sparrow (*Pocecetes gramineus*), White-crowned Sparrow (*Zonotrichia leucophrys*), White-throated Sparrow (*Z. albicollis*), Lincoln's Sparrow (*Melospiza lincolni*), Clay-colored Sparrow (*Spizella pallida*), Brewer's Sparrow (*S. breweri*), Baird's Sparrow (*Ammodramus bairdi*), McCown's Longspur (*Rhynchophanes mccowni*), and Chestnut-collared Longspur (*Calcarius ornatus*). The Seaside Sparrow (*Ammospiza maritima*), which nests on the Texas coast perhaps as far south as Brownsville, is to be looked for in Tamaulipas.

INDEX OF BIRD NAMES

*(Drawings in the text are indicated by italic page numbers,
color plates by plate numbers.)*

266

270

274

UNIVERSITY OF OKLAHOMA PRESS

NORMAN